D1598586

WATER SUPPLIES and ECONOMIC GROWTH

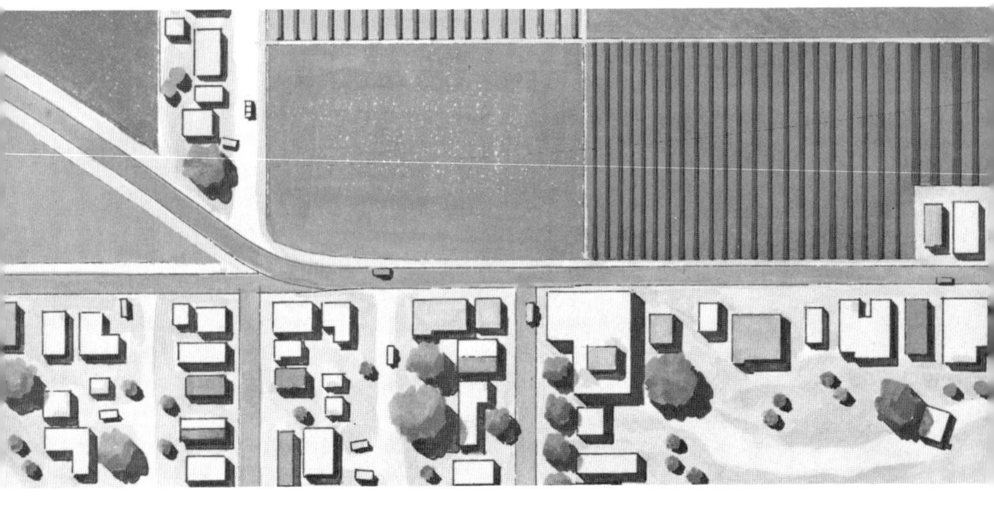

Water Supplies an

conomic Growth in an Arid Environment

AN ARIZONA CASE STUDY

MAURICE M. KELSO
WILLIAM E. MARTIN
LAWRENCE E. MACK

THE UNIVERSITY OF ARIZONA PRESS
Tucson, Arizona

About The Authors . . .

MAURICE M. KELSO, Professor Emeritus of Agricultural Economics and Emeritus Agricultural Economist in the Arizona Agricultural Experiment Station at the University of Arizona, has previously served as Chief of the Division of Land Economics in the Bureau of Agricultural Economics of the U.S. Department of Agriculture. He also has served as Head of the Department of Agricultural Economics and Rural Sociology and as Dean of Agriculture and Director of the Agricultural Experiment Station at Montana State College. He has authored numerous publications in natural resource economics and policy.

WILLIAM E. MARTIN, Professor of Agricultural Economics, and Agricultural Economist in the Arizona Agricultural Experiment Station, the University of Arizona, has authored many publications on farm management and water resources economics. His book (coauthored with Harland Padfield), *Farmers, Workers, and Machines,* won the American Farm Economics Association "Award for Outstanding Published Research" in agricultural economics for 1966. He has twice won the Western Agricultural Economics Association "Outstanding Published Research Award" for studies in interindustry analysis and Arizona water resources, respectively.

LAWRENCE E. MACK, Assistant Professor of Agricultural Economics, and Assistant Agricultural Economist, University of Arizona, received his B.S. degree in Agricultural Economics from South Dakota State College, and the M.S. and Ph.D. degrees from the University of Arizona. His primary research activity has been in compiling and analyzing data pertaining to the economics of water; his major teaching and research interests have been resource economics, production economics, and farm management.

THE UNIVERSITY OF ARIZONA PRESS

I. S. B. N.-0-8165-0368-0
L. C. No. 72-92106

Contents

TABLES

ILLUSTRATIONS

Preface

THIS PRESENTATION, first of all, describes the popular notion of the water problem and its cause in Arizona. It traces the physiography and climate of the state, the volume and rate of withdrawal of water supplies, and the economic development and associated water requirements, from which the popular image of the water problem was derived.

Next, it shows that the changing structure of the Arizona economy has permitted economic growth without the ruinous restraint of scarce water supplies that the popular image would expect. Our own conception of the water problem is deduced from and is consistent with the recent course of events. Our conception – that economic growth in Arizona need not be restrained by water scarcity – constitutes our problem hypothesis, the validity of which our empirical research has been designed to test.

Over the years each human society that has entered the part of the arid Southwest that now is Arizona has confronted the problem of developing a viable way of life in a water-scarce environment. The American-Indian societies solved the problem in their several ways. The Spanish-Mexican society, which intruded two to three centuries ago, also adapted in its own way. The Anglo-American culture inserted itself into the area in the mid-1800s, confronted the same problem, fashioned its own adaptations from within the dictates of its culture, and imposed a structure of institutions and patterns of behavior that survival in that environment seemed to dictate.

The Indian and Spanish-Mexican societies solved the social-survival problem largely by *adapting to* the dictates of the environment, including water scarcity. The Anglo-American society, true to its aggressive values, *struggled against* the dictates of the environment and increasingly sought to adapt the environment to the purposes of the society. This resulted in exploitation of the resources of the area and multiplication of their productivity to support an ever-growing population living at ever-increasing levels of material well-being. This penchant for adapting the environment to society, rather than adapting society to the environment, has continued to cause worry as to whether or not a truly viable society has, in fact, been created in this water-short area.

During the period of struggling against and gaining control over the societies already occupying the area, the Anglo-American society established its base for survival largely on a mining and grazing economy.

Later it began to develop a rural-agricultural base resting on control and development of water supplies for irrigation.

The limitations of the visible surface-water supplies placed an immediate and obvious restraint on continuing economic growth. Mining and grazing were not significantly restrained by water supplies, but irrigated agriculture was. The need to release that restraint on agriculture led to a search for means to develop all visible surface-water supplies.

Improvements in the technology of groundwater pumping opened up a vast invisible new stock of water, and irrigated agriculture took off at an accelerated pace, fueled by World War II and postwar demands for agricultural products. But new worries arose over the restraint ultimately to be imposed by the declining level of the groundwater stock.

A continuous search for a visible increase in the supply of water was given increased urgency during the 1950s and 1960s by the striking expansion in urban-industrial and recreation-retirement activities with their related increases in population.

The sense of urgency concerning water as a limitation on economic growth, even as a threat to long-run viability of the Arizona society, was the problem we set out to examine. What is the relationship between water supplies and economic growth in an arid environment? Can one quantify and project the timing of the relationship in terms of income levels and the structure of the dependent economy? What would be the nature and rate of change in the state's economic activity? Is decline inevitable, or is further growth possible? In either instance, why and by how much and how rapidly?

Under our hypothesis, we first develop the analytical ideas appropriate to the study – that is, we "conceptualize" the problem; we determine the structure of concepts and their functional interrelations needed to test it analytically. Because we examine the problem "economically," we develop our "conceptual model" for the problem analysis from the principles of economic decision-making.

First for a single point in time, then for an on-going span of time, we describe the analytical nature of demand, of supply, and of their functional interactions respecting water use in an economy like Arizona's. From these relations, in the face of a declining supply of groundwater, we deduce the likely consequences over time in acres cropped, water used, and income generated in Arizona agriculture, and the resulting affect on the nonagricultural economy.

Arizona water law and its general socioeconomic consequences are described. The empirical analysis of the role of water in Arizona's economic growth is then formulated in accordance with the conceptual structure of ideas and within the legal environment.

Certain *direct consequences* of increasing water scarcity (increasing water costs) are to be expected only *within irrigation agriculture* in the state. Specific conditions of agriculture are relevant to the analysis in each of several subareas of the state. For each subarea and for the aggregate of all subareas, the changes generated by increased water costs are projected over a span of forty-nine years (1966–2015) in respect to reductions in acres cropped, volumes of water used, gross outputs of agricultural revenue, and net revenues produced in agriculture. Demand curves for irrigation water by farmers for the base year of analysis – 1966 – are empirically derived.

Next, an analysis is made of the *indirect affects* on the *nonagricultural sectors* of the state's economy stemming from the direct effects of increasing water scarcity in irrigated farming. Projections are derived regarding the magnitudes of expected income losses in the aggregate nonagricultural sectors of the economy .

By adding the expected direct income losses in agriculture to the expected indirect losses in the nonagricultural economy, we determine the total expected economic loss generated by increasing water scarcity over the next fifty years. From these projections, suggestive figures are derived as to the magnitudes of payments that the economy of the state, or the people of the state who are adversely affected, could rationally make for additional water to forestall the projected declines in economic growth.

The analyses are made within the restraints of an assumption that no changes will occur during the fifty-year projection period in economic sectors of the state other than those affected, directly or indirectly, by growing water scarcity directly affecting irrigation agriculture only. We recognize, however, that rapid economic growth in nonagricultural sectors may more than offset declines in the agricultural sectors. Also, although growth in the nonagricultural sectors may not be restrained by increasing water scarcity now or for some time to come, such growth might be restrained eventually if water scarcity long continues or increases rapidly.

We examine these possibilities by projecting, over fifty years, several progressively more extreme patterns of possible change in the economic structure of the Arizona economy, determining for each the changing magnitudes of raw water demands relative to raw water supplies. This leads to the further hypothesis that policies and programs directed to changing the structure of economic growth so as to reduce the demand for water are equally as relevant to furthering economic growth as are efforts to increase the supply of available water. Such efforts to change the structure of growth may be cheaper and more effective in the long run.

Finally, this report summarizes the more cogent findings and the more relevant and striking implications relative to the question: What, in fact, is the relation between economic growth (or decline) and a growing water scarcity in an arid environment such as exists in Arizona?

The results are striking – so striking relative to the popular image of the water problem in Arizona that it is important that they not be lost to public discussion and debate concerning the nature, meaning, and resolution of the problem of water scarcity in Arizona and the nature of Arizona water policies, water programs, water laws, and water organizations designed to deal with them.

We are under no delusions that what we say concerning the Arizona water problem and its solutions is exactly right in all details; but the correct details, whatever they may be, could be different by several orders of magnitude from what we here elucidate without changing their implications for state water policies and programs in the slightest.

Because economic problems of water scarcity and the attitudinal problems of people toward that scarcity are similar throughout the arid Southwest, we believe that this case study of possible solutions to Arizona's water problems will have wide implications for economic growth in all arid environments. In fact, the analytical structure we have here developed could equally well be applied by other analysts concerned with water problems of widely different kinds in other and dissimilar areas, or, for that matter, by analysts concerned with other natural resource problems. By and large, only the definition and quantification of the parameters of our analytical models would require modification to such extensions of application.

The presently reported research, the relation of water supplies to economic growth in an arid environment, took the 1966 structure of water law and water administering and managing organizations; it then projected changing land and water use and income creation in the Arizona economy, assuming there would be no changes in that 1966 structure of water-related institutions throughout the fifty-year projection period.

A second research effort, follow-up companion to the one described herein, also was begun at the University of Arizona in 1966 to explore the economics of public water policy in Arizona, examine the existing institutional environment within which water-use decisions are made, and analyze plausible changes that would be fruitful in relaxing restraints on water use.

M. M. K.
W. E. M.
L. E. M.

Acknowledgments

RESOURCES BEYOND the capacity of the University of Arizona to provide were required for a research undertaking of the magnitude of that reported herein. Support funds from the Rockefeller Foundation were made available in October 1962; additional grants and extensions followed, terminating on June 30, 1970. The funds were supplied under grant numbers RF 62086 and RF 64009.

In conjunction with the Foundation Grant, the University of Arizona agreed to provide the facilitating services, the necessary professional staff, some of the research assistants, and the clerical assistance required. Responsibility for administering the Foundation grant and the University's contributions was centered in the Department of Agricultural Economics of the Arizona Agricultural Experiment Station and the University's College of Agriculture.

M. M. Kelso, Professor of Agricultural Economics, has been principal investigator for the research, responsible for its overall direction. Subsequently, the University also provided part of the research time of William E. Martin, Professor, and Robert A. Young, Associate Professor in the Department of Agricultural Economics, to provide professional direction to the research. Still later, it made available the research time of Lawrence E. Mack, Assistant Professor in the department, to assist in final stages of interpretation of the research results. Robert A. Young subsequently withdrew from the project. We, the authors, however, express our special indebtedness to him. He participated in the research from its inception, assisted in the overall conceptual formulation of the research endeavor, guided several of the subarea analyses, and participated in some of the aggregative analyses and interpretations.

In the course of this research, four Doctoral dissertations and three Master's theses contributing to the total research effort were financed wholly or in part from the Foundation grant. In addition, one Doctoral dissertation and four Master's theses financed from other sources contributed to the total effort. We express our appreciation to the twelve research associates and assistants who conducted these subphase studies. Without their contributions, this total effort would have been impossible.

The research associates were Harold M. Stults, Douglas M. Jones, Lawrence E. Mack (co-author), Ronald D. Finster, and Kenneth Hock. The research assistants were V. Wilson Lee, Billy M. Comer, Robert L. Spears, James J. Jacobs, Thomas G. Burdak, and James W. Goss.

Thanks are due the clerical staff of the Department of Agricultural Economics of The University of Arizona who typed and retyped the manuscript of this and subphase reports. Special expressions of appreciation go to Mrs. Paula Tripp and Mrs. Ruth Langer.

We acknowledge our indebtedness to the University Administration, especially to Jimmye S. Hillman, Head of the Department of Agricultural Economics, for their unstinting provision, within the limits of their resources, of the facilitating offices, equipment, supplies, services, and clerical assistance.

We express our indebtedness to The Rockefeller Foundation for its generous grant of financial aid, without which this work could not have been done at all, and for the complete freedom given us in how we planned, analyzed, and conducted the research with no administrative or professional restraints. Especially do we wish to mention Charles M. Hardin, J. E. Black, and Ralph K. Davidson of the Humanities and Social Sciences Division of the Foundation, under whose immediate jurisdiction the grant to us was placed, and who supported, encouraged, and counseled with us without stint or dictation from inception of the research to its conclusion.

Finally, we appreciate the assistance of the University of Arizona Press in bringing out this book under its imprint.

M. M. K.
W. E. M.
L. E. M.

WATER SUPPLIES and ECONOMIC GROWTH

If the University is to retain its value as an institution, it must find imaginative but practical ways to deal with this country's troubles. Society wants the University to help solve problems, not just go "tsk, tsk."

Steve Trachtenberg,
Dean (University Affairs)
Boston University

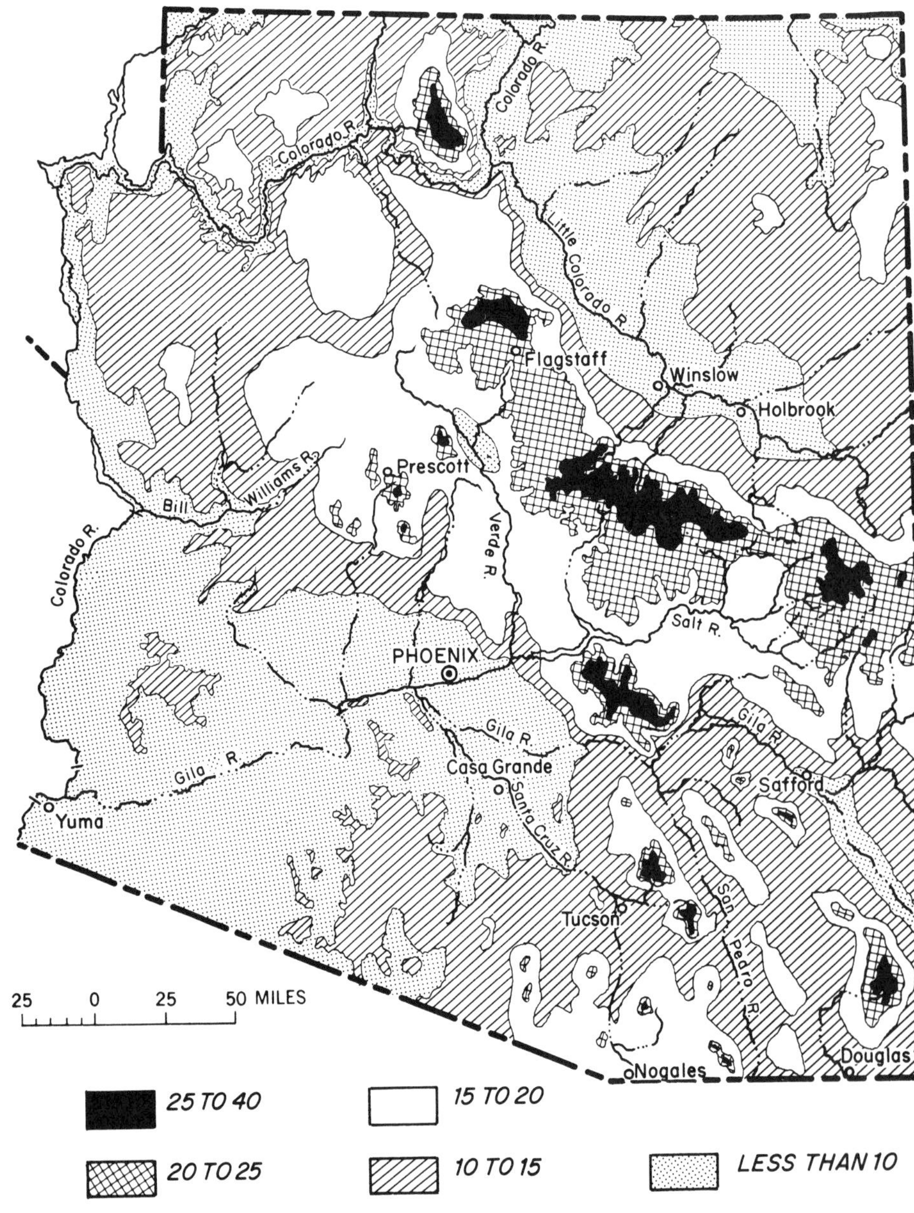

Fig. 1-1. *Average annual precipitation in Arizona.*
Source: *Harshbarger et al., 1966.*

1. The Water Problem in Arizona

Physiography and Climate

ARIZONA IS POPULARLY THOUGHT OF as a desert state. To resident and casual visitor alike, the vegetation, the clear skies and bright sun, the low humidity, and the dry water courses confirm the popular image. Deserts are dry and lack water. Clearly then, what is more to be expected than that Arizona would have a "water problem," especially as more and more people, attracted by the very aridity and heat that make the area a desert, are attracted to it as a place to live and work?

Arizona isn't, however, everywhere as dry and hot as the popular image has it. Figure 1-1 shows that less than ten inches of precipitation annually is received in two widely separated parts of the state. The first and largest area is in the southwestern part of the state and is part of the Sonoran Desert. To the east and northeast from this area, annual precipitation increases rather markedly to amounts in excess of 25 inches. But as one proceeds farther northeastward, precipitation again declines, and the second area of less than 10 inches is found.

Underlying this precipitation pattern is a marked physiographic pattern. The elevation is lowest in the far southwestern part of the state in the vicinity of Yuma. Elevation rises steadily but moderately as one moves north and east until one reaches a line that runs from the southeastern corner northwesterly across the state. Along this line elevations increase sharply from less than 1,000 feet to more than 7,000 feet, with marked increases in precipitation especially as snow during winter.

Beyond this line of high elevations, altitude drops slightly as one proceeds northeasterly and rises again as one approaches the far northeast corner of the state. This *high steppe* area, a part of the Colorado Plateau, tends to be dry because of the *rain shadow* effect of the sharply increasing and relatively higher elevations to the west and south.

Thus, the southwest and northeast sections are the driest, truly desert, areas separated by a belt of country diagonally across the state of markedly higher precipitation levels.

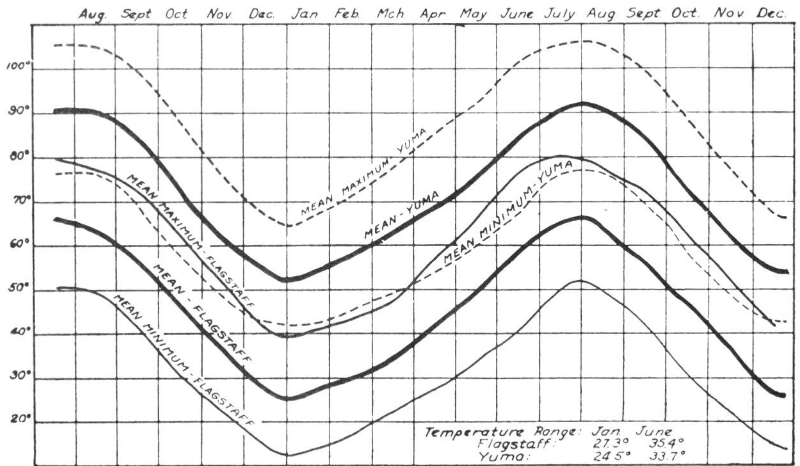

Fig. 1-2. *Monthly mean maximum, mean minimum, and mean temperatures for Yuma and Flagstaff, Arizona.* Source: *Smith, 1956.*

The physiographic pattern that underlies the precipitation pattern also is reflected in the temperature pattern of the state. Figure 1-2 shows that the summer temperatures at Flagstaff (7,000 feet) are almost identical with those during the winter months at Yuma (140 feet). Much of the area in the high country along the southeast-to-northwest diagonal exhibits summer and winter temperatures not far different from those experienced in the Rocky Mountain uplift as far north as the Canadian border.

Precipitation and temperatures taken together give Arizona three basic climates: desert, steppe, and highland, shown in figure 1-3, which cover, respectively, about 30, 53, and 17 percent of the state.

The desert and steppes are characterized by a lack of precipitation: the former more so than the latter. Practically all of the rain that falls in these regions evaporates; appreciable runoff and sub-surface storage occur only during the wettest period. As a result, the vegetation cover is restricted, and consists mainly of creosote bush, cacti, and sagebrush on the deserts, and mesquite, piñon-juniper and various types of grass on the steppes. In these dry regions irrigation is a must for successful farming. The highlands, on the other hand, normally receive sufficient precipitation during the year to support a moderately dense vegetation growth, with enough left over for substantial runoff onto the surrounding arid plains. This is particularly true of the cold highlands, which possess some of the finest and most extensive pine forests in the world, and where precipitation is reasonably dependable from year to year. In the warm highlands precipitation is less dependable, varying greatly in amount and intensity from one year to the next.

. . . Precipitation is heaviest and most dependable in summer, particularly in the highland regions of the state, which rarely experience a dry after-

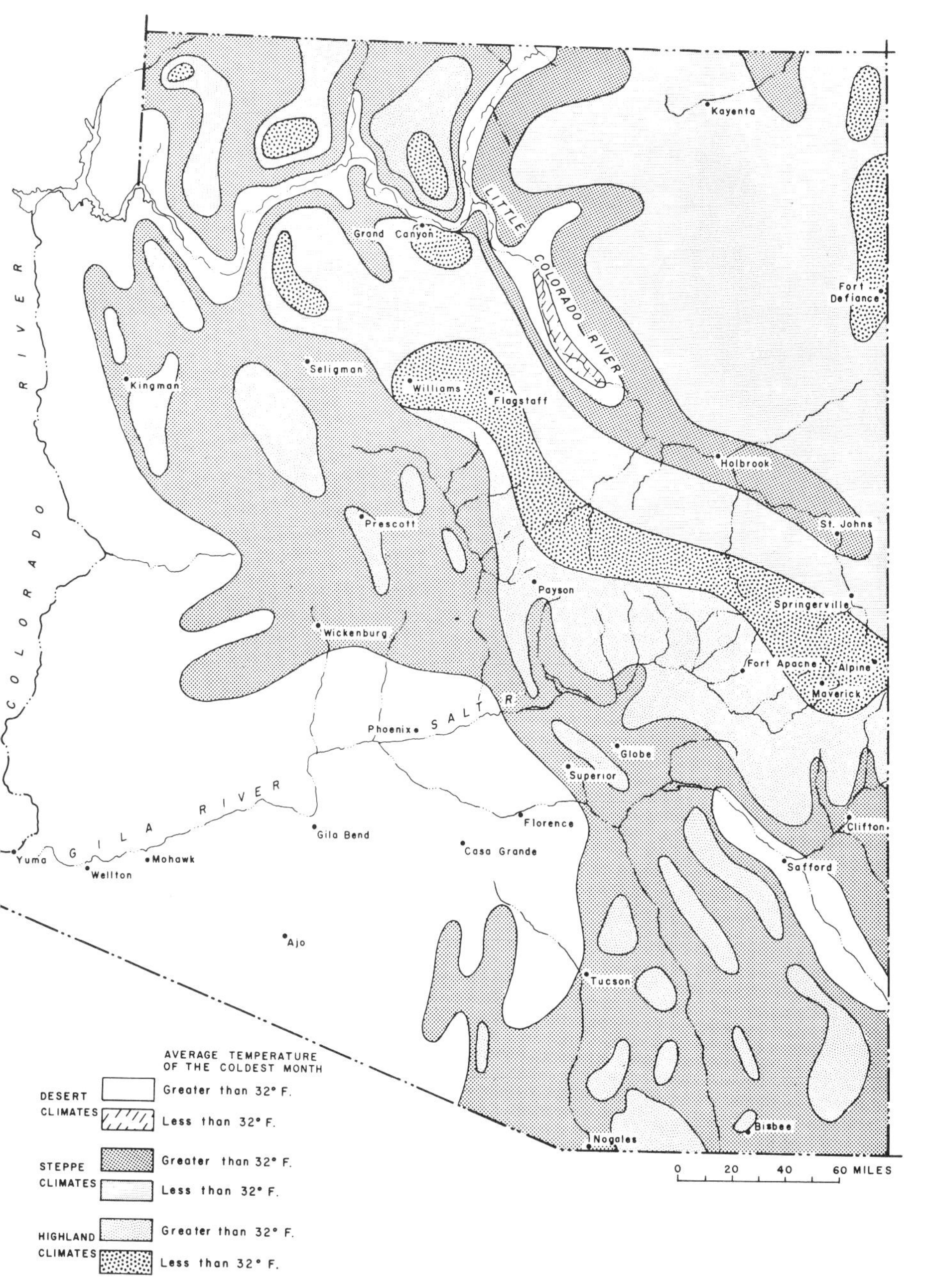

Fig. 1-3. *Climates of Arizona.* Source: *Cross et al., 1960.*

noon between the second week of July and the first week in September. Occasional cloudbursts may send torrents of water streaming down onto the surrounding valley floors, filling the washes and gullies to overflowing and doing considerable damage to roads and poorly located homes.

. . . Summer rains are associated primarily with very warm, moist, and unstable air which sweeps around the southern and western margins of a semi-stationary high pressure area over the Atlantic Ocean and advances into Arizona from the Gulf of Mexico. Widespread and frequently severe showers and thunderstorms develop in this air when it is forced to ascend over the numerous mountain ranges of the southern and eastern sections of the state.

Winter precipitation is generally less intense but more widespread than that of summer. Part of this precipitation is associated with the storm belt of the middle latitudes, which occasionally advances far enough south for its margins to affect Arizona. It is only when these cyclonic storms move in directly from the Pacific Ocean across the northern and central parts of the country that measurable amounts of rain can occur. When the storm track moves in a north-to-south direction east of the 105th meridian, about all Arizona can expect is plenty of wind and subnormal temperatures, particularly in the northeast part of the state.

Probably the heaviest rains of winter are associated with the so-called "Kona" storms or "cold lows" of the subtropical Pacific Ocean. These storms normally pass directly over Arizona, frequently advancing slowly, and since they retain most of their moisture supply while moving in from the Pacific, they can produce several days of moderate to heavy rain and snow, often accompanied by lightning and thunder. (Cross et al., 1960)

Thus the physiography of Arizona produces the precipitation, the temperature, and climatic patterns of the state. Through these elements of climate, it is responsible for the water-resource pattern. The latter, in conjunction with the settlement pattern and with man's demands, creates "the water problem."

Water-Resource Pattern

The water-resource pattern can best be understood in relation to the water provinces of Arizona pictured in figure 1-4. The Plateau Uplands, consisting largely of the cold steppe climate as shown in figure 1-3, are high, cold in winter, and dry. Groundwater is held in large quantities in the underlying sandstones, but these aquifers yield their water slowly to wells, resulting in pumped water of relatively high cost. Thus, large-volume low-return uses of groundwater such as for irrigation are well-nigh impossible in this province. Only small pockets of use are in local areas of alluvium close to the principal source of precipitation toward the eastern end of the Mogollon Rim on the headwaters of the Little Colorado River. Due to light precipitation, high rates of evaporation, and rapid

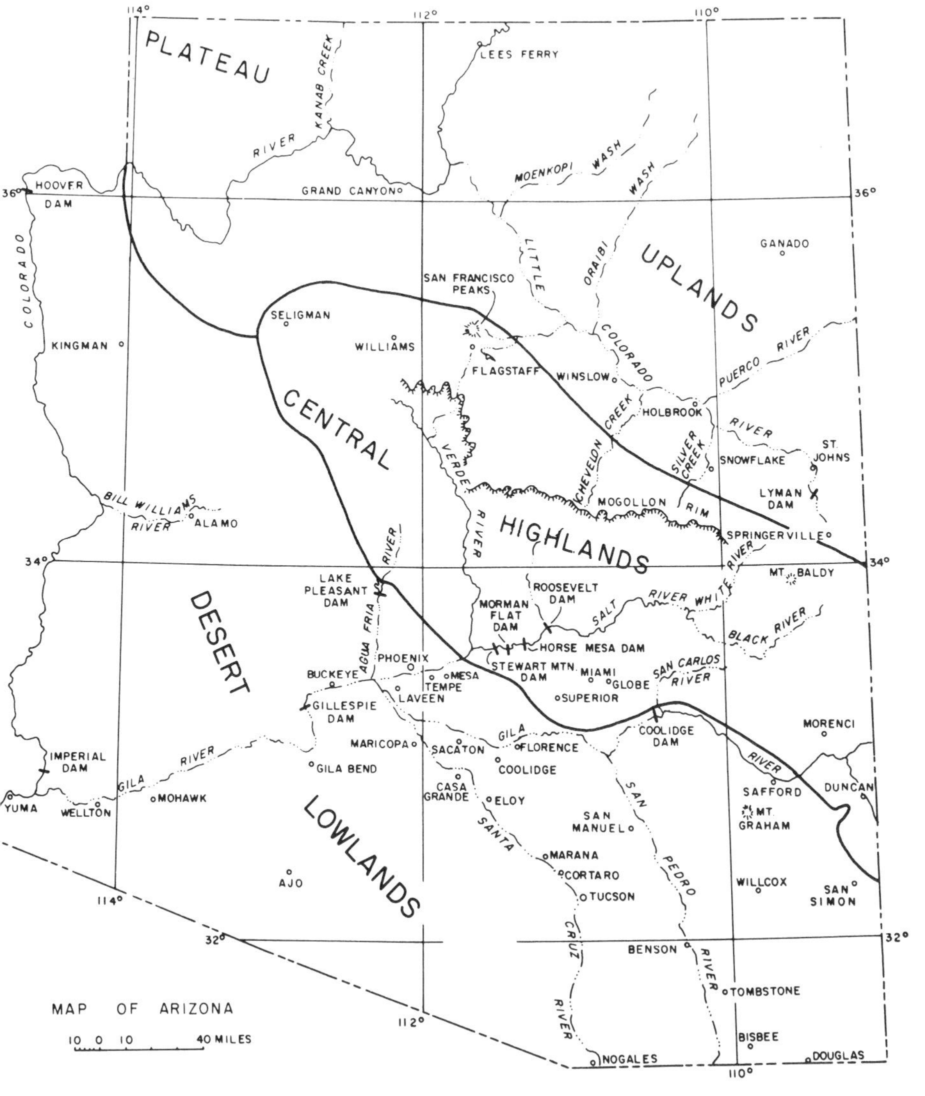

Fig. 1-4. *Water provinces of Arizona.* Source: *Cross et al., 1960.*

seepage into the fractured limestone substructure, run-off from and across the Plateau Uplands is small. Large-volume low-value uses of surface water are also restricted to limited areas along headwater streams close to the eastern end of the Rim. Thus, the Plateau Uplands Province is not an area of significantly large water supplies or water uses and is not significant in the state-wide water problem.

The Central Highlands Province, consisting largely of the highland climates of figure 1-3, is the principal source of water originating within Arizona. It receives the heaviest precipitation within the state, ranging from ten to thirty-five inches annually at various points along its length. Surface water from rainfall and snowmelt occurs in this province in relatively large amounts, causing it to be the chief area of perennial water supply in the state and the principal source of stream flow and groundwater recharge to the Desert Lowlands Province. The principal storm paths and the physiography of the Central Highlands are such that they produce most of this water supply south of the Mogollon Rim. Water uses in the Central Highlands Province are largely those dependent on direct evapotranspiration losses rather than withdrawals from stream and underground flows. Thus, its significance in the state's water problem is largely related to its significance as a supplier of water to the Desert Lowlands Province and to the magnitude and economic worth of the evapotranspiration losses its uses impose on the outflowing supply of both surface and underground water.

The Desert Lowlands Province, consisting largely of the desert and warm steppe climates of figure 1-3, is the beneficiary of the outflowing supplies from the Central Highlands Province. In addition, the province is the beneficiary of surface supplies entering the state from New Mexico in the Gila River and from the Upper Colorado River Basin in the Colorado River, as well as of underground supplies derived from precipitation on the highlands along its eastern and southeastern peripheries. It is by far the largest user of surface and subsurface supplies of water in the state. Of all measured diversions of surface-flowing supplies and of groundwater withdrawals, more than 95 percent occur in this province. Though this province comprises only about 45 percent of the state's total area, it contains more than 95 percent of the cultivated land, 85 percent of the state's total population, and more than 90 percent of its employment.

Only small quantities of water originate from precipitation within the Desert Lowlands Province itself, and then mostly as flash floods following summer thunderstorms. Storms originating in the Gulf of Mexico and occasionally in the Pacific off the west coast of Mexico extend into the southeastern corner of the province and drop their moisture in the scattered mountainous areas lying within and along the edges of that part of the province. As the resulting floodwaters move downstream (northwesterly) from these mountainous areas, the volume of flow decreases rapidly due to infiltration, evaporation, channel storage, and channel retention. What proportion of these flows seeps into the groundwater table and how much is lost by evaporation is not known precisely, but indications are that only a small fraction reaches the groundwater reservoir.

As shown in figure 1-5, most of the surface water yield from the Central Highlands flows southwestward through the Salt and Verde River systems into the Desert Lowlands east of Phoenix. From 1915 to 1945 approximately a million acre-feet of surface flow were discharged annually to the Desert Province through this river system. From 1945 to the 1970s the annual discharge has approximated three-quarters of a million acre-feet annually. The reasons for the lesser yields from the watersheds of these streams during the years following 1945 are not entirely clear.

Figure 1-5 shows two other sources of surface water to the Desert Lowlands Province – the Colorado River and the Gila River above its confluence with the Salt River. The Colorado River contributes approximately one and a half million acre-feet of water annually to Arizona on lands adjacent to the river below Parker Dam, most of it to the area around Yuma. The Gila River above its confluence with the Salt River contributes about three-quarters of a million acre-feet of surface-water diversions from where it enters Arizona near Duncan, downstream in the Safford Valley, and still further downstream in the San Carlos Irrigation Project in the vicinity of Coolidge and extending into the lower Santa Cruz area near Casa Grande.

Surface-water diversions for use within Arizona as shown in figure 1-6 totaled from 1.5 to 2.0 million acre-feet annually for several decades prior to 1957. In 1957 they began to increase, reaching about 3⅓ million acre-feet twelve years later in 1968. The increase during this latter period has resulted from increasing diversions from Arizona's and the Colorado River Indians' allotted shares of Colorado River water and from the favorable precipitation of the period.

Of the surface-water supplies available to Arizona, all are developed, controlled, and diverted for use within the state, except approximately one million acre-feet yet undeveloped in the Colorado River and claimed by Arizona for its use. Arizona's claim of a right to use these undeveloped waters of the Colorado was contested by the other states of the Colorado Basin, particularly by California, in a celebrated controversy extending over forty years. In 1964 the Supreme Court of the United States issued an opinion and decree confirming Arizona's claim to a right to develop-

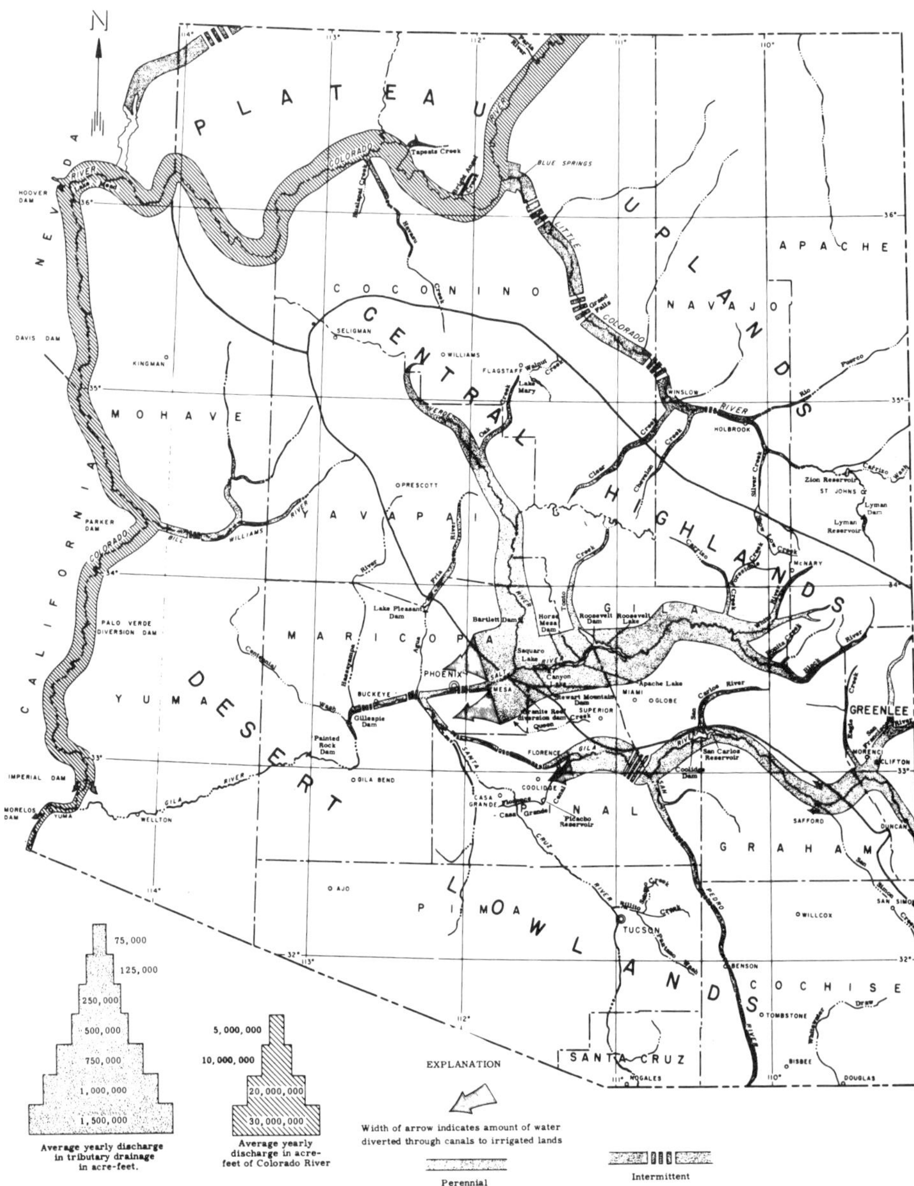

Fig. 1-5. *Annual discharge of Arizona streams. Width of stream indicates average yearly discharge in acre-feet. The Central Highlands Province contributes the most runoff within the state. The largest river is the Salt, followed by the Verde, Gila, and Little Colorado. Many of the smaller streams are intermittent and flow after dense showers, snow melt, or continued precipitation for several days. Area of lowest runoff is the southwestern corner of the state.* Source: *Harshbarger et al., 1966.*

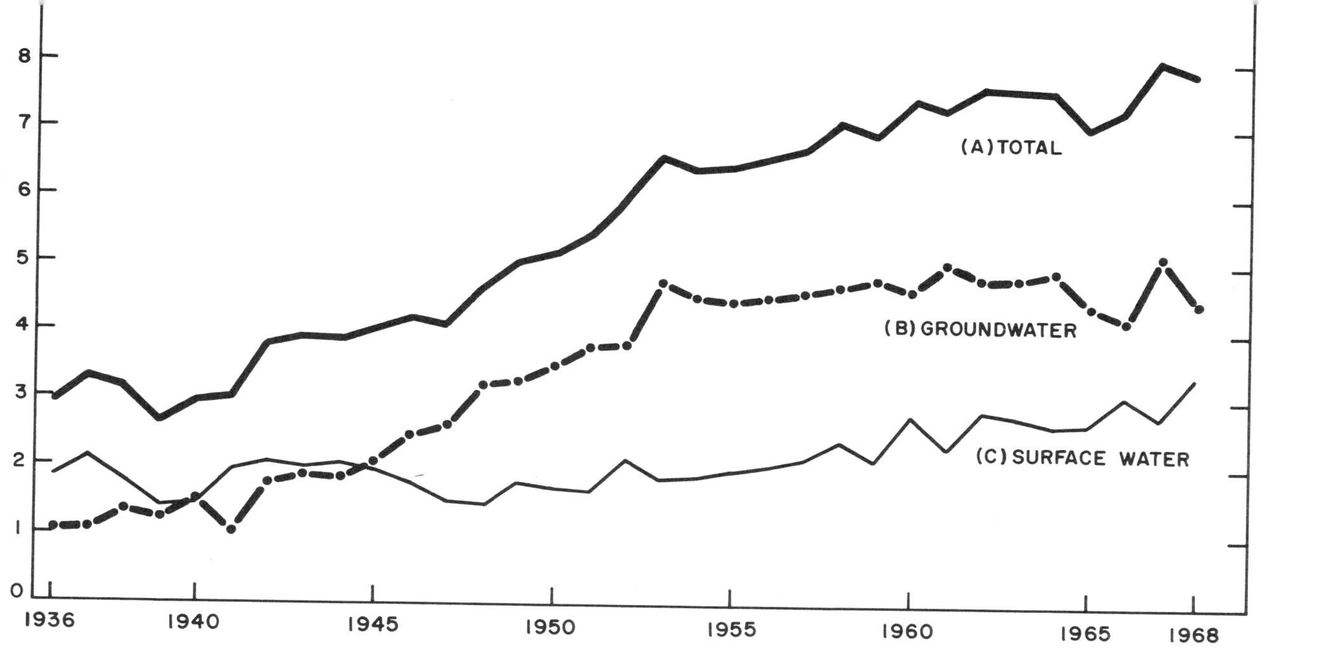

Fig. 1-6. *Surface-water diversions and groundwater pumpage, Arizona, 1936–1938.* Curve A *includes gross diversions from the Colorado River below Parker Dam, and hence includes water reported as "returned to the River or discharged across the Arizona-Sonora international boundary."* Curve B *shows groundwater withdrawals from 1936 to 1966 as per USGS* Annual Report on Groundwater *(1968), and withdrawals for 1967 and 1968 per the* Report *(February and December 1969, respectively).* Curve C *shows surface-water diversions for 1936 to 1945 as calculated from data in USGS (1954), for 1946 to 1962 from data in* Arizona Academy *(1964), for 1963 to 1968 from USGS* Annual Report on Groundwater *(relevant years, 1963–1969).*

ment and use of 2.8 million acre-feet of Colorado River water within the state. Plans for development and use of that part of the state's right to Colorado River water not presently (in 1972) used in the state, approximating one million acre-feet, are moving toward realization through joint action of the federal and state governments.

Almost everywhere in Arizona, in 1972, available surface-water supplies are over-committed. In that part of the Desert Lowlands Province lying generally around the confluence of the Gila, Salt, and Santa Cruz rivers and in other scattered intermountain valleys containing alluvial fill and receiving surface and underground flows from their surrounding mountains, large stores of underground water are available and have been developed for use on lands overlying them. In this province annual water use from the underground reservoirs exceeds in volume the annual supply of available surface waters.

These stores of underground water have accumulated in the gravels of the partially filled valleys over eons of geologic time. Generally, the gravels are deep and porous, storing vast quantities of water which may be pumped with an acceptable degree of efficiency.

But the rate of recharge to the gravels has been far less than the rate of withdrawal since at least the early 1940s. The result has been that, though rapidly increasing demands for water by the rapidly growing economy of the province have been met, doing so has been possible only by drawing on the accumulations of many millenia. The result has been, as shown in figure 1-7, that the levels of the groundwater tables in most of the developed groundwater areas of the province have declined, many of them by more than a hundred and twenty-five feet. But, because of improvements in well drilling and in the efficiency of pumps and motors, because of the declining relative cost of energy for the pumps and increasing economic value of the products produceable with the water, as of the early 1970s there has been no significant curtailment in the rate of pumpage. No large-scale abandonment of pumping activity has occurred. The volume of groundwater pumpage has held between 4.5 and 5.0 million acre-feet annually since 1953, essentially all of it in the Desert Lowlands Province. Groundwater withdrawals annually have been from 50 to 100 percent more than the total of surface-flow diversions during the same period, and are from a third to a fourth more than the total surface supply annually available, including the underdeveloped and undiverted portion of the Colorado River flow confirmed by the 1964 Supreme Court decree for use within the state.

The long-standing, widespread, and frequently large declines in groundwater levels throughout the Desert Lowlands Province give clear

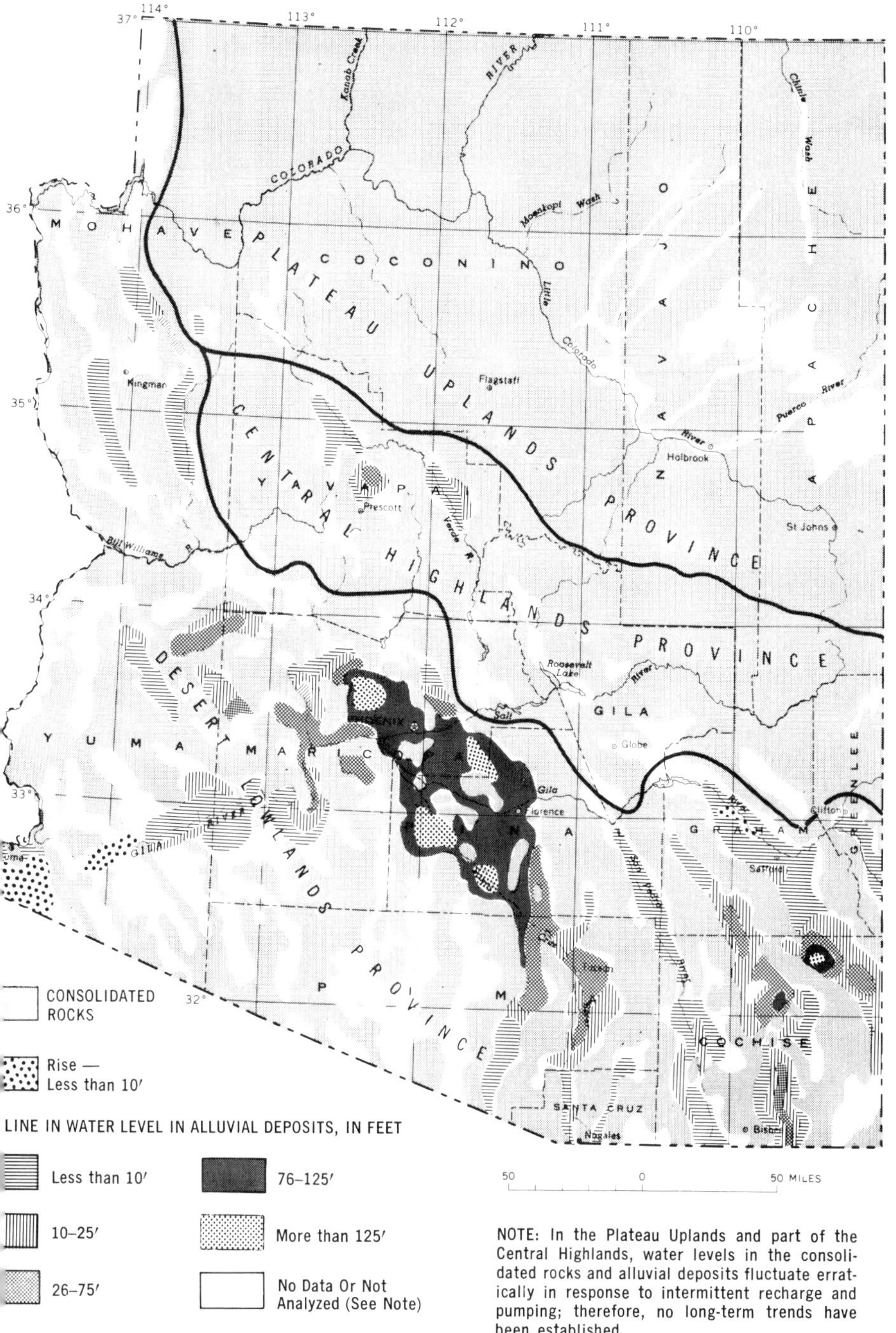

Fig. 1-7. *Approximate average change in water levels in developed areas, 1940–1968.* Source: *USGS, 1969.*

evidence that withdrawals have generally exceeded recharge to the groundwater reservoirs. However, how much of the annual pumpage withdrawals are net withdrawals from the groundwater stock is not precisely known. Data are too sketchy, and the technologies for getting such data are too primitive or too expensive. The most frequently mentioned figure is about 1.5 million acre-feet recharge to the groundwater reservoir annually. Thus, if one accepts this estimate for annual recharge, the net withdrawal from the groundwater stock has, on the average, been 3.0 to 3.5 million acre-feet annually since 1953.

If we look at Arizona's annual water budget in terms of an annually recurring *flow* supply and an annual withdrawal from the groundwater *stock,* we find that since 1953 the state has diverted 3.5 to 4.5 million acre-feet from annually recurring flows and 3.0 to 3.5 million acre-feet from the groundwater *stock.* Thus, since 1953, of all water diverted and withdrawn for use in the state, something over 50 percent has come from an annually recurring supply and something under 50 percent from a non-recurring stock.

Thus, three aspects of the water-resource situation in Arizona, when joined with the settlement pattern and man's demands, lead to the water problem in Arizona: (1) surface supplies are fully developed and used, excepting an amount approximating 1.8 million acre-feet remaining in Arizona's adjudicated share of water in the Colorado River; (2) groundwater supplies are vast and have been extensively developed and drawn upon to balance out water demands in the rapidly growing Arizona economy; (3) but this has imposed a draft on these underground supplies that is about three times the rate of annual recharge to the groundwater stock, gradually depleting the stock on which a large share of the Arizona economy depends.

Economic Development

The Anglo-capitalist economy of Arizona, like the similar economies of the other mountain and desert states of western America, depended in the beginning on direct utilization of three natural resources – mineral ores, natural forage, and water for irrigation. On these resources the mining, range livestock, and farming industries developed beginning about 1870.

Initially, the economy of the state was based largely on mining and grazing. Federal government expenditures for administration of the

Arizona Territory and for its policing and protection through the presence of the U.S. Army was the only other important, though not a resource-oriented, base for the state's economy. Almost all personal incomes earned in the state came directly or indirectly from these three general sources.

Incomes dependent on the use of irrigation water began to appear at an early date and assumed increasing importance with the development of the Salt River and Yuma areas.

But with further economic development, incomes received by the state's inhabitants came from sources other than grazing, irrigation, mining, and government. In 1929 (the first year for which such statistics are directly available) 28 percent of all personal income in the state was received directly from agriculture (including grazing) and mining (14 percent from each). An additional 10 percent came from government sources. A decade later (by 1940) the share received directly from agriculture had remained almost constant, declining from 14 to 13 percent, but the share from mining had declined from 14 to 9 percent. Together, the relative importance of these natural-resource-based industries had declined from 28 to 22 percent, but the share of personal incomes received from government had doubled to 21 percent. Thus, the share of personal incomes received in the state during 1940 coming from these three sources had increased from 38 percent in 1929 to 44 percent (table 1-1 and figure 1-8).

Decline in the relative importance of the resource-based industries – agriculture and mining – has persisted. Two decades later, in 1960, personal incomes received in Arizona from agriculture had declined to 7 percent of all incomes and that from mining to 4 percent. Together, the exploitation of grass, irrigation water, and minerals directly contributed only 11 percent of personal incomes in Arizona compared to 28 percent thirty years earlier. The share received from government held its own at 22 percent.

Although the proportion of personal incomes in Arizona derived from agriculture and mining has declined, the absolute amount of personal income received from each of these sources has held its own or increased slightly, even when expressed in dollar values of constant purchasing power (table 1-1 and figures 1-9 and 1-10). The relative importance of these resource-based industries has declined only because other sources of income have increased so much more. This changing importance of resource-based industries is a characteristic of economic growth wherever it is observed, and economic growth in Arizona has been vigorous and sustained during the period 1940 to 1970 (figure 1-11).

TABLE 1-1 — Personal Income, by Broa

Income Source	1929	1940	1950	1959	1960	196
Current purchasing power (in millions of dollars)						
Farms*	36	32	163	191	200	2
Mining*	36	22	49	85	104	1
Government†	25	52	205	539	587	6
Manufacturing*	17	12	52	253	275	2
All other sources§	140	133	522	1,364	1,542	1,6
Total‡	254	251	991	2,432	2,708	2,9
Constant (1957-59) purchasing power (in millions of dollars)						
Farms	60	66	195	188	194	2
Mining	60	45	59	84	101	1
Government	42	106	245	531	570	6
Manufacturing	28	25	62	249	267	2
All other sources	235	272	622	1,344	1,497	1,6
Total	425	514	1,183	2,396	2,629	2,8
Consumer's price index: purchasing power of the dollar (1957-1959 = 100)	167.5	204.8	119.4	98.5	97.1	9
Income by sources (percentage)						
Farms	14.2	12.7	16.4	7.8	7.4	
Mining	14.2	8.8	4.9	3.5	3.8	
Government	9.8	20.7	20.7	22.2	21.7	2
Manufacturing	6.7	4.8	5.2	10.4	10.2	1
All other sources	55.1	53.0	52.7	56.1	56.9	5
Total	100.0	100.0	99.9	100.0	100.0	10

*Annual personal incomes from farms, mining, and manufacturing, from table 70, **Survey of Current Busine**

†Annual personal incomes from government: income from government (table 70), plus wage and salary bursements to military personnel (table 50), plus transfer payments (table 50).

‡Total annual personal income: total from table 70 plus (from table 50) wage and salary disbursements military personnel, transfer payments and property income. This figure is larger than total personal inc as reported in the **Survey of Current Business** by an amount approximating the amount of personal contr tions for social insurance, as shown in table 50.

ources, Arizona, 1929, 1940, 1950, 1959-70

62	1963	1964	1965	1966	1967	1968	1969	1970
20	231	179	194	168	212	243	238	214
18	118	135	144	154	126	152	194	231
12	779	859	935	1,032	1,236	1,387	1,515	1,774
32	365	419	470	582	621	703	814	847
51	1,928	2,021	2,119	2,292	2,449	2,692	3,118	3,545
33	3,421	3,613	3,862	4,228	4,644	5,177	5,879	6,611
09	216	166	177	149	182	200	186	158
12	111	125	131	136	108	125	152	171
76	730	795	851	912	1,063	1,144	1,186	1,311
15	342	388	428	514	534	580	637	626
56	1,806	1,868	1,927	2,027	2,107	2,222	2,442	2,620
68	3,205	3,342	3,514	3,738	3,994	4,271	4,603	4,886
.9	93.7	92.5	91.0	88.4	86.0	82.5	78.3	73.9
.8	6.7	5.0	5.0	4.0	4.6	4.7	4.0	3.2
.6	3.4	3.7	3.7	3.6	2.7	2.9	3.3	3.5
.0	22.8	23.8	24.2	24.4	26.6	26.8	25.8	26.8
.3	10.7	11.6	12.2	13.8	13.4	13.6	13.9	12.8
.3	56.4	55.9	54.9	54.2	52.7	52.0	53.0	53.7
0	100.0	100.0	100.0	100.0	100.0	100.0	100.0	100.0

de up of contract construction; wholesale and retail trade; finance, insurance, and real estate; transportion, communications, and public utilities; services; property incomes.

ce: **Survey of Current Business,** U.S. Dept. of Commerce, Office of Business Economics, tables 50 and 70, relevant monthly issues reporting data and analyses concerning total and per capita personal income by regions and states, relevant years.

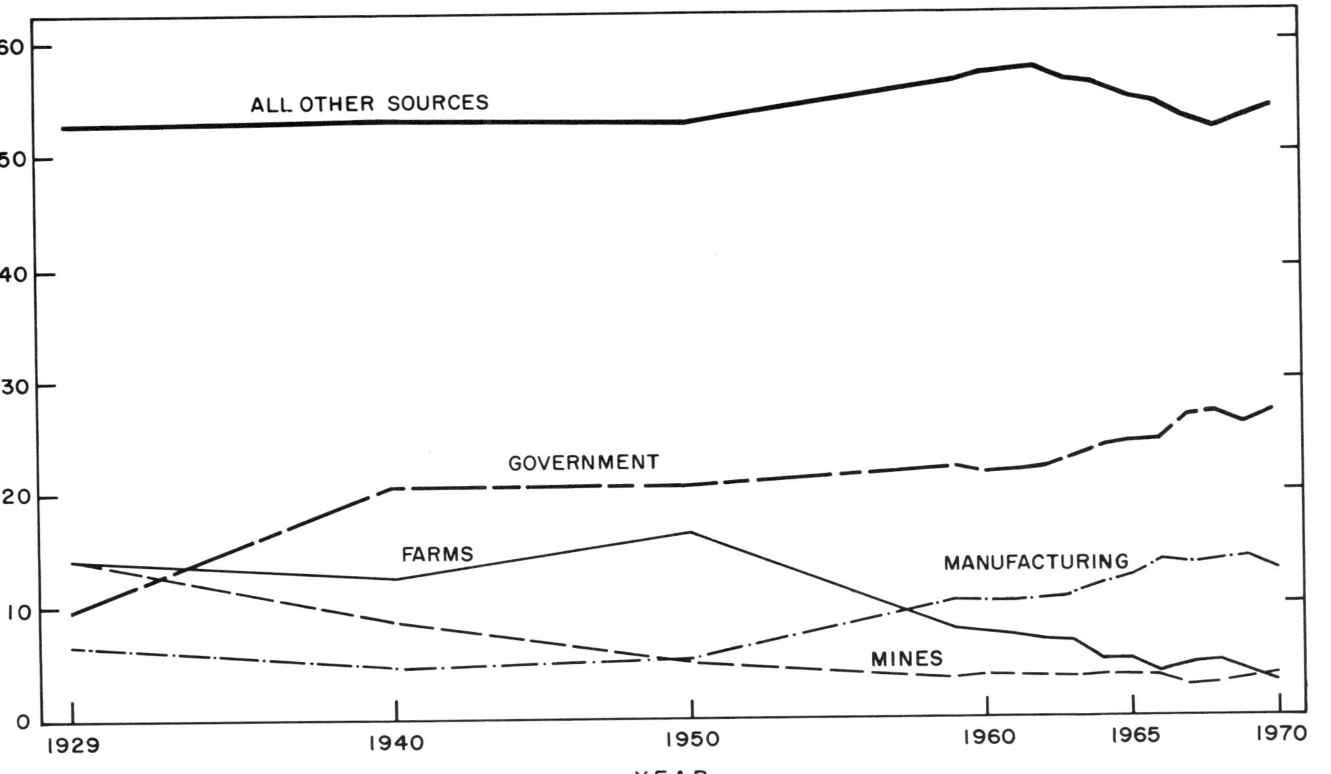

Fig. 1-8. *Percentage of personal income by broad source, Arizona, 1929–1970*. Source: *table 1-1*.

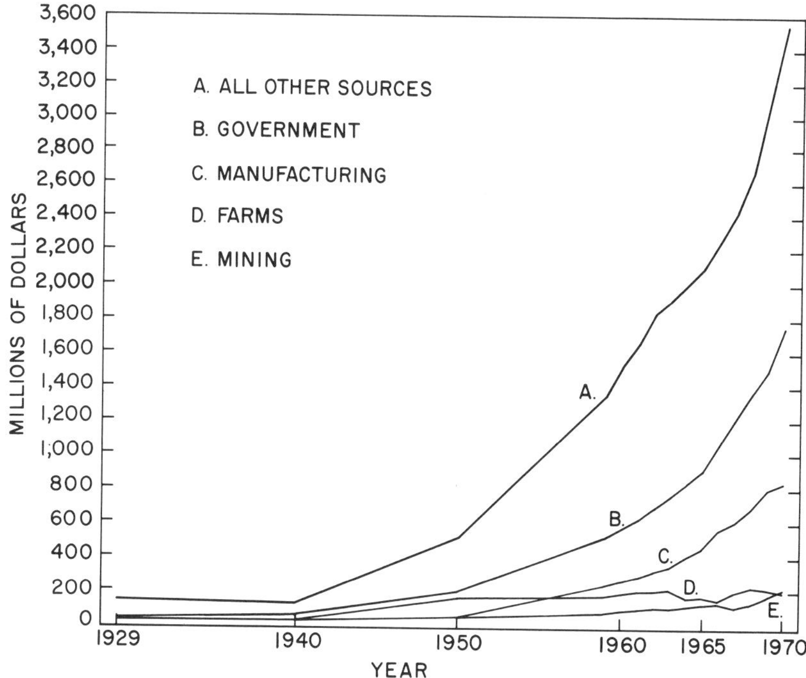

Fig. 1-9. *Personal income by broad source, Arizona, 1929–1970, in dollars of current purchasing power.* Source: *table 1-1.*

Popular Image of the Water Problem

This vigorous growth in a desert setting where water is obviously limited has precipitated and given a sense of urgency to the popular notion of "the water problem" in Arizona. Agriculture was an early and leading sector in the state's economy and is still an important sector in the early 1970s. Among all economic sectors, it is, however, the largest user of water per unit of production or per dollar of income created. Because of this large-volume demand for water by agriculture, and because there existed only a narrowly limited surface water supply, agriculture early established and perfected its property claims to all readily available surface-water supplies by the time vigorous economic growth got underway.

Economic growth, however, meant expansion in many other industrial, manufacturing, commercial, and service sectors of the economy (table 1-1 and figures 1-9 and 1-10) all of which require varying amounts of water in their processes. Concomitant with their growth was a rapid

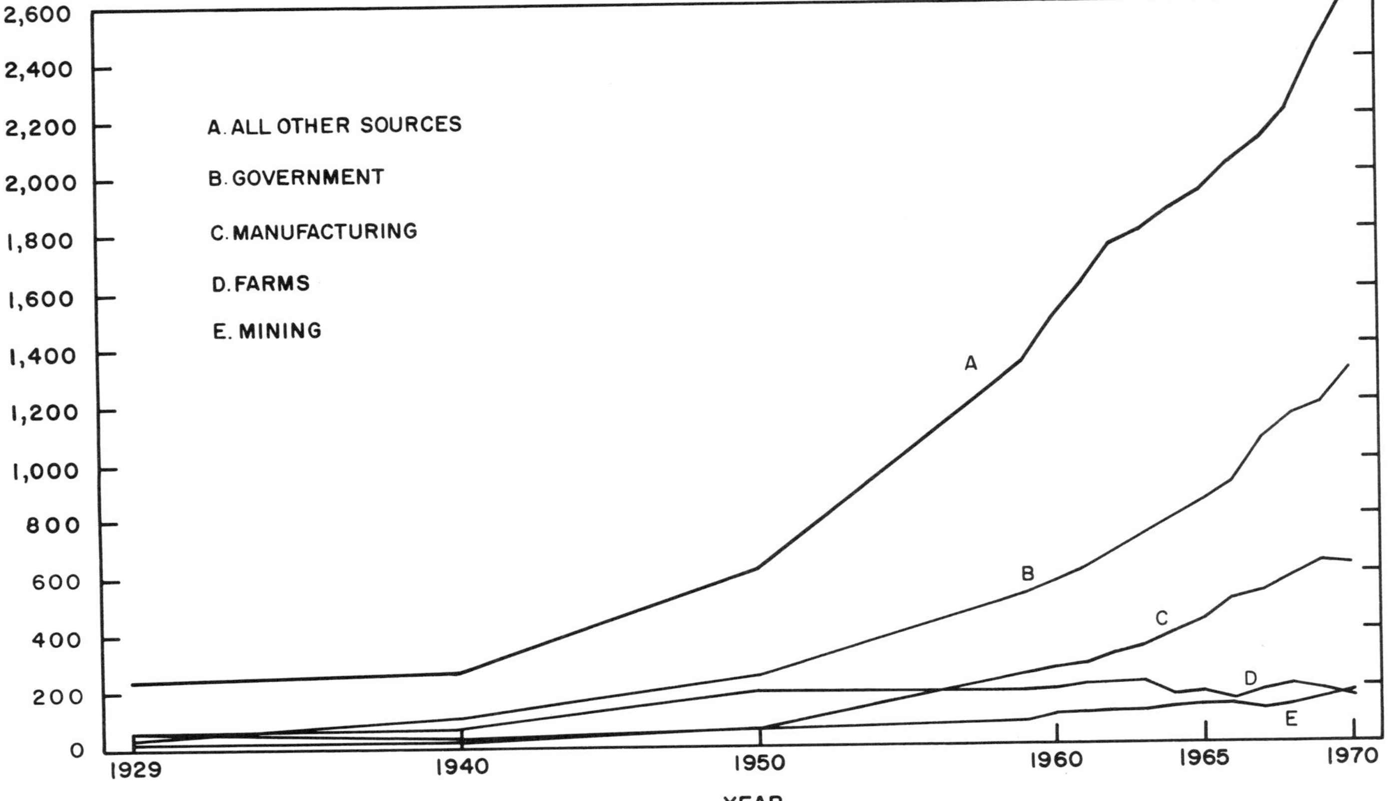

Fig. 1-10. *Personal income by broad source, Arizona, 1929–1970, in dollars of*

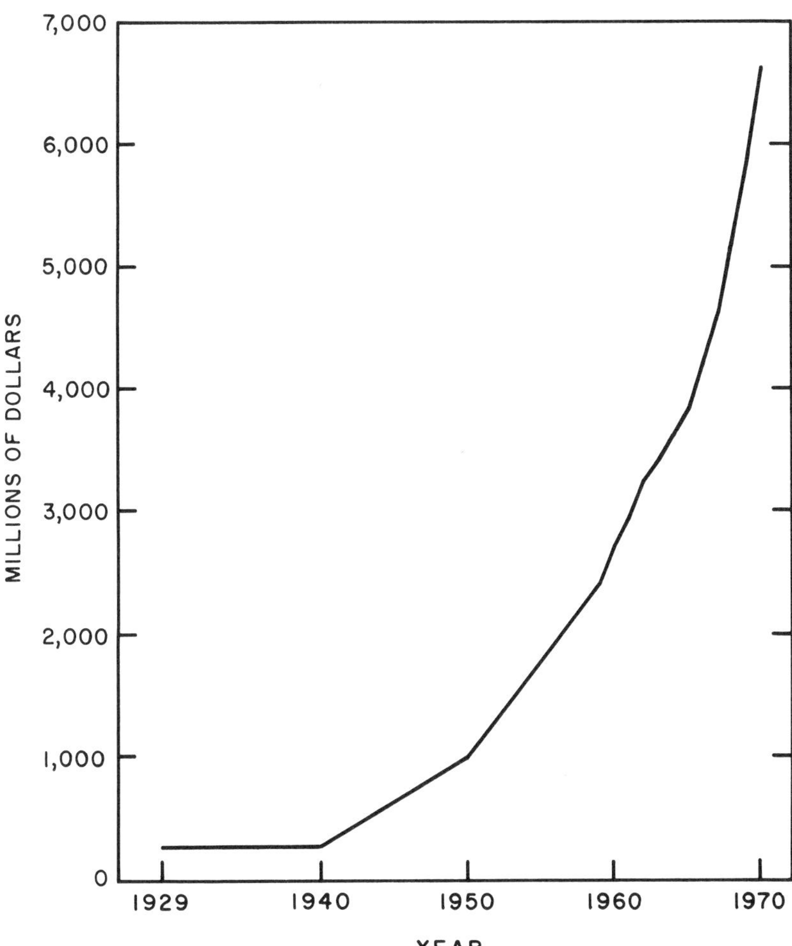

Fig. 1-11. *Total personal income from all sources, Arizona, 1929–1970, in dollars of current purchasing power.* Source: *table 1-1.*

growth in numbers of people who also are consumers of water (figure 1-12). Thus, the popular notion of the water problem was posed as follows: with existing limited supplies already appropriated by an important but heavy-water-using sector (agriculture) and other demands for water increasing rapidly, how were the growing *water requirements* to be met and economic growth kept going? All in all, it appeared that limited water supplies in the state might prove to be the number one restraint on continued growth of the Arizona economy.

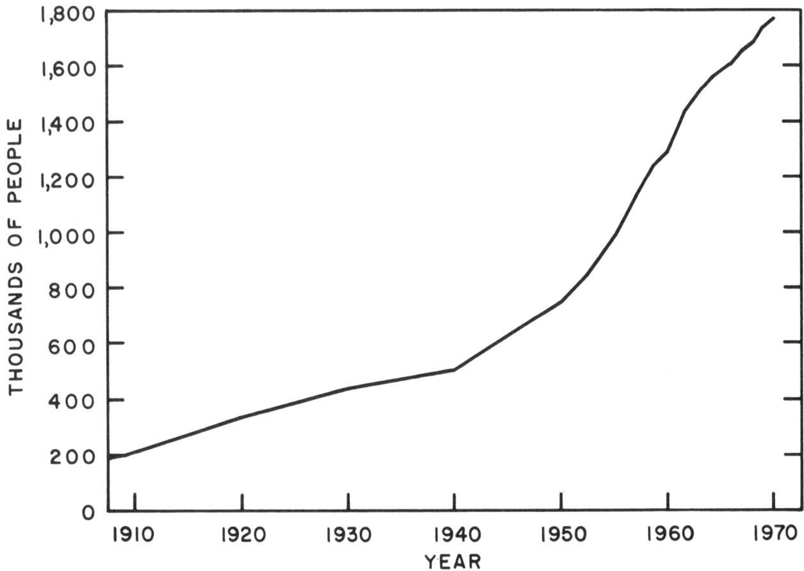

Fig. 1-12. *Arizona population, 1910–1970.* Source: *Statistical Abstract of the United States (relevant years).*

Therefore, a much discussed problem in Arizona for many years has been the degree to which water shortage will be a drag on the state's economy and what, if anything, can or ought to be done about it. This is the problem to which the study reported herein is directed.

Limitation on the growth of the mining industry in Arizona has always been and still is its competitive economic advantage relative to other mineral-supplying areas in the world and its ability to locate additional economically exploitable ore-bodies within the state. Water as an input to the mining and smelting industry, though essential in relatively small quantities per unit of output in both weight and value terms, rapidly exhausts its productivity as larger quantities are used per unit of output or income. In the language of economic theory, water, in the mining and smelting industry, produces a high marginal and average value per unit of water for small quantities of water use per unit of output, but its average and marginal value productivity per unit of water use falls rapidly toward zero as quantities beyond these initial small amounts per unit of output are applied. Thus, the industry can, if need be, and often does, pay handsomely for small quantities of water. But, as of the early 1970s, water availability has not limited the mining sector of the Arizona economy.

The limiting factor in growth of the range livestock industry has been the relatively unchanging ability of man to produce natural forage per acre and to convert the forage produced into marketable product. Along with a relatively fixed productivity per acre of forage-producing land, the range livestock industry has had a shrinking area available for its use. As with mining, water is essential to the range livestock industry in small quantities per unit of product. Its value in those small quantities is high, but its marginal and average value productivity falls rapidly after those small requirements per unit of output have been met. Water has not been and will not be a limitation on the growth of the range livestock industry.

Essentially the same point can be made for all the presently expanding economic sectors of the state's economy, including household consumers. Some, relatively small, quantity of water is essential to each of these expanding uses, and these small quantities generate high marginal and average values of productivity. Hence users can and often do pay handsomely for these small initial quantities. But beyond these small and highly valuable initial amounts, the value of additional quantities of water declines rapidly. Given the ability to obtain these modest amounts of highly valuable water, water supplies are no restraint on growth. Comparative economic advantage of Arizona firms versus competing firms outside Arizona derived from market location, transportation, and communication advantages are the decisive restraints on growth of the manufacturing and commercial sectors of Arizona's economy.

This brings us to the crop-farming sector of the state's economy. Because of the desert nature of the state, crop agriculture is wholly dependent on irrigation for the moisture supplies essential to plant growth. The water that falls on Arizona is too thinly distributed and falls on many lands not suitable for crop growth. Therefore it must be transported to and concentrated on fewer acres or supplemented with water brought to the cropland areas from natural storages (largely underground) or from distant areas that have more water than they can economically or legally use. Thus, crop agriculture in Arizona has been and always will be limited by the volume and cost of legally available water supplies.

Large-scale irrigated crop agriculture in Arizona was made possible by two developments in the state occurring at two different points in time. The first was the development and expansion of the Salt River Project over a forty-year period under the financial and management assistance of the Bureau of Reclamation. Through this development, the run-off waters of the Salt and Verde rivers flowing from the highest water-yielding area within the state have been totally captured by six storage reservoirs and are transported to approximately 239,000 acres eligible to receive them in and around Phoenix.

The second development was the rapid technological improvement since World War II in well-drilling techniques, in deep-well pump efficiencies, and in lower costs of power (both electricity and natural gas) for driving the pumps. As a consequence, the vast underground aquifer underlying much of Maricopa and Pinal Counties, as well as scattered aquifers in numerous other valley areas of the state, have been extensively tapped. Now, more water is provided annually by pumps from underground than from surface sources.

It is evident that crop agriculture has exerted a steady pressure for development and procurement of additional water supplies, because the primary restraint on expansion of that industry always has been the water supplies available to it.

One facet of the water problem in Arizona has stemmed from this steady pressure by the crop-producing industry for additional water supplies. One source of this pressure has been the internal logic for expansion of any industry. Requisite land, labor, management, and capital were available. If only more water were available, additional desert could be made verdant and productive, additional product could be generated, and additional activity generated in the Arizona economy. Hence, the pressure to develop more water for agriculture.

Another source of the pressure from the crop industry for more water supplies has been the need for more reliable supplies of water to satisfy its needs in all seasons of each year and for all years in the face of fluctuating seasonal and yearly supplies.

A second facet of the water problem in Arizona emerged with the expansion of agricultural crop production based on expanded groundwater pumpage. This facet of the problem is expressed as a concern over the "long run" supply of water for agriculture as well as for all other water uses. Extraction of water from nature's storehouse in annual amounts greater than nature's deposits results in a steadily diminishing quantity of water in the storehouse and a steadily increasing depth from which it must be drawn.

This development added a new and more urgent dimension to the concern over water supplies. Now, in addition to the internal logic of an industry for expansion and for seasonal and annual stability, there was added the far more potent logic of economic survival. In time, the storehouse would be emptied (or lowered beyond the economic reach of crop agriculture). At this point crop agriculture must shrink, to its own economic detriment, but, also to the detriment of those parts of the state's economy related directly and indirectly to the crop producing industry.

To these problems, a third facet has been added. Although it might with justification be said that until World War II Arizona was basically an economy of primary industries exploiting minerals, grass, and irrigation water, since then there has been a shift at a steadily increasing tempo from an economy of primary industries to a manufacturing and service economy (table 1-1 and figures 1-9 and 1-10). General urban-industrial growth has added significantly to the demand for water for municipal-domestic and industrial purposes. In addition, rising levels of living have increased the per capita demands for municipal water both for private and public uses.

Increases in nonagricultural demands for water have led to proportional increases in the volume of municipal and industrial water use, but, what is more important, they have led to anticipations of still greater increases to come. However, all existing annual surface-water supplies are now claimed by existing users, and the groundwater storehouse is being depleted by 3.0 to 3.5 million acre-feet per year by existing claimants. Viewed simplistically and uncritically, this leaves much doubt as to where those increasing municipal-industrial supplies of the future are going to be obtained.

Thus, the third facet of the popular view of the state's water problem has been concern over future water shortages. Not only will these shortages put a damper on continued expansion of the state's economy but, more importantly, may even cause it to shrink due to the persistent overdraft on the underground water storehouse.

We summarize the popular image of the Arizona water problem:

1. Water is being used annually in larger quantities than become annually available.

2. Existing uses must in the long run be curtailed, resulting in shrinkage of the state's economy.

3. Population growth and new uses for water in the state will be stymied unless additional presently unclaimed and unused supplies can be found and developed from either within or outside the state.

Changing Economic Structure and Relative Water Requirements

Different economic sectors of the Arizona economy have greatly different demands for water per unit of output or income and in the aggregate. Growth of the economy is not followed by proportional growth in total water demand in the state except in the unlikely circumstance that all economic sectors of the state grow in similar proportions. Figures 1-9,

1-10 and table 1-1 clearly show that since World War II the structural make-up of the economy has changed drastically, a matter of considerable importance when assessing the relation of water to economic growth. During the period from 1929 to about 1940, the structure of the economy was relatively stable (table 1-1) and so was the total of annual water diversions and pumpage at about three million acre-feet (figure 1-6). During the period from the early 1940s to 1953, the structure of the economy began to change (table 1-1 and figure 1-9). Growth centered in agriculture and government. Irrigated crop production increased from 0.5 to 1.3 million acres and from about 65 million dollars to about 200 million dollars of personal income creation. Government grew as a source of personal incomes from something over 100 million dollars to about 250 million dollars and total of all personal incomes from about 500 to about 1,180 million dollars. (Income figures in this section are given in dollars of constant purchasing power, as shown in table 1-1, in order to remove the "red herring" of inflation from these income comparisons.) Population increased by about 80 percent, or by 400,000 persons. Water diversions and pumpage during this period increased from about 3.0 million acre-feet to about 6.5 million acre-feet, or more than doubled (figure 1-7). Up to this point, experience seemed to support the popular notion of the nature of the water problem. Continued economic growth would continue to require increasing quantities of water.

However, beginning about 1953, the changing structure of the growing Arizona economy entered a new phase in which irrigated crop production and livestock grazing remained essentially unchanged (in fact, irrigated acreage decreased slightly though irrigated agriculture held constant in income creation) but all other sectors entered a period of accelerated growth. Between 1953 and 1968 income created in the government sector increased from 250 million dollars to 1,150 million dollars; manufacturing from 60 million dollars to almost 600 million dollars; mines from 60 to 125 million dollars; and the total of all personal incomes increased from 1,180 million to 4,270 million dollars. Population more than doubled from 1953 to 1968, increasing by another 845,000 persons.

In spite of this phenomenal increase in income generated within the state's economy between 1953 and 1968, water diversions and pumpage increased only from about 6.5 million acre-feet to about 7.8 million acre-feet. (There is some question as to how much the increases in diversion and pumpage figures reflect true increases and how much they reflect improvements in data collection. Though the increase includes some of the latter influence, its magnitude is not known and at most it is probably a small proportion. Thus, we use these data herein as reported by the USGS and make no attempt to correct them for this factor.)

The great importance of the changing structure of the economy on economic growth and water demand in Arizona is strikingly apparent from these data. Also apparent is the degree to which structure of the economy can change with attendant large increases in income with but modest demands for increased diversions and pumpage of water. As summarized in table 1-2, between 1940 and the early 1950s when irrigated crop acreage increased significantly, total income from irrigated agriculture was equaled or surpassed only by government and "all other sources," and population increased by less than one-half million, total water diversions and pumpage increased by about 3.5 million acre-feet, and total income increased by 669 million dollars.

But, between 1953 and 1968, when the increase in total state income took place almost wholly in the nonagricultural sectors and net incomes increased by 3,088 million dollars, together with a population increase of 845,000 people, water diversions and pumpage increased by only 1.27 million acre-feet.

TABLE 1-2

Changing Structure of the Arizona Economy Related to Water Diversions and Pumpage

Factor	1940 Amounts	Changes from 1940 to early 1950s*	Changes from early 1950s* to 1968
Water (acre-feet annually)†	2,954,000	+3,579,000	+1,266,000
Irrigated acres‡	665,000	+ 635,000	− 96,000
State income			
(million dollars annually)§			
Agriculture	66	+ 129	+ 5
Mines	45	+ 14	+ 66
Manufacturing	25	+ 37	+ 518
Government	106	+ 139	+ 899
All other sources	272	+ 350	+ 1,600
Total	514	+ 669	+ 3,088
Population (number)	499,261	+ 395,000	+ 845,000

*Various years from 1950 to 1953, depending upon availability of data.

†From figure 1-6.

‡From **Arizona Agriculture** for relevant years.

§Incomes are in dollars of constant purchasing power (1957-59 = 100) as given in table 1-1.

These data underscore a significant consideration in analyzing the relation between water supplies and economic growth in an arid economy, namely, the importance of the *changing structure* of an economy as a means for meeting the threat of water shortage as a restraint on growth. This phenomenon led us to realize the importance of another avenue of inquiry in our analysis of the water problem. To what degree can or might the problem of water shortage as a restraint on growth be circumvented by changing the structure of the Arizona economy? And, stemming from this question, what are the prospects that the economy will, responding to ordinary market processes, "automatically" change its structure in the desired directions? And, do existing institutions facilitate or hinder such "automatic" changes in economic structure? Or, if purposive policy actions by the state can be used to *change the supply of water* available, what might be the purposive policy actions it could use to *change the demand for water* without adversely affecting, even, possibly, favorably affecting income creation and economic growth of the state?

A New Conception of the Water Problem

We began this research with the popular image of the water problem in Arizona in mind, and nothing more. We had no reason to disavow it; it seemed plausible on its face; the relevant water data seemed to support the popular conception. Our goal was to measure empirically and to project into the future the increasing economic cost of the problem to the state's economy. We reasoned that by doing so we would add concreteness and economic dimensions to the understanding of the state's water problem both by those inside and by those outside of the state, thus providing a justification for and a measure of the magnitude of the needed expenditures to solve the problem.

As will become clear as we reveal our findings, our analysis did not bear out our beginning notion of the nature of the water problem – the popular notion. In the spirit of scientific method, this led us to reject our beginning ideas of the popular notion of the problem and to seek new ideas concerning the real nature of the state's water problem that our findings would support.

We thus were lead to the following notions as to the real nature of the state's water problem and its solution, the validity of which the description of our findings and their meanings will reveal:

1. Water is *economically* scarce in Arizona but not so *physically* limited as to be a serious threat to the viability of the state's economy.
2. Much of the scarce water supplies are, by legal devices and by

reasons of location, locked into uses in which the marginal value of the product of the water is extremely low – approaching zero in some cases.

3. Curtailment of these low-valued uses because of increasing water scarcity (revealed as rising costs of pumping from the stored groundwater supply) will have but modest effects on the state's economy because of the low value productivity of the marginal units of water that were being used in this fashion.

4. Changing the structure of the state's economy by curtailing water uses producing lowest net incomes per unit of water used, and expanding water using sectors of higher production of net income per unit of water, can release growth of the Arizona economy from all restraint by water, well into the twenty-first century.

5. Such transfer of water use is economically advantageous to the state's economy, as it means, simply, that the state is using its scarce water in higher income producing activities, thus adding to the economic growth and income level of the state's economy.

6. By creating a water market or establishing an allocative agency charged with facilitating water transfers from uses of lower value productivity to uses of higher value productivity, the Arizona economy can continue to grow without significant restraint stemming from "water shortage."

In sum, the Arizona water problem is more a problem of the lack of man-made institutions (policies) for developing and transferring water than a problem of physically short supplies. At least, the problem can be resolved more cheaply for many years to come if it is approached through institutional (policy) reform relating to water transfer rather than through development and/or importation of additional water supplies. The water problem in Arizona is a "man-problem" rather than a "nature-problem."

2. Conceptualizing an Economic Analysis of the Arizona Water Problem

Analysis at a Point in Time: Statics

Static Demand for Water

Any commodity or service is wanted in order to satisfy someone's desires. The strength of the desire for the first few units of the commodity or service may be great. However, as more units become available, given no change in the demander's structure of preferences, the desire for additional units of the commodity or service becomes less and less. The economist refers to this phenomenon as *diminishing marginal utility;* it means simply that as more units of a commodity or service become available to a user (or use), he (it) will be willing to pay less and less for successive additional quantities. This condition applies to water as to all other economic goods which are desired for final consumptive uses.

As with any good, material, or service added to a mixture of other inputs in order to produce some product, water when added to a production-input mix adds fewer and fewer units of output (product) as more and more units of water are added, given no change in the kind or amount of other inputs in the mix or in the technology of the production process. This condition the economist calls *diminishing marginal productivity* or diminishing returns.

Thus, we expect to find the value of quantities of water *added* to existing quantities of water to be *smaller* than that of the existing quantities. Conversely, the value of units of water *lost* to existing uses is that of the lowest valued uses of the existing supply – given, remember, no changes in the conditions underlying demand or the production process. This is what is meant by *marginal value productivity;* the value added or lost by adding or deleting a unit of water to or from an existing use.

This phenomenon occurs whether the using unit is a single household, a single farm or industrial producer, or an aggregate of such users as a whole industry of users, or a whole economy of users such as make up a county, region, or state. It can be illustrated as shown in figure 2-1.

Suppose this graphic picture represents the marginal water demand by one average urban family. The family will pay handsomely – more than

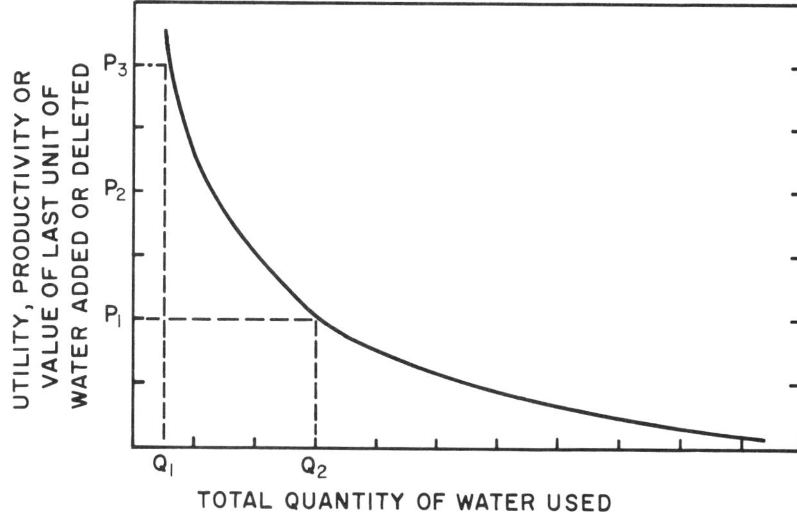

Fig. 2-1. *The marginal value of additional units of water (hypothetical).*

a price of p_3 – to get the first small quantity, q_1. But its willingness to pay for additional quantities falls rapidly until some modest quantity (say q_2, or 50 gallons per day) is obtained. This family will be happy to obtain much more water than 50 gallons per day, but only at much lower prices per additional unit of water. For example, it would only pay a price of p_1 for the last unit of water that would bring total water use to q_2. The line in this picture is the *marginal value* or *marginal productivity* of water to a consumer household. Rationally, one would pay no more for a marginal unit of water than its marginal value. Notice the broken-backed appearance of the marginal value curve. This appearance is typical of such marginal-water-demand curves by all types of users whether urban consumers, urban businesses, manufacturers, miners and smelters, or irrigators, and whether for one user or for an aggregate of users.

The broken-backed shape of the demand curve for additional water arises because there are, for any user, certain uses for water that are crucial to him, for which he will pay handsomely but for which only small quantities are required. Examples are water for drinking, for cooking, and for cleanliness by a household consumer, or for irrigating high-valued crops such as lettuce or citrus by a farmer. But these same users have other uses for water, not crucial to their happiness or well-being but "worthwhile." For these uses the consumers would be willing to pay smaller amounts, and for these uses they could use considerably larger quantities of water. Examples are irrigation of lawns and shrubbery for the urban consumer; irrigation of barley, sorghum, and alfalfa by a farmer; and flushing out tanks, troughs, and floors by a manufacturer.

Not all individual users are exactly alike in this relation of *value* and *additional water demanded,* but their marginal demand curves for water all do tend to have this broken-backed shape. If we know the exact shape of this marginal demand curve for each water user and add them together to determine the total quantity of water required at each level of cost, we have an aggregate marginal demand curve for all water users in Arizona; or, if we add together the curves by groups of different types of water users, we have aggregate marginal demand curves for urban consumers, for mines and smelters, for irrigators, and so on.

From what we know about these relations between value and quantity in water demand between different kinds of uses and users, it appears that some uses (users) attach much higher values to the first few units of water they want than do other users, whereas some of these other users will take much greater quantities of water at low relative prices. We illustrate the aggregate marginal demand curves for several types of users in figure 2-2.

Urban consumers attach a higher value to a small quantity of water than do any other users, but they don't take much water. At the other extreme, irrigators attach a much lower value than do any other users, even to their most valuable water. However, at relatively low values for

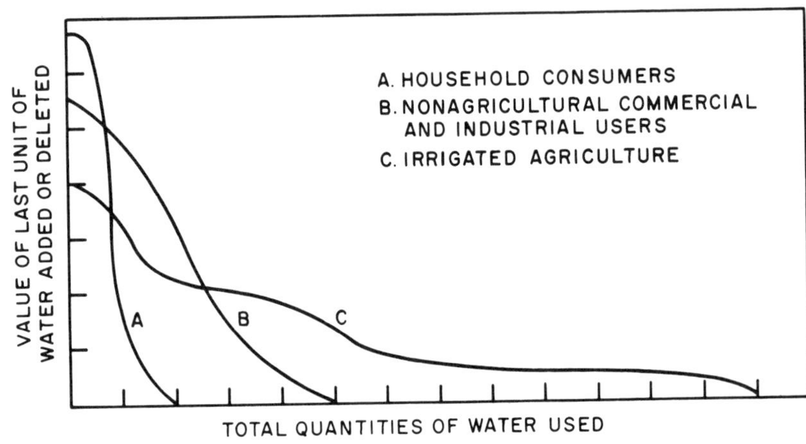

Fig. 2-2. *Aggregate marginal demand curves for water for several types of users (hypothetical).*

water, irrigators use much more water than do any other class of users. Nonagricultural commercial and industrial users stand midway between these two groups. We can add together these several marginal demand curves for water and get a composite marginal demand picture for all water users. This composite curve is shown as figure 2-3. It may be read as follows.

Suppose the cost of water in the area is "a" and that this cost applies to all users. Then the aggregate demand curve for water says that urban householders would use quantity of water "OA," nonagricultural, commercial, and industrial users would take quantity "AB," and irrigated farming would use quantity "BC," or, in all, a total quantity of "OC" units of water would be used.

We observe two things about aggregate water demand:

1. Within each *class* of users, some uses by that class are more valuable to it than are other uses; there are marginal uses within each class.

2. As between classes of users, some classes of users are "more marginal" than others in the sense that they do not compete strongly for the first small supplies of available water but compete strongly for large quantities of water at low levels of per unit cost.

The second of these characteristics of aggregate water demand applies strongly in Arizona as it does in any "irrigation" state or area. Irrigated agriculture is a user of large quantities of water at low water values. In Arizona, for instance, all urban household and nonagricultural, commercial, and industrial water uses combined (quantities OA plus AB in our water-demand picture of figure 2-3) amounted to 600,000 acre-

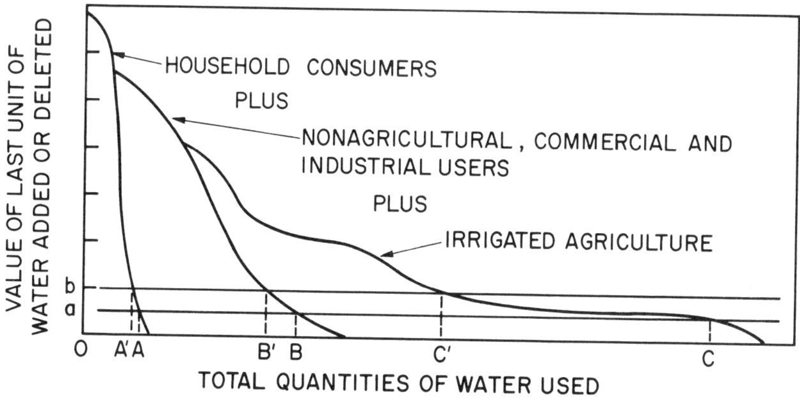

Fig. 2-3. *Composite aggregate marginal demand curve for water for several types of users (hypothetical).*

feet in 1967, whereas quantity BC (agricultural use alone) accounted for 6,400,000 acre feet, more than ten times as much as all nonagricultural uses combined.

But suppose the cost of water rose to level "b" in Arizona because of increasing cost of pumping or the need to import "replacement" water for disappearing groundwater at higher levels of cost. Notice what happens to quantities of water taken by the various users. Agricultural use is cut about in half (from BC to B′C′) while all other uses outside agriculture are cut only from B to B′. Most of the cut in nonagricultural use is in commercial and industrial uses. Urban households are affected hardly at all (from A to A′ only).

In other words, a small increase in water cost will reduce agricultural use greatly and all other uses only slightly. This conception of marginal water demand led us to our first decision on how to approach the study of the impact of growing water scarcity on Arizona's economy. Agricultural irrigation is the *marginal* use (or class of users) and by far the largest user of the limited available quantities of water in Arizona. The impact of any changes in costs of available water will affect agricultural irrigation much more than any or all other classes of uses taken together. Thus, we decided to concentrate our initial analyses on the relations between water quantities and marginal values in the irrigation agriculture industry of the state and ignore, for the time being, impacts on all other segments of water demand in the state.

Having selected irrigated agriculture as the economic sector on which to concentrate our analysis (because it constitutes the *marginal sector,* and by far the largest user among all sectors), recall, then, the other characteristic of aggregate water demand, namely, that within each class of users some uses by that class are more valuable to it than other uses; some uses within a class of users are marginal to other uses within the same class. This characteristic is especially important within the irrigated agriculture class of users where the marginal demand for water by irrigated agriculture looks as depicted in figure 2-4.

The first quantity of water, OX, is highly valuable to agriculture. This amount might represent the water used on intensive vegetable and fruit crops and on citrus orchards and can, if need be, be quite costly. The quantity XY is next most valuable, can be next most expensive, and might represent the quantity used on cotton, potatoes, sugar beets, and similar semi-intensive field crops. The quantity YZ is the least valuable water. It must be *cheap* and might represent that water used on feed grains and forage crops, largely barley, sorghum, and alfalfa.

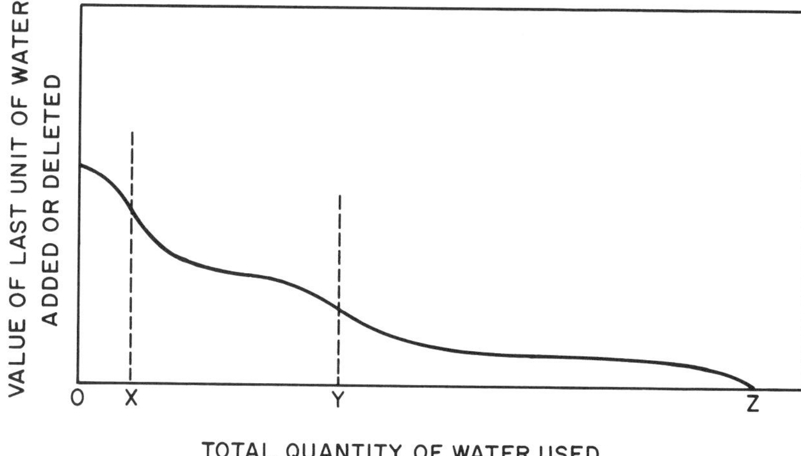

Fig. 2-4. *Aggregate marginal demand curve for irrigated agriculture (hypothetical).*

If there is no interrelating production linkage between these three classes of crops, it is obvious that, as water becomes scarcer or of higher cost, the grains and forages will be sacrificed first because they are the marginal, or *sensitive,* uses within agriculture. Cotton and other semi-intensive crops are next in marginality or *sensitivity* to water cost; vegetables, fruits, and citrus are least marginal or most *insensitive.*

This reasoning led us to our second decision on how we would approach this study. We would determine the empirical shape and level of the marginal demand-for-water curve within irrigated agriculture pictured hypothetically in figure 2-4 and identify which crops, in what amounts of acreage and output, constitute the various points along that marginal demand curve. By doing so, we would determine the net value of product produced by each successive unit of water used in irrigating crops in the state. On the reasonable assumption that irrigators would cut back on their least valuable uses of water as it becomes more expensive, we could also determine how much net product value in agriculture would, as a consequence, be lost to the Arizona economy. Furthermore, by estimating the rate of future year-to-year increases in water costs due primarily to falling groundwater levels, we would be able to chart the rate of year-to-year decline to be expected in agricultural net incomes in the state over future years.

Static Economic Supply of Water

As the preceding discussion implies, we need to know something else about the economics of water use in irrigated agriculture, in addition to economic consequences of water scarcity. We must know the amounts of the demand for water at a point in time, before we can determine the economic consequences of water scarcity. We must know the amounts of water available to agriculture at alternative plausible levels of costs at a point in time (what the economic analyst calls the *static economic supply* of water).

The economic problem of water doesn't rest on the physical quantity of available water alone but on the physical quantities available at particular costs. It isn't enough to know that a million acre-feet of water, for example, are physically available. One must know what quantities, totaling a million acre-feet, are available at what cost for each quantity.

First, however, we need to be sure what we mean by *available*. To be physically available is one thing, but to be legally available may be something else again. This takes the analyst into water law and the law governing the operating policies controlling water-managing organizations. The next chapter describes the Arizona situation in this regard. It is sufficient for our purposes here to be clear only that when we refer to economic supply we mean that quantity or quantities of water that are *legally* or *organizationally* available for use at a range of costs.

Typically, different quantities of water are available to agricultural users at different levels of cost. Under conditions of water supply where the farmer purchases his water from an irrigation district, it is usual for the irrigator to have the right to acquire some specified quantity of water at a price, some further quantity at a different price (usually higher), through two or more such steps. Such a supply curve can be pictured as in figure 2-5.

This graphic picture of water supply says that this user can obtain any quantity of water he wants up to the quantity OA at a price of Oa for each unit. Any additional amount up to AB would cost Ob per unit. Any further amount up to BC costs Oc per unit. No water at all can be obtained in excess of quantity OC. The original source of any of these supplies could be either surface water or pumped water, where both types of water are being developed and sold to the farmer by the irrigation district.

The static marginal water supply curve for irrigators who pump their own water also would have this same general shape, as illustrated in figure 2-5, if they were pumping from several different depths. Quantity OA would be the maximum quantity that could be pumped in one year

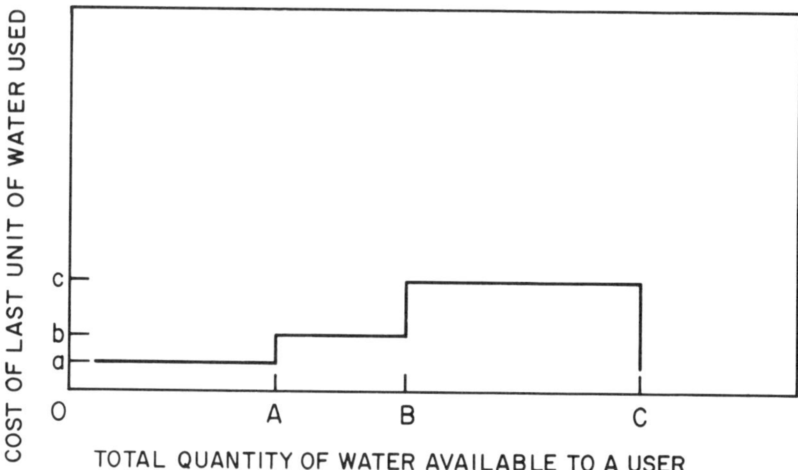

Fig. 2-5. *Marginal supply curve for water (hypothetical).*

from the shallowest depth at a cost of Oa per acre-foot. Larger quantities of water are available at higher costs from wells of deeper pumping lifts.

Figure 2-5 shows the marginal supply curve facing a single user of either district delivered or pumped water. Just as we did with the individual marginal demand curves, we can add together the supplies available to any number of individual users and derive an aggregate marginal supply schedule for the total number of users. But in doing so a complication intrudes that must be taken into account.

The picture of demand for water, as developed in the preceding section, was for water available to the users *where they want to use it.* Thus, our picture of available supplies must likewise be put in terms of supply available at the same location as demand – that is, where the irrigators want to use it. In other words, we must picture supply at *delivered prices.* The cost of available water must reflect not only its cost at point of pumpage or diversion but also the costs of its delivery to point of use.

Hence, a meaningful aggregate marginal water supply function can include only those potential users of the water who are confronted with identical or closely similar delivery costs for the water in question. Consequently, we will have as many aggregate marginal water supply curves as there are areas within which delivery conditions for water are the same for everybody within each area.

Because in our analysis it is necessary to relate marginal demand for water to the marginal supply of available water, it will be necessary to picture aggregate demands separately for each group of users for whom separate supply curves are determined. The result is that our analysis of demand for and supply of water must be disaggregated into area units of relatively uniform internal water delivery cost conditions. Then, the results of these disaggregated area analyses can be summed to portray the statewide consequences of the state's total water problem.

Fortunately, surface water supplies in Arizona are quite localized and are in all cases distributed to agricultural users through organized districts in each of which all users are charged uniform prices; thus the disaggregation problem is relatively simple. Relative to *surface* water supplies for agriculture, we find it necessary to consider only the following aggregate areas: (1) the Gila River above San Carlos reservoir, (2) the San Carlos Irrigation District below San Carlos reservoir, (3) the Salt River Project and its related Roosevelt Water Conservation District, (4) the several Yuma irrigation districts and the Wellton-Mohawk project, and (5) the Maricopa County Municipal Water Conservation District No. 1 and the Buckeye Water Conservation and Drainage District.

The economic supply of groundwater clearly is not simply all the water contained in the aquifers underlying the demanders. It is a function of the costs required in lifting it to the surface. These costs will be a function of depth to water, efficiency of the aquifer in giving up the water it holds, the "draw down" or cone of depression resulting from pumping, the costs of power and equipment, and the costs for well drilling, deepening, and casing.

Because, in most cases, groundwater is self-supplied by its users, distribution costs of the produced water at the surface are negligible. Generally, only extraction costs need to be incorporated in the groundwater supply function. In some cases groundwater is pumped by an organization and delivered to its many members. In such cases, it is typically priced to all members at uniform prices as delivered water. However, extraction costs vary by depth to water and by aquifer efficiencies so that economic supplies of self-supplied groundwater are composed of those quantities pumped from nominally common aquifers at ranges of cost reflecting variability in pumping conditions. Given appropriate considerations in delineating a common groundwater aquifer, it is possible to derive a marginal supply curve for groundwater for a single common aquifer. This curve would be similar to that shown in figure 2-5 but would have many small successive steps instead of only the few steps shown.

In Arizona, developed and exploited groundwater aquifers are widely dispersed and highly diverse in hydrologic characteristics. This poses a difficult problem for our analysis. We must compromise between the greater analytical cost and complexity confronted by including all diverse aquifer characteristics in the analysis and the loss of accuracy experienced with lesser cost and complexity by grouping aquifers into "representative classes" for purposes of our analysis. After weighing the advantages and disadvantages in accuracy versus cost and complexity, we chose to group the groundwater aquifers into study areas as follows:

1. The area of the Salt River Project and its related Roosevelt Water Conservation District. (Note that this area is also one of the surface water areas segregated for our study. Thus it comes about that we study the Salt River Project-Roosevelt Water Conservation District area as a problem of joint surface water-groundwater use.)

2. The Santa Cruz-Gila groundwater complex in Pinal-Pima Counties. (The San Carlos Irrigation District in Pinal County is also an area of joint surface-groundwater use.)

3. The complex of aquifers that compose Maricopa County *outside* the SRP-RWCD area (further complicated by surface waters in the Maricopa County Municipal Water Conservation District No. 1 and the Buckeye Water Conservation and Drainage District).

4. The purely groundwater areas of the San Simon-Aravaipa-Wilcox-Douglas basins of Cochise County.

We recognize diversity *within* each of these areas by subclassifying each area into subareas of similar pumping lift and dynamic characteristics of groundwater decline.

The frequent but small upward steps in the marginal supply curve of groundwater reflect two things: (1) the fact that some users must pump from deeper groundwater levels than others and/or that some must pump from less efficient aquifers; (2) that as the volume and duration of pumping from each individual user's wells increase, the cost of water to him will rise because of deeper "coning." In either event, the cost of groundwater in the area rises as volume produced increases.

There is a further difficulty. Though irrigation water originating from surface flows and water pumped from the ground may be essentially indistinguishable for irrigation purposes, they are so different in respect of the legal-administrative structures that surround their production and distribution as to make them wholly different *economic* supplies. This requires that we usually must keep groundwater supplies distinct from surface-water supplies and consider them to be two distinct economic inputs. As a result, we have, for each separate area where both groundwater and surface water are used, marginal supply curves for surface water and separate marginal supply curves for groundwater. In some areas of the state, only *one or the other* of these supplies will be relevant to the analysis. In other areas *both* may be relevant, the demanders having available two different supplies to which they may turn to satisfy their demands. Our analysis will be concerned with how much of each at what costs each of the irrigation areas will use.

The water-supply conditions discussed so far are short-period, single-cropping cycle, or annual supplies; the cost increases shown do not reflect declining levels of groundwater due to withdrawals in excess of recharge. The supply curve shown is *static,* meaning it shows conditions existing at a point in time; the increases in costs because of water-table decline from year to year are *dynamic* and will be considered below.

Static Economic Consequences of Marginal Demand and Supply

Let us see how the relationship of demands and supplies described so far may be used to derive information about economic activity related to water uses.

Because we are focusing our initial analysis on water use in irrigated agriculture, we assume for our illustration an area in which the aggregate demand for and the aggregate supplies of surface and groundwater for irrigation use might appear as shown in figure 2-6.

In figure 2-6, the various segments of the marginal supply curve might have the following interpretations:

1. The segment from O to X might be the supply of surface water available under surface-flow rights. The cost to the irrigator of the first

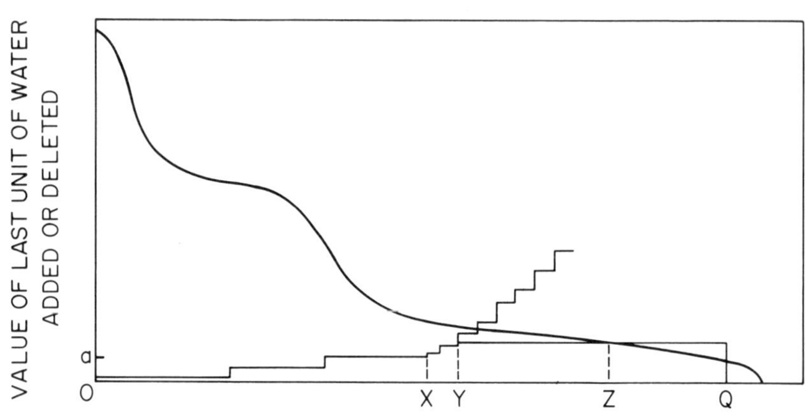

Fig. 2-6. *Aggregate marginal supply of and marginal demand for irrigation water in a given area (hypothetical).*

quantity of water is almost zero, with gradual increases in cost for the next two increments of water supplied.

2. The small rapidly rising steps beginning at X represent the supply of groundwater available from individual user owned and operated pumps. This curve rises from the first curve for surface water beginning at a cost of Oa, indicating that Oa is the lowest cost for any individually pumped water in the area.

3. The supply segment from Y to Q might be an additional supply of groundwater available to the irrigator from organization owned and operated pumps for which all members are charged a uniform price.

Under the hypothetical marginal demand and supply conditions depicted here, agriculture will use OX acre-feet of surface water, XY acre-feet of individually pumped water, and YZ acre-feet of organization pumped and supplied water. No more than OX acre-feet of surface water are available. All of these sources will be used because no other source is cheaper, and all of this water can be used to produce output worth more than the water will cost. Considerably more than XY acre-feet of individually pumped water are available, and somewhat more than XY could be used profitably, but only XY acre-feet will be used because only that much is cheaper than any other available additional supply. Beyond XY, organization-pumped water is cheaper than individually pumped water. The organization's ability to produce and deliver pumped water is YQ, but only YZ will be purchased by irrigators. Beyond a total quantity of water of OZ, additional available sources of water cost more than they are worth. Thus, the organization will have unused capacity of ZQ. Individual owner pumpers also have some amount of unused capacity beyond quantity XY if they are not using their wells to capacity as is implied in the graph.

Aggregate net farm income produced by the agricultural use of water in this hypothetical area is represented by the size of the area between the marginal demand and marginal supply curves from the zero line at the left of the graph rightward to the water quantity where the marginal demand and marginal supply curves cross at Z. Completing such analyses for all irrigated crop-producing areas in Arizona and adding up the aggregate net farm incomes generated by irrigation water in all such areas will give us the total net farm income generated by irrigation water in the Arizona economy for the particular year (or years) to which the data refer.

Net personal income produced in this area by use of water quantity OZ will be found to be the area of net farm income described above, less fixed cash costs of crop production, and plus the wages paid to farm labor that were included as farm costs when calculating the marginal farm demand curve for water.

Comparative Statics Over a Span of Time: Dynamics

Everything described in this chapter to this point has concerned itself with demands for and supplies of water in crop agriculture for a short period in time, such as one cropping season or a single year. These demands and supplies are called *static,* because none of the conditions effecting their magnitudes change within the period of the anlysis. This static picture gives only a *basing point,* or a point of departure, for the analysis of the water problem with which we are concerned, namely, what will happen in the future as conditions do change. Changes will occur in economic and population growth, in groundwater levels, in technologies of production, in levels of per capita incomes and leisure time, and in price relationships. These, of course, are the real stuff of which the water problem in Arizona is composed.

The *dynamic nature* of these demand and supply curves because of time related changes in any one or more of these conditions *reveals itself as a shift in the position of either the static marginal demand or supply curve or both* between specified (dated) points in time. To make the problem tractable to analysis, it is usual to specify particular future points in time (such as every fifth or tenth or twentieth year, depending on how rapid the rate of change is expected to be and how accurate the analysis required) and to consider the dynamic consequence of change in only one of these conditions at a time all other conditions held unchanging in the analysis. Since this procedure actually does not trace out all the dynamics of the situation between the two points in time but shows only the final effects as new static relationships at the new point in time, the procedure is referred to as comparative statics.

Dynamic Economic Supply of Water

Of major concern in the makeup of Arizona's water problem has been the steadily declining economic supply of groundwater and the possible effect this dynamic element will have on long-run economic health of the Arizona economy. Let us examine this element in detail.

As pointed out previously, a dynamic element in supply shows up as a shift in the position of the supply curve. When we speak of a declining supply of groundwater for irrigated agriculture, we mean in economic terms that, because the water table is falling from year to year due to over-pumping, the cost of lifting a unit of water to the surface is increasing, over time, because of increased power requirements and the need for increasing well depths and the size of power units and pumps (holding constant all other conditions, such as technology, prices, and quality of the water). The consequence is that though equal quantities of water can be pumped (so long as the aquifer has not gone dry), doing so will cost more per acre-foot of water pumped. In terms of the static economic supply, this means that the supply curve for groundwater in a particular area will, at future points in time, rise faster and higher for equal quantities of water. An economic analyst would say, "the supply curve will shift upward and/or to the left," as illustrated in figure 2-7. For this illustration, we keep the demand for water constant.

The marginal groundwater supply curves S_1 are the same as the curves shown in figure 2-6. Consider them the static marginal supply curves for 1970. The marginal supply curves S_2 and S_3 reflect the changes that are expected to occur in the groundwater supply at future points in time, say 1980 and 1990, respectively. In our empirical analysis, presented in a later chapter, these curves are projections derived from hydrologic data of rates of groundwater decline caused by volumes of pumpage and conditions of the aquifer during the years between the dates specified.

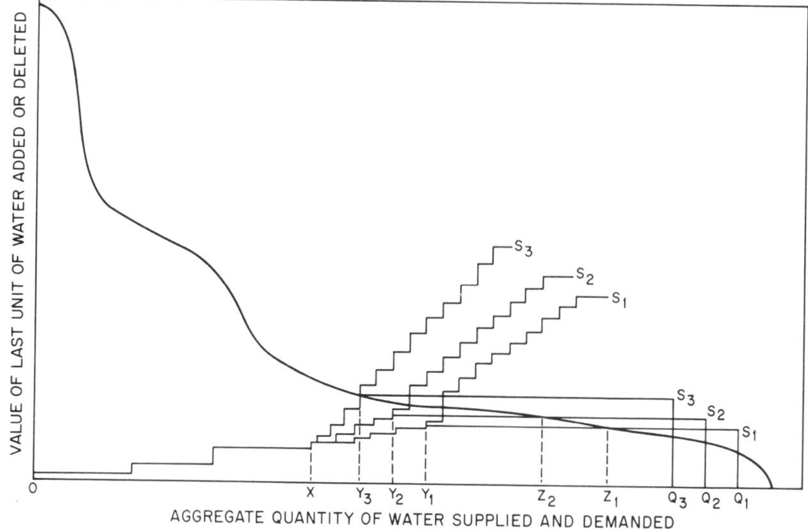

Fig. 2-7. *Projected aggregate marginal supply curves (hypothetical).*

Projected Economic Consequences of Demand and Supply

Notice what the curves of figure 2-7 tell us. Surface water use will not be affected. The volume of individual pumpage will be reduced from XY_1 in 1970 to XY_2 by 1980. The quantity of organization-supplied groundwater will fall from Y_1Z_1 to Y_2Z_2. By 1990 no organization-pumped groundwater will be used, and individually operated pumps will be extracting only XY_3 acre-feet of groundwater. Groundwater withdrawal will by 1990 amount only to XY_3 acre-feet compared to XZ_1 acre-feet twenty years earlier, but surface water use will remain constant.

Of course, net farm income – the area in figure 2-7 between the demand curve and the relevant supply curve – will have declined somewhat in the intervening years. But, net farm income will have declined only modestly because only acreage of low-valued crops will have been abandoned. All effects occur at the relatively horizontal, low end of the marginal demand curve. The volume of pumpage will have declined significantly. It may be that the decline of pumpage will have been sufficiently great that pumpage in 1990 will not be in excess of recharge and the whole system will be stable at a modestly lower level of net income. At least the rate of decline in the water level will have been greatly slowed, and, so long as the conditions assumed continue unchanged, the water level may ultimately become stable.

Changing Demands for Water

Just as marginal supply curves will shift over time, so will marginal demand curves. Demand could either decrease (the curve would shift downward and to the left) or increase (the curve would shift upward and to the right). The major possible cause for a decrease in demand for water by irrigators in Arizona would be decreases in farm prices for crops grown in the state. If such a situation were to occur, the intersection of future marginal demand and marginal supply curves would be lower and to the left of the intersections shown in figure 2-7. Less groundwater would be pumped, and net farm income would decline somewhat more than if only supply shifts were to occur.

However, there are several possible reasons for an increase in demand over time, and thus a shift in the marginal demand curve upward and to the right. An obvious cause would be higher prices for agricultural crop output. Another reason would be technological advances in crop production resulting in greater output per acre at an unchanged or lower cost. (Technological change will always shift the demand curve to the right. We do not adopt "bad" technologies that would shift it the other way.) A further reason for the marginal demand curve to move to the right over time is that the average size of individual farming operations is continually becoming larger. As farms become larger, they are able to produce at lower per unit costs even without a change in the overall level of technology. If the net effects of dynamic change in the irrigated agricultural sector of the Arizona economy is to move the marginal demand curve for water upward and to the right, the intersection of the projected marginal supply and demand curves will be upward and to the right of those shown in figure 2-7. More groundwater would be pumped, and net farm income would decline somewhat less, than if only supply shifts were to occur.

Empirical Analysis of Direct Effects of the Problem

In the empirical analysis to come in a later chapter, we examine the direct economic effects of the projected changes in marginal water supply on Arizona agriculture, using the concepts of comparative statics previously described. The empirical technique of representative-farm linear-programming models is described in detail in that chapter. However, the basic assumptions about change that affect the conceptualization of the empirical problem are specified here.

Our basic interest in this research is analysis of the effects of water scarcity. Therefore, factors originating within the water-using system that are expected to affect the shape and position of the marginal water supply curve over time will be examined in detail and allowed to change, with most other factors arising outside the system but affecting the agricultural economy held constant. This procedure is used because we want to sort out the effects of water scarcity from the effects of all other factors.

Thus, the technology of both water supply and agricultural production are held constant. Technology will surely change over time, but we are not interested in its effects in this analysis. For the same reason, the prices of agricultural outputs and inputs (except for water) are held constant. Agricultural prices will surely change, and farm income will be affected, but the effects will not be because of water problems.

However, two factors other than the cost of irrigation water will be allowed to vary. We are studying agricultural adjustment to increasing water scarcity. In addition to adjustments in water use, land use, crop mix, and output per acre, farmers will adjust by changing farm size. Change in farm size affects water use. Therefore, projected changes in farm size are included in our analysis. The other factor is urbanization. It would be folly to project changes in agricultural water use due to rising water costs if farmlands were no longer in agricultural use because of urbanization. Therefore, agricultural demand for water is adjusted to be consistent with projected urbanization of farm lands.

The net effect of these assumptions is as follows. Our projections will depict direct adjustment in Arizona agriculture arising because of increasing economic scarcity of water (rising water costs), given that urbanization of farm lands continues at its exogenously projected rate and that farm size continues to increase (a function both of rising water costs and other general economic factors which would hold even if water were not scarce). All other assumptions take the most conservative position relative to the deleterious effects of water scarcity; that is, any reasonable projection of these other factors would show water scarcity to be *less* of an economic problem. For example, increases in pumping technology would decrease water cost and prevent agricultural decline; increases in production technology would increase the value of water and prevent agricultural decline. If agriculture does not decline because of water cost, there is no reason to invest in new water development. If increased agricultural prices increase the demand for water, agriculture will not decline. If decreased agricultural prices decrease the value of agricultural products and thus the demand for water, agriculture would decline more than projected. But, of course, this additional decline would not be because of rising water costs, which has already been included in the analysis, but because of falling agricultural prices, a situation that would require a completely different solution.

Multiplier Effects on the Nonagricultural Economy

The conceptual analysis of the water problem, described so far, has focused only on the *direct* relation of water to the irrigated agriculture sector of the economy. However, in addition to the direct effects on the agricultural economy, there will be *indirect* effects on that part of the nonagricultural economy stemming indirectly from water through its effects on the agricultural sector. These indirect effects are often referred to as the "secondary" or "multiplier" effects of the initiating influence, in this case, the water problem operating on the agricultural sector.

When agricultural outputs and incomes decline, some other outputs and incomes outside of agriculture may fall as well. Purchases by agriculturalists of both production and consumption goods and services may decline as their agricultural production and incomes decline, thus lowering the volume of business and hence the net incomes produced in those nonagricultural sectors that provide goods and services to irrigators. Further, if the economic sectors selling goods and services to agriculture and buying and handling products from agriculture have their business volumes and net incomes reduced by declines in agriculture, they too, will make fewer purchases from *their* production and consumption suppliers, reducing business volumes and net incomes of *those* suppliers, and so it will go in ever widening circles. This part of the impact on the total economy resulting from a decline occurring in one part of the economy (in this case, in irrigated agriculture) is called the *multiplier* effect, that is, the total income loss to the economy resulting from each dollar loss of income in irrigated agriculture is some multiple of that initial dollar loss.

Thus, we introduced another element into our analysis of the economic consequences of increasing water shortage in Arizona, namely: How much additional income will be lost in Arizona from each dollar loss of income in irrigated agriculture in Arizona, and how much total income will be lost in the state from the total dollar loss in income in agriculture? Then, because we can project ahead the likely year-to-year rate of decline in income in agriculture, we can project ahead the likely year-to-year decline in total income in the Arizona economy as water becomes more scarce and more expensive for irrigated agriculture.

The method we employ in making these estimates of the multiplier effects of income loss in agriculture is a well-established method known as *Input-Output* or *Interindustry* analysis (frequently abbreviated to I-O analysis). The method rests on the obvious truism that the expenditures by each spending unit are some other unit's income. That which is income and that which is expenditures is, in fact, the same thing viewed from different sides of the transaction; to the receiver it is income, to the relinquisher it is expenditure. Being the same thing, the total of incomes and the total of expenditures in an economy at each point in time necessarily must balance; if incomes decline from one point in time to another, expenditures must decline equally. Thus, I-O analysis is a flow-of-funds analysis. It traces out how the expenditures by a spending unit are distributed (as income) among other units with which the spending unit is economically related as a buyer of the other unit's product or services. Then, it further traces out how those incomes received by each of those other units are in turn distributed by them as expenditures among still other units with whom they in turn are related. This chain of events continues in ever-widening circles of relationship until the amounts thus shared, and net incomes resulting, fritter away to nothingness, becoming lost in the vastness of the whole economic system.

Once having determined these expenditure sharing patterns of relationship, and income consequences for all spending units in the economy, it is possible to determine by how much incomes throughout the economy are affected by each dollar of change in expenditure by any one unit taken as the initiating unit. This, then, is the *multiplier* – the amount by which incomes in the whole economy are changed by a change of one dollar of production in the initiating unit.

It is manifestly impossible to consider every spending unit – person, firm, or governmental unit – separately in tracing out these I-O linkages. But it is possible to group similar units into classes and trace out the I-O linkages among classes of spenders and receivers. These classes are called *sectors* of the economy. Thus, all agricultural producers can be lumped together as the *agricultural sector,* or all irrigation crop farmers as the *crop irrigation sector,* or all irrigated cotton producers as the *irrigated cotton sector,* and so on. The degree of refinement in the groupings (in the sector breakdowns) is a choice based on convenience, complexity of the resulting linkages, magnitude of the analytical problem created, desired degree of accuracy in results, and, of course, the available research funds. In our use of this technique, we divided the Arizona economy into 26 interrelated I-O sectors, of which 10 were subdivisions of agriculture and the other 16 were nonagricultural sectors ranging from 5 agricultural processing sectors to sectors for wholesale and retail trade and transportation (Tijoriwala et al, 1968).

In our analysis, irrigated crop agriculture sectors are taken to be the initiating sectors for purposes of determining aggregate economic impacts of shifting water supply or rising water costs. Output in these sectors will decline; each dollar decline in output in these sectors will reduce expenditures in them, and declines in expenditures will flow through their interrelated sectors generating ever-lessening but ever-widening declines in them. From these relationships it can be determined how many dollars of income will be lost in these other sectors by each dollar lost in irrigated crop agriculture. The total loss to the Arizona economy will then be the dollar loss in agriculture plus the generated losses in all interrelated sectors of the rest of the economy.

Our analysis, were it to end at the point described above, namely, multiplying the net income decline in irrigation agriculture by some factor to determine the total income lost in the Arizona economy by virtue of the decline in agriculture, will, true enough, determine the total *gross* decline in income produced by the Arizona.economy. But, it will grossly exaggerate the extent of the *net* income decline experienced by the people affected. The gross decline in income is the total amount of income that would not be produced in Arizona in irrigated agriculture and in those businesses directly and indirectly related to agriculture. But this *gross* amount of income will be the *net* amount lost by the people of Arizona only if the income receivers, who would have received it had it been produced, have no other income-producing employment to which they can turn, thus being unable to recoup much or all of the loss income stemming from the curtailed irrigation agriculture. It is necessary to estimate the extent of substitute employment and income that will be available to all those income receivers whose incomes in or related to irrigated agriculture will be lost or lessened. The *net* loss in aggregate income due to a dollar loss in irrigation is only the decline that occurs in incomes over and above the alternative opportunities open to those whose incomes are curtailed. We discuss this problem in detail in a later chapter.

Economic Analysis of the Problem

We can now summarize our way of looking at the problem of the Arizona economy as a water user and how we approach its economic analysis:

1. There are numerous different water demanders, each with some use(s) for a small quantity of water of great value to them and each with other uses for larger quantities of water but of markedly less worth, up to the point where no more water would be used even if it were "free."

2. The typical water demander's curve is a broken-backed curve – small quantities of water of high value or productivity and relatively large quantities of low values or productivity.

3. Although each water demander is an individual, household, or firm, they can be classified into groups on the basis of relative similarity in patterns of water use. For our purposes, irrigated agriculture is the important class because it uses such large quantities of water at low levels of value of productivity. Thus, irrigated agriculture is the marginal class of users among the totality of all classes of users.

4. Within the irrigated agriculture class of water users, there are some uses that use relatively small quantities of water at relatively high levels of value or productivity, and other uses that use relatively large quantities of water at relatively low levels of value or productivity. The graph picturing this relation of values and quantities is the marginal water demand curve by irrigated agriculture.

5. The volumes of water that will be available, by areas or by state total at various levels of rising cost, can be determined and shown in tabular or graphic form. These are economic marginal supply functions for in-state water.

6. As water costs rise, one can determine from the combined demand and supply curves for water how much less water irrigated agriculture will use and how much loss of gross output and net income in irrigated agriculture this curtailment will cause.

7. By projecting rising costs of water over time, one can project the likely pattern of decline in cropped acres, output per crop, gross dollar output, and net income in irrigated agriculture over time.

8. By determining a multiplier factor between gross output in irrigation agriculture and incomes generated in all related economic activities, and adding in the income not produced in agriculture because of its decline in gross agricultural output, one can estimate the decline in total income in the state resulting from any projected decline in irrigated agricultural gross output resulting from projected growing water scarcity.

9. By estimating the alternative employment opportunities available to men and resources displaced by curtailment of irrigated agriculture, and subtracting that magnitude from the total income decline determined through item 7 above, one can estimate the net loss in income that will be experienced by affected people over time because of the projected curtailment of irrigated agriculture. This estimate may be put on a per-acre-foot-of-water basis to obtain the real value of an acre-foot of water developed to counteract such agricultural and nonagricultural adjustment to water scarcity.

Structural Change of the Economy Relative to the Problem

So far, we have confined our attention to water use in the agricultural sectors of the Arizona economy and the resultant multiplier effects. Approaching that problem, as we did, solely as the problem of a diminishing groundwater supply, it is obvious the results of the analysis will show a declining level of agricultural incomes over the next fifty years in Arizona and, through them and the multiplier effect, a declining level of total incomes in Arizona. This conclusion points to a declining economy in Arizona due to the water problem, exactly what the popular view of the water problem has feared. The actual size of this estimated decline and its relative seriousness are discussed in later chapters.

But this is only a partial view of what is and will be happening in Arizona. The analyses so far described have explicitly assumed that the rest of the Arizona economy – all the agricultural and nonagricultural sectors that will not directly be affected by rising water cost – will remain constant at the level of income creation they exhibited in 1966 or will decline in income creation because of indirect effects.

This is manifestly unreal. In fact, one element in the water problem as popularly conceived is that most nonagricultural and a few high-valued agricultural sectors are growing rapidly, requiring increasing quantities of water for their use. Where is that water to come from unless agriculture is curtailed still further or water supplies are increased by importation or both?

It is obvious that we must expand our analysis to include changing water demands, especially in these rapidly growing nonagricultural sectors, and relate this dynamic demand to the water supply and assess this relation in the state's water problem.

The preferred way to do this, obviously, would be to project the rate of change in water demands by these nonagricultural sectors over the next fifty years as we did for agriculture, combine all projections into one analysis, and see where it takes us in terms of excess water demand (relative to the limited water supply). Projecting the rate of change in the nonagricultural sectors, however, is more complex than projecting agricultural change. No data or system analysis available will permit a single projection with even a modest degree of assurance as to its reliability.

So we took another approach. The Arizona economy, as any economy, can be viewed as a structure of economic sectors. The I-O model of the Arizona economy mathematically pictures that economy as an interrelated structure of economic sectors. We know the water demand for each of these sectors in terms of acre-feet required for each one thousand dollars of its output. Thus, we can project water demand by sector and total water demand by all sectors for any projected level of output for each sector and for all sectors. Though we cannot predict a single pattern of sectoral growth in output for the Arizona economy, we can project a realistic rate of growth in output for the overall Arizona economy and, through the I-O model, determine several alternative and realistic patterns of sectoral growth of the economy that are consistent with realizing the projected rate of overall growth. We then can project for each alternative structure of sectoral outputs of the economy the changing total quantities of water each alternative structure will demand.

Then we can see what the prospects are among the alternative structures of the state's economy for balancing total water demands with supplies if the projected rate of overall economic growth in the state is to be realized. We then can describe what changes in the structure of the state's economy will be required and how drastic they must be if we are to live within our water budget. Or, we may estimate how large the importations of water or development of new internal supplies must be, as among the several structural alternatives, if we are to get the projected rate of overall economic growth. This we have done; the results are reported in a later chapter.

Though this analysis does not predict the overall demand for water by the state's economy, it does indicate how serious the problem relative to water supplies may become, and suggests what and how complex the required changes in the state's economy may be over the period 1966 to 2015 to meet the problem.

3. Arizona Water Law and Its Socioeconomic Consequences

Water law consists of two distinguishable bodies of law: (1) those laws that define property rights in the use of water (water rights) and (2) those laws that establish the organizations (public and private) for the administration of water rights and the development and management of water. Professor Clark (1964) describes the law of property rights in water in semiarid regions as trying to answer these questions:

> . . . *who is* entitled to *how much* for *what purpose* from *what source; who* will receive *preferential use* during periods of shortage; and *what rights* attach to *subsequent consumptive uses,* or are to be enjoyed by *nonconsumptive users?* [Italics in the original]

Laws establishing public or quasipublic water developing and managing organizations prescribe the structure of the required or authorized organizations, define their authorities, and specify their relations to one another, to the holders of the water rights they are charged with administering, to nonholders of those rights, and to the general public.

Water law, like all law, is partly constitutional (derived from "basic law" of the society), partly statutory (enacted by legislative bodies), partly administrative law (codified rules and regulations established by the administering organizations themselves), and partly court (that is, judge) made law (derived from decisions rendered in the settlement of specific disputes over the meaning and application of the provisions contained in any of these laws). Thus, water law, like all law, is a somewhat amorphus, somewhat uncertain body of principles, provisions, and precedents evolving out of conditions of the past, being applied to problems of the present, in a manner thought to be equitable among contemporaries and between contemporaries and those who will follow. All law is tentative, a norm to be applied in specific circumstances. Thus, water law is never perfectly definitive, always includes elements of uncertainty, sometimes pervasive and fundamental, sometimes particular and superficial, but always evolving with changing conditions and values in the natural and social environments.

Water law in Arizona is no different. In some respects it is more uncertain, more out-of-touch with the conditions of its rapidly changing social and economic environment, than in some other of the western states, all of which confront comparable water problems in relation to social and economic growth and welfare.

Socioeconomic Issues in Water Rights

This volume reports research into the economic implications of water and water policies in Arizona. Thus, the research is not centrally concerned with the hydrology of the water system or with its related biologic system, though obviously these are important elements in the analysis. Neither is it centrally concerned with the technologic relations of water inputs to outputs in production and consumption, though this too is an essential part of the analytical structure.

Central to this research is the behavior of people using and developing water in Arizona *and the interactions among them and between them and others* as they strive individually and collectively, competitively and cooperatively, to use and develop, to exhaust or conserve, the state's water supply to improve their social and economic well-being. Behavior is central to this research because people's actions relative to water comprise the real meaning of water use, allocation, and development. What people do in this regard is a consequence, in part, of their goals interacting with their understanding of the hydrologic cycle, the biologic system, the technology of water in production and consumption, and the restraints of markets and prices. However, of equal importance, their behavior toward water will be affected by the restraints and opportunities imposed by the law to direct their interpersonal and intergroup relations of competition and cooperation in their access to and in their development and use of water.

This research concerns what people do, why they do it, and with what consequences to the attainment of their goals insofar as these grow out of their relations to water and its related resources. Obviously, what people do and why is determined in part by their technical knowledge about water, but it is also determined by the nature of the social, political, legal, and economic environment within which they act. The former is their relation to nature and is the field of technology and natural science; the latter is their relation to other men as individuals or as groups and is the field of behavioral science.

Men's relations to other men will be in part economic relations of supply and demand, markets and prices, but also there will be relations of rights-duties, liberties-exposures specified by the law of water rights and the actions of administering organizations. Although economic relations are the primary focus of this research, the restraints imposed and the freedoms permitted by law and its administration constitute part of the environment within which economic relations take place. When analyzing the economics of water, an understanding of these legal and administrative institutions is as necessary as an understanding of bio-hydrology.

Two aspects of water rights most significant for an understanding of men's behavior relative to water and to one another over water are: (1) the security of their expectations that whatever rights they hold to water and its use will be stable and dependable over time, and (2) the flexibility permitted to them to effect changes in use and location of use of the water covered by their rights, and to acquire and transfer water rights from and to others.

The degree of security in their rights provides certainty or uncertainty to men's expectations that they may enjoy the benefits that will flow from their use or nonuse of their investments in or related to water; flexibility in their rights permits change in rights and expectations made desirable by changing circumstances of themselves, of others, or of nature. Security gives stability to rights and the confidence based on predictability of expectations; flexibility provides assurance of adaptability to unforeseen changes in conditions that will confront the water-right holder.

Security of Water Rights

Security of water rights assures the user and developer of particular waters that he knows where he stands relative to the rights and liberties of other persons respecting control and use of those waters. Security of rights also guarantees that the user will continue through time to enjoy whatever benefits and to suffer whatever harms may flow from his control, allocation, use or nonuse, and development of that water, unaffected by unilateral and capricious acts of others, whether they are public officials or private citizens. Committing labor and capital to the development and delivery of water supplies and to the application of the water to production or consumption is essential in water use. The consequences of those acts occur after them, sometimes a long time after. These actions won't knowingly be taken by the water-right holder without some assurance that known portions of their fruits will belong to or known burdens of any detriments attributable to them will be borne by him. This is security of expectations or, since property is involved, tenure security of water rights.

It is not security against all the hazards of life, against the actor's own mistakes, or against capricious acts of nature, but only against unilateral or capricious acts of other men that may deprive the water-right holder of the fruits of his actions or that may shift to him losses stemming from the actions of others. This is the essence of *tenure security* and is essential to an effectively functioning system of water rights.

But this is only half the story. Security of expectations (tenure security) can be a straitjacket from which the water-right holder cannot escape. Passage of time changes the conditions of action. The actors, through experience, increase their knowledge of technology and devise more productive equipment and ways of production; conditions of the water and associated resources change with use and development; preferences of the society and its individual members as between satisfactions and sacrifices resulting from water use change from time to time, thus altering the preference weightings of alternative gains and losses.

Flexibility of Water Rights

Tenure security must be accompanied by *tenure flexibility* (or transferability). There must be some way for the holders and would-be holders of water rights to alter their access to the benefits and their exposure to the losses that may flow from their use and development of the water covered by their rights. The water-use decision-makers must, in some way equitable to others, be able to invest themselves with or to divest themselves of the rights and liberties, the duties and exposures imposed on them by water rights and by the behavior of water. This is tenure flexibility. It makes possible shifts in water development, delivery, and use made imperative by changing natural conditions, institutions, technology, population, and preferences if the welfare of the individual is to be protected and that of the society is to be maintained and improved.

Tenure security and tenure flexibility seem to be contraries, but they are not. The essence of tenure security is security against unilateral and capricious acts of other citizens and officials. It is not security against unilateral rule changes by the rule-making body, so long as those changes are "constitutional," or against capricious acts of nature. The essence of tenure flexibility is freedom on the part of the actual or potential water user to acquire or dispose of rights or liberties relating to water or to subject himself to the rights or liberties possessed by others. Tenure flexibility is not a *unilateral right* to take gains from or thrust losses upon others; it is an *inter-personal freedom* to negotiate such exchanges.

Tenure flexibility must involve two or more parties. It requires bilateral or multilateral, not unilateral, decisions, and considered, not capricious, acts based upon negotiations and agreement among affected parties. For freedom to be real and effective, if a decision is reached, channels must be open to effectuate the decision and to shift between individuals the agreed-upon incidence of benefits and costs and the rights-duties and liberties-exposures that constitute property in water.

Security and flexibility are the twin essences of socially efficient property relations wherever they are found and relative to whatever objects they apply. Relative to many property objects, tenure security and flexibility are both highly developed – for example, home and automobile ownership; relative to other property objects, they are primitive – for example, atmospheric moisture and scenic views. Water rights stand somewhere between these extremes, in some circumstances relatively secure, in others less so, in some circumstances relatively flexible, in others more rigid.

Discussion of *water rights* in Arizona must be divided into two different but related topics – (1) *surface-water* rights and (2) *groundwater* rights.

Surface-Water Rights

What are usually referred to as *surface-water rights* are, in Arizona, both narrower and broader than the name implies. They are narrower in that they pertain only to surface waters flowing in defined natural channels, thus not to nonflowing surface water such as lakes or to waters moving across the surface in undefined channels; and they do not attach to drainage waters resulting from applications of water to land. The rights to surface waters are broader than the name implies in that they pertain also to subsurface (or ground) water moving in defined subsurface channels with definite beds and banks. In Arizona, however, the overwhelming proportion of surface-water rights pertain to waters moving on the surface in defined natural channels.

In Arizona, as in the western states generally, surface-water rights are appropriative, not riparian, rights. The holder of an appropriative right does not *own* the physical body of the water *allocated* to him but only a right to its use for beneficial purposes. The physical body of the water is owned by the public, held in trust by it for the benefit of its members. Thus, an appropriative right is, in effect, a license to a designated party to use a specified part of the flow of a specified stream for purposes and by means deemed beneficial to him and not unreasonably harmful to others.

In general, the appropriative right in Arizona endows its holder with these rights, liberties, duties, and exposures:

1. The holder need not be adjacent to the stream or even within its

watershed but need only be able to put the water to use at the point on the stream to which his right attaches, or to divert the water from the stream and convey it to the point of his use.

2. His right to use water in the stream or to divert it stands in order of priority to the rights of all other in-stream users or diverters on the same stream strictly in the order of time at which the right was first claimed and put to use. This is the "first in time, first in right" principle of the prior-appropriation doctrine of water rights. Under this principle the appropriator can at any time claim the water allotted to him by his right, but *only* if there is sufficient water in the stream to fill *all* the rights of other appropriators senior to his in time, whether or not these senior appropriators are located above or below him on the stream.

3. The quantity of flow he can claim in-stream or can divert under his right is expressly stated in his right as a quantity per unit time and was determined or authorized by some administrator or by a court at the time of the first granting of the right as the limit of flow he could then *beneficially* use without waste.

4. What constitutes *beneficial* use is extremely vague. In fact, it is a criterion for the acceptability of an appropriative right only at the time of perfecting the initial claim to the right. Once the right has been granted, the beneficial character of any subsequent use of the water seldom, if ever, arises as a criterion for deciding the content of the appropriator's right. Usually, in those instances where the nature of the water use under a right has changed, any question about the validity of the right will turn, not on the question of whether the changed use is beneficial but on whether associated changes in the proportion of consumptive use and volume and flow of drainage and effluent discharges adversely affects other water users drawing upon the same hydrologic system – hence, not on beneficiality but on reasonableness of impact on other affected water users.

5. The appropriative right is appurtenant – that is, tied – to a specific land unit, and the water can be used only on that site. (This rule applies strictly only to appropriative rights for irrigation users. But since irrigation is the overwhelming user of water in quantity terms in Arizona – well over 90 percent – this manner of stating the case should be appropriate for purposes of this report.) On what part of the site it can be used is not specified in the right. Thus, all the water can be used in a highly concentrated fashion at a point on the site or uniformly over the site. Changing the established pattern of use on the site may raise questions of the reasonableness of its impact on other water users and, through an administrative act or judicial decision, be enjoined.

Prior to 1962 in Arizona, appropriative rights were not transferable by their holder to land sites other than that specified in the original granting of the right, whether unilaterally for his own purposes or by assignment to another. The only exception to this locational inflexibility of water rights arose when the original site was destroyed or impaired by natural calamity or act of God. Under such circumstances the right could be *moved* with confirmation by administrator or court.

Since 1962, this restraint has been removed and water rights are, in principle, freely transferable to other lands with or without change in use. However, the hydrologic effects on other users of water in the system affected by the transfer may be so difficult to predict and quantify that extensive activity on the part of a public administrator or the courts may be required to determine their existence and magnitude and the outcome of such investigations may be highly uncertain, thus rather effectively discouraging any significant number of attempts to effect such transfers.

Furthermore, even if the facts about adverse effects should turn out to be readily determinable, it could frequently result in authorizations to transfer, not all the water covered by the right, but only that quantity of the water that had been consumptively used at the original location. This would, in effect, be a reduction in the quantity of water allowed under the right subsequent to its transfer and rarely would be acceptable to its original holder. Thus, he is further discouraged even to consider a transfer of location.

6. Not only is the area of use of diverted water specified in the right but so is the point of in-stream use or of diversion and even the route of conveyance to point of use. None of these attributes of the right can be changed unilaterally by the right holder but must be approved by administrator or court (which really means by other water users in the same hydrologic system who might be harmed by such changes).

7. Water available under an appropriative right must continue to be used in order to maintain the right. Abandonment of the right or nonuse, in whole or in part, of the water available under the right causes the unused water to revert to the public domain as unappropriated water subject to appropriation or claim by another. In Arizona, nonuse for five consecutive years is considered to constitute abandonment. Readily apparent is the pressure on the holder of an appropriative right to use all of the water allotted to him even when all or part of it produces little or no or even some negative value product.

Though nonuse or abandonment may constitute loss to the holder of the unused right, it may not represent any opportunity to others to claim an appropriation of the unused water. If the stream is extensively over-appropriated, as most streams are, the unused or abandoned water will probably accrue to the benefit of existing right holders so far down the appropriative "queue" that their rights had previously been filled intermittently or not at all. A new appropriator of the abandoned water on such a stream does not appropriate the former right holder's place in the queue but must join the queue at its outer end. On an over-appropriated stream, what actually occurs is that, at the instigation of the existing right holders, the administrator or courts rule that the person who has permitted some or all of his right water to escape unused must continue to do so. The unused water has become a part of the "public" flow of the stream available to fill previously unfilled rights.

Appropriative Rights: Security of Expectations

Though the foregoing is by no means a complete legal description of the law of appropriative water rights in Arizona, it is sufficient to assess its essential social, political, and economic consequences. We first examine the degree of certainty or uncertainty of expectations – the degree of security in the expectations of the right holder that he will secure the benefits or suffer the costs of his acts in using or not using and developing water under these rights.

Two kinds of security-insecurity in water rights should be distinguished. The first – physical security – is that security on the part of the right holder that the natural flow of the stream will be sufficient to fill his own claim in addition to all claims senior in time to his. The other kind – *tenure security* – concerns the degree to which the water-right holder feels that the content of and the limits on the lawful actions of all other right and non-right holders in exercising their rights and freedoms of access to whatever water may be flowing in the stream are definitive and not unilateral and capricious.

It is obvious, of course, that there is little if any relation between the nature of water rights and the volume of the natural flow of a stream. Hence, there is not much relation between the nature of surface water rights as a whole and the physical security of right holders as a group on a natural stream. As a group on a natural water course, they will be physically secure or insecure, depending on the volume of natural flow rather than on the nature of the right. However, the physical security of the right of an individual right holder on the stream depends not only on the natural flow of the stream but also on where he stands in the time-priority queue of all right holders on the stream.

Because of the security of expectations bestowed upon right holders by their appropriative rights, together with (1) the physical insecurity of many right holders brought about by the unstable or insufficient flow of the stream, and (2) the considerable economies of scale implicit in most surface water developments, they may, as a group sharing a common water source, find it advantageous as a group to undertake water conserving improvements and management of their water-delivery system. They may also as a group invest in facilities to store seasonal excess flows, to increase water yields from the watershed on which their source is dependent, and to transfer water from other basins to theirs. The long-run tenure security bestowed by appropriate rights encourages group investment in, and group management of, water to enhance the physical security of their water rights.

But appropriative rights also may, as between individual right holders on a common stream, cause some to resist participation in long-run investments in development of the stream. The holder who is sufficiently senior in the priority queue that his rights are physically secure, will feel no economic motive for participating in improvements the economic benefits of which will serve to fill more adequately and to make more physically secure, not his rights but the rights of holders lower in the queue. Of course, those standing low in the queue whose water expectations, though secure in tenure, attach to a highly insecure physical supply, will be seriously interested in supply-increasing investments and will seek to spread the investment over as many persons as possible.

If those appropriative right holders on a stream whose rights are physically insecure are sufficiently numerous relative to those whose rights are physically secure, and if rules by which public districts are formed can force a minority into a district, they may be able to force all right holders on the stream into group action for further development of the stream's available water supply. Where this cannot be done, those whose rights tend to be physically insecure may organize themselves for their own group-furthered development of the stream's water supply, the rights to the augmented supply vesting only in them as a group. In this case, rights in the augmented flow of the stream will be held co-equally by all members of the developing group instead of in the time hierarchy characteristic of the usual appropriative right. The physically insecure appropriators will, if so organized, hold an aggregate or group appropriative right at the end of the appropriative queue, but all in that group will share co-equally in it.

Thus, the tenure security of appropriative rights tends to encourage group investments in surface-water-conserving and surface-supply-increasing developments. And because the action will usually be group action, strong efforts will be taken to make the group as inclusive as possible by legal action and by stressing the wide-spreading and far-reaching gains to be realized from the investment.

Appropriative rights in Arizona exhibit a considerable degree of both physical and tenure security due to extensive group development and management of surface waters and because each holder knows exactly where he stands in the hierarchy of holders and how much claim to water is senior to his. About the only tenure insecurity in appropriative rights in Arizona stems from the power of a public body to condemn water rights for a public purpose with compensation for the value of the water rights taken (a power not clearly established in Arizona). Another source of tenure insecurity may be the *reserved right* held by the federal government as prior claim on all or most of the waters arising on federally reserved lands, as distinguished from federal public domain, sufficient for their ultimate development. Condemnation of water is a seldom if ever used right of uncertain status in Arizona, which, even if exercised, will be accompanied by compensation of right holders for values taken. The federal reserved right is still more of a threat and a worry than real. Therefore, these insecurities in Arizona's appropriative structure have not so far been much of a restraint on long-run investments in the augmentation and stabilization of surface-water supplies.

Appropriative Rights: Flexibility

Flexibility and inflexibility are those characteristics of a water right that make easy (flexible) or difficult (inflexible) the transfer of an appropriative water right among and between users, uses, and locations of use. Transfer of surface-water rights among users, when accompanied by no change in kind or location of water use, is easy in Arizona – as easy as any real estate transfer, because the water right can be, even must be, transferred as an appurtenance to the land to which it is attached. Transfer of the right with transfer of the land to which it is appurtenant, even when accompanied by change in use of the transferred land and water, is relatively easy under current Arizona water law so long as the change in use of the water is accompanied by no significant change in the proportion of the water that is consumptively used or in the manner of disposal of the unconsumed portion.

The restrictive effect of surface-water rights on economic change in Arizona – their detrimental inflexibility – arises whenever a water transfer that changes location of use, diversion, or conveyance, or changes consumptive use or the manner of disposal of unconsumed water, will increase economic productivity of the water, but is restrained for one or more of three reasons: (1) when it may adversely affect some other water user leading him to register objection to the transfer with appropriate authority; (2) when it may be prohibited by conditions laid down by the agency financing the water development (for example, by the

Bureau of Reclamation's usual requirement, under Reclamation Law, that surface water supplies developed by its assistance must be used for "agricultural purposes" only); or (3) when it may be restrained by regulations prohibiting transfer of the water for any purpose whatever outside the legally established boundaries of the district through which the water is allocated and distributed for use. In an economy as dynamic as Arizona's it frequently arises that surface water would be considerably more productive if it were transferred from points of less to points of greater relative water scarcity, or to quite different consumptive uses. Under the Arizona law of surface-water rights, though these transfers are not prohibited, the administrative workings of the law impose severe restraints upon them. The severity of the restraints derives in major part from technical uncertainties as to who would be harmed and by how much from these changes if they were permitted. It also derives from the total absence of any market or administrative mechanism through which the allocation and assessment of damages for such adverse occurrences can be effected. The legal right to flexibility exists, but an operating method, whether that of market bargaining or administrative negotiation, for effecting it does not.

Even he whose water right is excessive for purposes of his present or anticipated use is pressured by the nature of surface-water law to apply it to uses from which the return to him will be small, zero, or even modestly negative. Under existing institutions, about his only alternative is to abandon it, which constitutes a donation by him of his excess water to the public domain, a degree of beneficence but rarely found.

It is not unusual for critics of the system to urge stronger enforcement of the principle of beneficial use as a solution to this problem. Indeed, the Arizona code bearing on surface-water appropriative rights says explicitly, "Beneficial use shall be the basis, measure, and limit to the use of water" (Arizona Revised Statutes, 45-101B).

Struckmeyer and Butler (1960), in commenting on this provision in Arizona law, simply say, "The meaning of the words 'measure' and 'limit' is not defined, nor has recourse been had to the courts for an interpretation of the terms." Furthermore, they add, "No case exists in Arizona where the decision has wholly turned on a definition of 'beneficial use,' although it has been held that appropriation is limited by beneficial use." Thus, although beneficial use might appear to be a clear mandate under appropriative rights for the transfer of surface water from locations and uses of lesser to locations and uses of higher economic benefit to users and through them to the state's economy, it has been and still is an ineffective criterion. Possibly the growing economic scarcity of water resulting from Arizona's rapid economic growth, and the increasing disparities between economic efficiencies in its present uses compared to how it could be used, will at long last open the door through class actions in the courts, through legislation, or through pressures on administrators to application of the statutory rule of beneficial use as the basis, measure, and limit to the use of surface water.

A possible but unclear degree of flexibility in Arizona surface-water rights rests in the right of eminent domain under which municipalities may be able to condemn surface-water rights with compensation to damaged parties to get water for municipal consumers. A severe restraint on the application to surface water of this universal right inherent in government lies in the technical uncertainties in determining, assessing, and distributing damages. So far, municipal shortages of water have not been sufficiently severe to warrant the time, expense, and litigation these determinations would involve. But, with the growing demands of metropolitan areas for water where available surface supplies exist, the use of this device may receive increasing attention.

Socioeconomic Implications

The "first in time, first in right" principle of the appropriative system of water rights, the requirement that the water to which the rights are attached must be developed and used or it will be lost by abandonment, the tenure security in that water with which the appropriative right endows its holder together with the rigidities (that is, the transfer inflexibilities) that militate against its transfer among uses and locations of use once it has been granted, has, in Arizona as elsewhere in the West, resulted in extensive but often premature group investments in the development of additional surface water supplies. Any group of users who are currently, or fear at some future date to be, short of fully adequate water supplies and which discovers a source of unappropriated surface water is under heavy pressure to claim, develop, and use that supply *now* rather than wait until the need for it becomes pressing. Failure to do so invites the probability that somebody else will get there first, thus depriving the first group of access to that water forever. Other means to meet the problems of water shortage, often means that are socially more efficient because they increase the productivity of existing surface supplies through transfer and strict application of the statutory rule of beneficial use, have been largely prevented by the present form of the appropriation doctrine of surface-water rights.

Thus, surface-water rights in Arizona – designed as they are to encourage development and use of water, the early filing of claims upon available or potentially available surface waters, and requiring their prompt development and use else they will be declared abandoned – together with the rigidities built into these rights, lead to the ever-present specter of water shortage and the ever-pressing demand to find and develop "new" supplies to meet the ever-increasing demands of the state's developing economy. It is plausible to presume that the specter of water shortage is, at least in part, a consequence of man's clumsiness regarding the institution of surface-water rights established to regulate surface-water use and development in addition to being a consequence of the niggardliness of nature in a desert climate. The research reported herein is, in part, a test of the validity of that presumption.

Groundwater Rights

"Underground water, groundwater, or percolating water, as it is variously called, is that water which oozes or percolates through porous soil and gravel beds beneath the surface of the land" (Arizona Academy, 1964). "It does not include water flowing in underground streams with ascertainable beds and banks" (Arizona Revised Statutes, 45-301).

Rights of access to and use of groundwater in Arizona are quite different in the behavior they invoke in their holders than are the rights that attach to surface water – that is, flowing water. It is almost as if they are different resources, although they are indistinguishable in the technology of their use once they are diverted or extracted and in the conveyance channels for use.

Groundwater in Arizona is not subject to the law of prior appropriation that attaches to surface water. Groundwater is, at least nominally, subject to the common-law rule that each owner of overlying land owns not only the surface of his tract but everything beneath the surface, including water "oozing and percolating through the soil and gravel beds" found thereunder. Thus, the common law rule in Arizona creates a property right in the owner of land to the subjacent groundwater lying within and beneath that land.

(The same rule, of course, applies to ownership of petroleum, minerals, rock, gravels, or anything else lying beneath the overlying land surface. It is common, however, under this common law rule, especially with respect to petroleum and minerals, for the surface owner to separate and transfer to others rights of varying degrees to these subsurface resources. These are known as "mineral reservations," or "oil rights," and so forth; they may be owned separately from the balance of the tract and its subsurface content. However, this common practice has not developed relative to groundwater in Arizona. Hence, it is not incorrect to say that the owner of the surface in Arizona also "owns" the groundwater lying beneath that surface though he might not similarly "own" the petroleum or minerals found there, these resources being "owned" by another.)

But, after having said so much, the seemingly clear common law rule with respect to the ownership and control of groundwater begins to slip away; we find it doesn't really apply with the simple clarity that the above way of stating it implies. For, as with surface water, the landowner doesn't really own the groundwater as he does petroleum or minerals that he may remove and dispose of however and whenever he sees fit. His use of *his* groundwater is restrained by the rule of reasonable use on his overlying lands. As with surface water, he doesn't really own the water beneath his land but only a right to its reasonable use for purposes incident to the beneficial enjoyment of his land from which it is obtained. Beneficial enjoyment has, in this connection, the same meaning, the same inchoate quality, as in its application to surface-water rights. However, the more significant restraint on groundwater use lies in the phrase "enjoyment of his land from which it is obtained," for this effectively restricts the use of groundwater to that land and precludes its transfer to other lands belonging to himself or others not located over the aquifer from which the water is withdrawn except where doing so is clearly not harmful to other landowners overlying the same aquifer. The burden of proof in such cases rests on the landowners wishing to make such transfers.

However, groundwater rights are in one respect more unrestrained than are surface-water rights in that the quantity of the extraction, subject only to the rule of reasonable and nonwasteful use, is unrestrained. The overlying landowner may extract from beneath his land all the water he needs wherever, however, and for whatever legitimate purpose he needs it on that land without limitation (except that it not be wasteful). He has no liability of any kind to owners of other lands overlying the same groundwater aquifer for adverse effects on their groundwater stocks resulting from his pumping, provided that the water pumped is used for the purpose of putting to use the overlying land from which it was drawn.

What constitutes "wasteful" use as a restraint on groundwater extraction remains ill-defined. Struckmeyer and Butler (1960), in their pamphlet on water rights in Arizona, make this interesting statement: "The trouble and expense of applying water to land, if it is not in some way 'beneficial,' would be an unlikely occurrence." Clearly implied is the presumption that what the water user does is *ipso facto* beneficial or non-wasteful because no rational man would use costly water in a way not beneficial to him. Under this dictum the beneficial-use rule as a rule of reasonable use is not much help, because whatever water use exists is beneficial. In this connection, however, they cite the interesting California case in which it was held that running water on land in winter for the purpose of exterminating gophers was held not to be beneficial use. It would seem that beneficiality is thus not, as implied by them, a rule that applies to the owner's benefits from use of his groundwater, because that is impliedly always beneficial to him as it was even in the "gopher" case, but a rule regarding the beneficiality or harmfulness to other individuals or to the public resulting from the owner's use of groundwater. No Arizona case has ruled on this or any similar issue.

The only exception of any importance to the restraint imposed on the use of groundwater away from the land of origin lies in a provision of the Groundwater Code of 1948. It provides that no permit for the construction of an irrigation well within a critical groundwater area is to be issued by the Arizona State Land Department except to the owner of the land where the well is to be located or to an "irrigation or agricultural improvement district or other organized irrigation project for use upon lands within the district or project." The research report prepared for use by the Arizona Academy's (1964) Town Hall on Arizona's Water Supply says,

> This provision appears to allow an irrigation district to pump groundwater from beneath one tract in the district for use on other tracts some miles away. This may conflict with the restrictive rule of the Bristor vs. Cheatham case that the use of underground water must be confined to the reasonable enjoyment of the owner's overlying land.

However, no court has ruled directly on this point in Arizona, so the rule stands and is applied within several irrigation districts in the state. It is an interesting question why no litigation has arisen over this rule, considering the jealousy with which pumpers of groundwater have protected their supplies from such transfers by other individual pumpers in their areas.

The generally unrestrained removal of groundwater by overlying land owners is restrained, though weakly, by the Groundwater Code of 1948, as amended (Sections 45-301-324, Arizona Revised Statutes, 1956). In groundwater areas declared by the State Land Commissioner to be critical, new and additional wells for irrigation purposes cannot be constructed and water from any existing irrigation well can be used only on lands that had been used for irrigation purposes at some time during the five years immediately preceding the declaration of the area as critical. However, this apparent restraint on groundwater withdrawal is much weakened by the provisions of the Code itself and subsequent court decisions that (1) wells for all purposes other than for irrigation are wholly exempt from restraint under the Code; (2) new irrigation wells replacing existing wells may be constructed without restraint as to size and depth and existing wells may similarly be deepened and/or pumped more vigorously; and (3) water from existing irrigation wells within "critical areas" may be used on any of the pumper's own lands within the area, even those that have no history of irrigation use during the five-year period preceding the declaration of the area to be critical in spite of the apparent legislative statement to the contrary (State V Anway, 87 Arizona, 206 [1960]).

Groundwater rights in Arizona may be summarized as follows: The owner of land may use as much water from beneath his lands as he wishes, with whatever timing of extractions he desires, for any legitimate purpose, without liability to any other landowner for damage to his groundwater supply, subject only to the following three restraints:

1. The use to which the water is put and the quantity withdrawn must be for reasonable or beneficial use of the owner's overlying land and be not wasteful.

2. In critical groundwater areas the landowner cannot increase his extraction of groundwater for irrigation purposes by drilling additional wells, though he can do so by pumping existing wells harder or, on a showing of need, by deepening them or by abandoning existing wells and constructing bigger and deeper wells to replace them.

3. He cannot transfer the water (export it) from his overlying land, either for his own use or for use by another, when other landowners object with a reasonable showing of presumptive damage to their groundwater supplies. This restraint apparently does not apply to organized irrigation or agricultural improvement districts, which seemingly can extract groundwater from beneath one tract within the district for use on other tracts within the district.

It is not clear what constitutes the geographic limits to the area of overlying land on which groundwater from a given well can be considered to be reasonably used. That it must be used on the spot where the well is located is patently absurd. But how far away from that spot it can be used, even though still on the well-owner's land, is not specified. May water be used on one contiguous tract, regardless of size? Could it be used on separated though small tracts? If so, how far separated is reasonable? In irrigation districts and in municipalities, water pumped by either is used throughout either's service area rather than only on the tract from which it is pumped. In the absence of legislative action on these and similar points in groundwater law, the question can only be answered in specific instances on the basis of specific complaints placed before the courts.

The greatest single shortcoming in Arizona groundwater law is that it is largely judge-made law, not statute (that is, legislated) law except to a limited degree for critical groundwater areas. Its judge-made character may be illustrated by two circumstances:

1. The Constitution of Arizona specifies that the American common law derived from that of England shall be the basic fabric of law for Arizona except where legislation has been adopted to the contrary. As stated previously, groundwater law has, with a few modest exceptions, never been legislated in Arizona. Therefore, according to the common-law rule of property, all that is below the land surface inheres to the owner of the surface or to his assigns (for example, as in the case of minerals). Yet, according to judge-made decisions, the overlying land owner doesn't really own his subjacent water so freely and unrestrainedly; modifications have been made following other rules of reasonableness and equity – but by courts, not legislature;

2. The legislature provided that in critical groundwater areas water drawn from approved (licensed) wells cannot be used on lands that were not irrigated during the five years immediately prior to the declaration of the area as critical. However, the court has held that it may be so used on previously unirrigated lands belonging to the well owner – a judicial act rather than (even contrary to) a legislative act, no doubt with judicial legitimacy on arguments of due process in the taking of property – but again judge-made rather than legislature-made law.

Hence, groundwater law, as a guide to action for the development and use of groundwater, is not a body of codified organic law but is an intangible, amorphous body of law deduced from particular court decisions on specific issues in specific conflicts. There always remains the uncertainty in each groundwater user's contemplated use of his water and in each brewing dispute over groundwater rights-duties and liberties-exposures how the particulars of that contemplated use or dispute square with the precedents of court decisions settling previous, presumably similar, issues. How frequently uncertainty over the outcome of any such present or possible conflicts, if brought before the courts, discourages the parties from making decisions or entering conflicts for adjudication is, of course, unknown. It would seem probable that it is considerable. Thus, the uncertainties persist, continuing to leave the basis for decision making and the relations among groundwater users nebulous, equivocal, and uncertain.

Security of Expectations

As with surface-water rights, security or insecurity of expectations on the part of the holder of rights to underground water has several facets – physical security, tenure security, and whether the expectation is short-run or long-run. The physical security of groundwater rights will differ between landowners, due to (1) local differences in depth from the surface to the water table, (2) local differences in the efficiency of the aquifer as a water yielder, (3) local differences in the quality of the aquifer water, and (4) local differences in the "draw down" or "cone of depression" in the water table during pumping. Physical security in groundwater rights refers to the degree of certainty on the part of the right holder that the physical supply of water available to him will not be affected by fluctuation in nature. In this sense groundwater rights are quite secure because the physical supply is not much affected from year to year by fluctuations in natural conditions of precipitation and run-off. Given the conditions that determine the individual landowner's ease or difficulty of access to the water table and of extraction therefrom, his expectations regarding the natural conditions of that supply are highly secure.

The security of his expectations regarding his *tenure rights* to that water, however, can be quite different. Tenure rights can exhibit considerable insecurity in the long run but considerable security in the short run. Tenure security in groundwater refers to the landowner's certainty as to the effects on his water supply he can expect that stem from the legal acts of other landowners. So long as landowners who share a common aquifer are not as a group extracting water in excess of natural recharge of the aquifer, all will be secure in their expectations regarding their future supplies of groundwater. But, as soon as collective withdrawal from the common aquifer increases to the point that it exceeds natural recharge, each affected user of water from that aquifer finds the security of his tenure in his water supply diminishing, the degree of his insecurity depending on the volume of withdrawals in excess of recharge and the time horizon of his expectations. Tenure security may be but little affected in the short run by such excess withdrawals but greatly affected in the long run.

On the other hand, tenure rights to groundwater can be quite secure in that (1) the right of access to whatever groundwater lies beneath the owner's land is protected by law and largely unrestrained, and (2) protection of each groundwater developer against unreasonable use of the water by other pumpers and against unreasonable export of that water from the tract of origin by other pumpers is firmly developed.

Tenure rights in groundwater, thus, are quite secure in some respects and somewhat insecure in others. They are insecure in the long run whenever collective extraction from the common aquifer exceeds recharge and are more insecure in this regard the greater the relative amount of this excess removal. Their insecurity in this regard is enhanced by the relative freedom each pumper has to extract all he reasonably needs for use on his land, unrestrained by other pumpers. Tenure rights to groundwater are quite secure, on the other hand, because the right of access by the landowner to his water is largely unrestrained and because restraints are imposed upon other pumpers on the same aquifer to protect each against unreasonable extraction and use or export of the pumped water from the area.

The chief insecurity in tenure rights to groundwater arises from their being judge-made rather than legislature-made law. The tenure right holder to groundwater never knows for sure what a court may decide the "law" to be. He can protect himself from this uncertainty by not bringing his disputes before a court, but he cannot prevent other parties from embroiling him in a court conflict regarding his use of his groundwater.

Long-run tenure insecurities in groundwater law in Arizona tend to overshadow the securities. The socioeconomic consequence is heavy pressure on the groundwater user to get as much water out of the ground as he can, economically and legally, in as short a time as possible. The obvious result is rapid extraction of groundwater for so long as marginal-value product from its use is equal to or above the operating cost of the pumps by which it is extracted. Thus, short-run security is gained by each at the expense of long-run insecurity on the part of all.

Such tenure securities and insecurities, together with the relative ease of access to the groundwater by each potential user, has encouraged individual user investment in developments for groundwater extraction. The conditions of groundwater tenure put a premium on using the water *now,* rather than conserving it for the future, even for the owner's future.

Furthermore, pressure on each groundwater user to bolster his individual short-run security at the cost of long-run insecurity for all, forces users heavily dependent upon rapidly deepening groundwater stocks to search eagerly for replacement water supplies. Groundwater law encourages rapid depletion of groundwater stocks, thus forcing long-run search for developable replacement surface supplies. The interests of many groundwater pumpers and of rapidly growing municipal-industrial sectors of the state's economy thus coincide in a need and search for developable surface supplies and for the financing required to effectuate them.

Flexibility

The second element in water rights is flexibility – the ease or difficulty the owner experiences in transferring the use or location of use of water to meet changing socioeconomic conditions.

Groundwater rights are about like surface rights in their tenure flexibility; they are somewhat more flexible than surface-water rights in the ease of their transfer among uses on-site, but somewhat less flexible compared to surface-water rights in the ease of their transfer off-site. Groundwater tenure is more flexible on-site than are surface-water rights because there are no restraints on the amount or purpose of groundwater withdrawal so long as it is reasonable for use on the site (except for the weak restraints found in critical groundwater areas). Flexibility of groundwater tenure is further enhanced because even in critical groundwater areas the weak restraints imposed on groundwater withdrawals therein do not apply to wells for purposes other than for irrigation.

Groundwater rights are almost totally inflexible regarding changes in the location of the water's use, particularly if the change is to sites beyond the limits of the aquifer and even to sites other than the site of withdrawal though still overlying the same aquifer, especially if some other groundwater user on the aquifer registers a complaint about the shift in location of use. Groundwater rights are somewhat more flexible than surface-water rights regarding transfer to off-site uses, however, if pumped by an irrigation or agricultural improvement district for use within the district.

Tenure flexibility of groundwater use tends to be impaired by extreme obscurity and inadequacy of the technical data needed to determine the adverse effects of water transfer off-site. The mere assertion of presumptive damage by another pumper on the same aquifier may be sufficient to stop these transfers.

Thus, groundwater tenure in Arizona is quite inflexible relative to off-site tranfers but quite flexible relative to changes of use on-site. The socioeconomic consequence is a rigid "locking in" of groundwater to existing sites and to existing uses. Only when the new uses for the water are feasible on the site where it is presently being used, or, possibly, where the new use, though on a different site, is still on the same aquifer, can transfers of use of groundwater occur in Arizona with some reasonable assurance they will be upheld in the courts. Groundwater in Arizona is effectively though not totally restrained from shifting to new and more effective economic uses.

Socioeconomic Implications

Rights to the development and use of groundwater in Arizona endow their owners individually and collectively with a complex mish-mash of (1) securities and insecurities in their expectations that the waters will continue to be available to them over time and (2) flexibilities and inflexibilities in their abilities to shift the uses to which their waters can be put in order to adapt to changing technologies, preferences, prices, and institutions. But, if we look at this mish-mash as a whole, we can discern certain consequences it has had on the development and use of Arizona groundwater.

1. Because supplies of groundwater are readily accessible to their overlying landowners over wide areas in Arizona and are somewhat insecure over time, and because surface waters are "locked up" in largely nontransferable appropriative rights, and because of the high cost of developing increased supplies of surface water to meet increasing demands for water, the pressure to increase water supplies has encouraged individual landowners to invest in the development of increased extractive capacity for groundwater. Groundwater pumpage grew from about 1.5 million acre-feet in 1940 to 3.5 million acre-feet in 1950 to 5.0 million acre-feet in 1953, the level at which it has remained into the early 1970s.

2. Short-run tenure security in groundwater with long-run insecurity arising from its common property character puts a premium on short-run development and extraction of groundwater by the individual owners of its overlying lands. Because tenure rights in groundwater are tied so directly to individual ownership of separate tracts of overlying lands, each owner having considerable tenure security in his rights of access to that water, there has been no encouragement to group action by overlying landowners on a common aquifer to conserve or develop increased supplies of the underlying water for which they are all competing (as there has been with respect to surface water supplies). The only exception, and it a weak one, occurs when the groundwater is pumped by an organized district for use throughout the district.

3. Because, typically in Arizona, groundwater is more costly to its user than is surface water and is more subject than surface water to increasing cost over time due to the deepening water table, and because each individual pumper-user bears the whole cost of developing and extracting his groundwater supplies (except where an organized district is the developer-pumper and partially subsidizes water costs by using electricity incomes available to the district), the groundwater user is under more economic pressure than the usual surface-water user to conserve the groundwater once he has extracted it (though not that which remains in the ground).

Economic Critique of Water Law

In Arizona, groundwater and surface water are quite different kinds of water, not in their physical character and productivity but in the institutional restraints and opportunities attaching to them that influence the decisions made relative to their development, allocation, and use by water producers and consumers. Each of these two kinds of water is subject to quite different kinds of property (tenure) rights; each moves in a quite different physical system, observable and measurable to quite different degrees of complexity and accuracy. Adding to the complexities of the problem, some using-systems rest on surface-water supplies and rights only, some on groundwater only, and some on combinations of groundwater and surface water in widely differing proportions.

Both surface and groundwater rights in Arizona emphasize security of expectations over tenure flexibility or transferability. Groundwater and surface-water rights are about equal in tenure security in the short run, but in the long run, surface-water rights have greater tenure security than do groundwater rights. In physical security, groundwater users and surface-water users who stand high in the queue are about equal. But, groundwater rights are physically more secure than are surface-water rights of those who are far down the appropriation queue. Both surface and groundwater rights in Arizona play down flexibility in the transfer of rights – surface-water rights somewhat more so than groundwater rights for transfer among on-site uses, but groundwater rights somewhat more so than surface-water rights for transfer to off-site uses.

The result has been extensive *group* investment to make the flow of surface waters regular and to increase the supply and level of management of those surface supplies. Except for some undeveloped supplies yet remaining in the Colorado River, there are no more readily developable surface-water supplies remaining in Arizona.

In contrast, the nature of groundwater supplies and the rights attaching to them has resulted in extensive *individual* user investment of capital to increase withdrawal capacity for these waters. Exceptions to individual investment in groundwater extraction works have been (1) certain irrigation districts that have district installed pumping and distribution capacity, and (2) municipalities that have developed groundwater supplies for use by their domestic and industrial customers. In addition, only groundwater has been developed and distributed by private, corporate firms for sale to domestic and industrial, though rarely to agricultural, customers. Furthermore, because of the nature of the rights attaching to surface waters in contrast to those attaching to groundwater, administrative rationing allocates surface waters among users and locations of use for both the short and the long run; but greater reliance is placed on economic rationing, emphasizing short-run exploitation, to allocate groundwater among users and uses, with public (in this case judicial) rationing to allocate groundwater among the locations where it can be used.

The emphasis given to security of expectations in water rights, without equal emphasis on locational flexibility in those rights, causes water in Arizona to be "locked in" to lands of early appropriators (surface water), which are largely agricultural, or to lands overlying groundwater aquifers (groundwater) which because of their inevitable geographic extension are also largely agricultural. Thus, rapidly increasing nonagricultural, urban, and industrial users find it difficult to satisfy their increasing demands for water. Only two methods of obtaining water are open to them. They can (1) acquire lands suitably located for their uses that already hold a surface-water right eligible for their intended use or that overlie an accessible groundwater aquifer, or (2) join in group activities to develop underdeveloped surface-water supplies for importation from outside the area of need. Such additional supplies presently must be from outside the state, carry a high cost, and require broadly based public participation in the necessary financing of the venture.

Finally, because private rights to the use of water, whether surface or groundwater, attach only to the acts of storage, diversion or extraction, and use, and not to ownership of the body of the water itself, the idea is implanted in the public and administrative minds that the only cost of water is the direct outlay cost for constructing and operating the storage, diversion or extraction works, and the conveyance system. Water in its natural state is considered to be free. Neither the public nor administrators recognize the social opportunity cost of water that is involved, for example, in its allocation to use A rather than to use B. The net value foregone to society by denying its use to B is part of the cost to society of use A. To derive the greatest social value from the water's use, this cost must be recognized as a charge for the water against use A which must be able to produce enough value from use of the water to be able to outbid use B for it. This real social cost arises whether use A actually pays the cost or not; it is a sacrifice that the whole economy incurs, regardless of who pays it.

In a typically functioning resource-allocation system, private property rights attaching to the resource insure that user A will be required to pay the true economic cost of his use of the resource because he will have to purchase it in a competitive market economy where use B is also competing for its use. But under water law (in Arizona as elsewhere) private property rights do not attach to the water but only to the rights to its use. Surface water is public property. The property status of groundwater is unclear, but it is clothed with a public character. Hence, allocation of rights to use natural water supplies as to location, nature, and timing of the use is not carried out primarily by economic charges (prices) but largely by administrative rules and regulations. No other natural resource in our economy is allocated among possible users and uses in this fashion, except air, highway space (on other than toll roads and bridges), and access to fish and game and most public recreational areas.

The problem this creates is that water allocations either ignore these opportunity costs altogether, to the economic detriment of the dependent society, or, where these costs are considered in some measure, the non-market administrative methods by which they are brought into play are so wooden, so cumbersome and unresponsive, so uncertain and inflexible, that available water supplies tend always to be allocated and used at less than the socioeconomic efficiency of which they are capable. The creation of a much more refined and responsive administrative rationing system, or some form of a market-like economic rationing system, or some combination of the two, is much to be desired if the limited water supplies of the state are to make their full contribution to the socio-economic development of Arizona.

4. The Direct Consequence of Increasing Water Scarcity on the Arizona Economy

We have defined the concepts necessary to the analysis of water scarcity and outlined the conceptual model that we will use to examine the effects of water scarcity on the Arizona economy. We have sketched the legal environment within which water is used in Arizona and the general socioeconomic consequences of the Arizona water law. The remainder of this book will be concerned with obtaining empirical estimates of the consequences of water scarcity in Arizona, using the conceptual model, within the restraints imposed by the legal environment.

We have chosen to estimate consequences of water scarcity over the ensuing fifty years. In doing so, as our conceptual model has shown, we must first estimate the direct effects of water scarcity in agriculture, the marginal use of water in Arizona. Then, having projected the direct effects of water scarcity in agriculture on agriculture, we may use the results as a base to project the indirect effects of water scarcity in agriculture on the rest of the economy.

Method of Analysis

Our problem is to project the reactions of Arizona farmers, in terms of the crops they will grow and how they will grow them, over the next fifty years as they respond to increasing irrigation water costs. As our conceptual discussion pointed out, any resource is scarce if it is not free; that is, if it is available only at a price. Water in Arizona is scarce only in terms of the demand for water being such that the quantity demanded is supplied at a positive price. Most irrigation water in Arizona is supplied at such a low price that many thousands of acres of low-valued crops may be grown. The prices of surface waters are low and are not increasing. Only the costs of pumping groundwater are increasing over time as the level of the vast groundwater reservoir below the surface of Arizona falls in response to pumping without an equal quantity of recharge.

The actual size of the groundwater reservoir is unknown. We know only that it is vast and not in danger of complete depletion in the foreseeable future. Therefore, irrigation water scarcity in Arizona is exhibited only by a rising cost of water to some farmers in some areas. The absolute cost and the rate at which the cost is rising depend on the physical conditions of the aquifer from which the farmer obtains his water. Thus, instead of speaking of farm adjustments due to water scarcity, it is more accurate to speak of agricultural adjustment due to rising water costs. It is this phenomenon of rising water costs over time that allows us to make projections of agricultural adjustment over the coming fifty years through use of a formal economic model.

Representative-Farm Linear-Programming Models

A linear-programming model is a mathematical system for maximizing a stated objective within the bounds of a set of stated restrictions. For example, a linear-programming model for a farm might be constructed so as to show what crops to grow (and in what quantities) in order to maximize the farm's profits subject to restrictions such as the quantities of land, water, and capital available to the farm operator.

A representative-farm linear-programming model is a model for a farm situation which has been selected as representative of the situation facing farmers of a particular area. If one were to define a representative-farm model for each different situation facing farmers over a large area such as the state, and then were to sum the results of all of the models in proportion to the frequency with which each model situation actually exists, one could obtain estimates, for the entire state, of aggregate quantities of crops, gross and net income, water use, and any other quantities of interest.

The accuracy of the aggregate estimates would depend on (1) the accuracy with which representative physical, biological, and economic situations are perceived and defined, and (2) the accuracy with which the stated objective to be maximized reflects the actual objective of the population of farm operators. The physical, biological, and economic situations as discovered and defined by us are outlined in this chapter and in the appendixes. We have attempted to achieve a high degree of accuracy by intensive stratification of our population into some 150 representative-farm models of homogenous situations. Solutions to the models were obtained by using the objective of maximization of profits – a goal which we believed adequately represented the overriding motivation of commercial crop farmers in Arizona. Empirical results of our models, which were solved for past years, checked closely with statistics of farm output for past years and adjustments in farm output between past years. Thus, we concluded that model construction was adequate, that the objective to be maximized closely approximated the actual objectives of farmers in the state, and that the models would be useful in projecting agricultural adjustments in future years, given that surrounding conditions in future years could be adequately described.

The Projection Procedure

The general operational procedure for making projections of agricultural adjustment over the fifty-year time horizon is explained below, although some differences in procedure were used in different areas of the state, depending on actual conditions found in that area. A simplified flow diagram of the procedure is presented as figure 4-1. Operation of the model begins by specifying the initial conditions affecting farmer decisions in period t. These are (a) the net return over variable costs for each potential use for irrigation water (for example, the expected net return from one acre of cotton grown with a specified set of practices); (b) the depths to water, and thus the costs of water, in the various subareas of the study area; and (c) the constraints on land and water availability by subarea and size of farm.

These conditions are inserted as the parameters of the linear-programming models of representative farms of the areas. Solution of the programming model on a digital computer gives the cropping patterns that would maximize net income for the individual farmers of the areas, given the constraints they face in terms of resource availabilities and government policies, and at the same time provides the quantity of pumped water necessary for this cropping pattern for each subarea for the given time period.

The quantities of water pumped in each subarea for that time period are the inputs used in estimating the changes in depths of water in each subarea and for each representative-farm model.

After computing the average change in depth of water over each subarea, new constraints in terms of maximum pumping capacities by depth to water and subareas are developed for the beginning of time t + 1. Because pumpage depths have changed, the costs of water to be entered into the new linear-programming model are changed as well.

Several other adjustments in the parameters of the water-demand model are made at this time. These adjustments are made outside the main computational procedures and require some subjective judgment on the part of the researchers.

In each year, a certain number of the wells in the area reach the end of their useful life. A decision must be made between replacing the

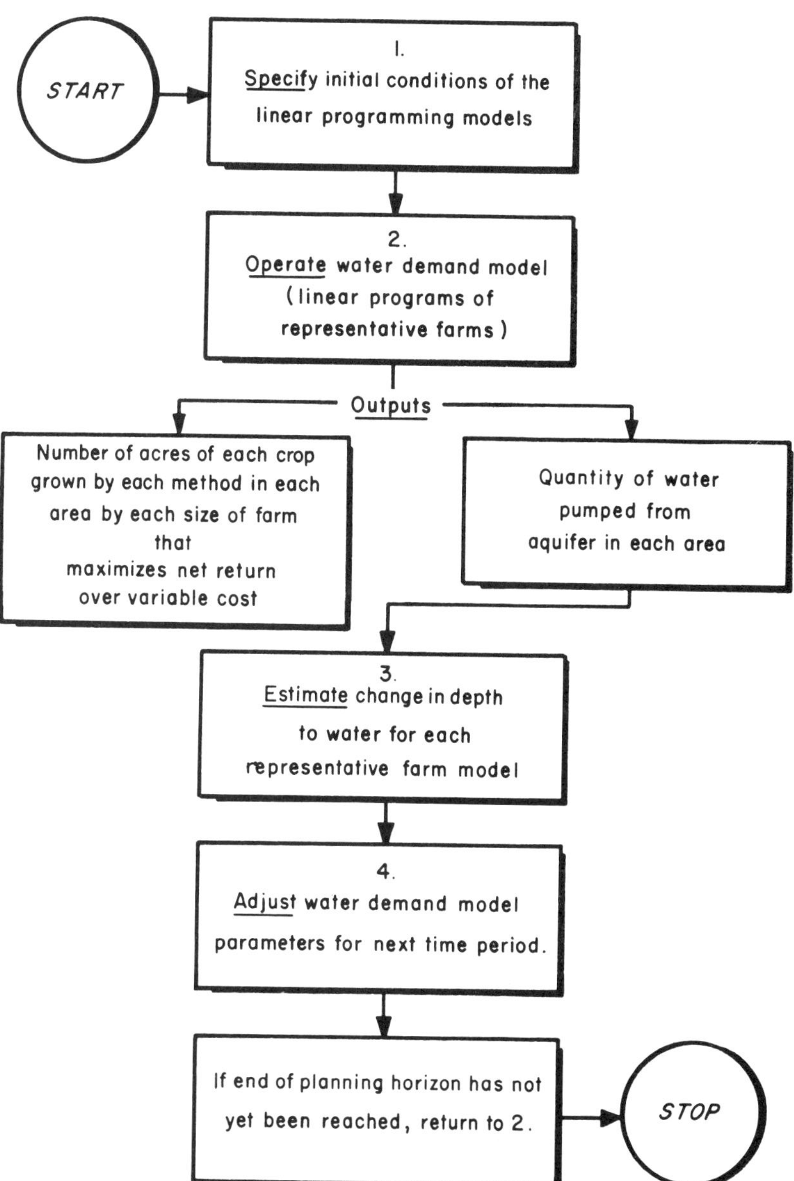

Fig. 4-1. *The irrigated agriculture projection model.*

well or abandoning a given amount of irrigated acres. Well replacement requires a large fixed investment which must be amortized over succeeding years. Well abandonment, on the other hand, requires sacrificing the expected net return from the crops that could then no longer be grown. Note that the crops that would be sacrificed are the marginal low-valued crops such as barley and alfalfa, not the high-valued crops such as cotton or vegetables. Furthermore, because large farms are more efficient than small farms, large farms can better afford well replacement and will experience a slower rate of well abandonment and thus of land abandonment.

The amortized cost of replacing the wells must be compared with the stream of expected net returns of potential crops to be irrigated. This comparison is made for each size of farm. If the smaller farms cannot afford to replace a well at the depth necessary for continued use, but the largest farms can, the acreage that the smaller farmers would have had to sacrifice is assumed to be purchased by the large farmers, and the well is replaced. Thus, the model postulates that land is not abandoned because of lack of water until the largest, most efficient units can no longer afford the water cost. This procedure agrees with the observed change in farm size over time in the study areas. Because the larger farms use different production technologies than the small farms and have certain other advantages, such as purchasing efficiencies, the procedure of projecting changed farm size over time provides the projection model with some dynamic properties.

In areas where urbanization is projected to absorb agricultural acreage and create new urban water requirements, adjustments are also made in the total land and water availability constraints.

With all of the constraints of the linear-programming water-demand model adjusted to the new conditions, the model is solved for the period $t + 1$. This cyclical procedure is continued until the end of the planning horizon is reached.

Data With Which to Implement the Models

The basis of the economic projection models consists of extremely detailed descriptions of the organizations, costs, and returns of irrigated crop farms in Arizona.

At the outset of this investigation, little was known about the details of irrigated cropfarm agriculture in Arizona, even as to the number and size of farms within the population. Data for 1959 from the U.S. Census of Agriculture were used as a starting point in determining acreages, numbers, and types of farm firms; however, the census did not present sufficient detail to be useful for more careful analysis. Thus, it was necessary to develop our information from detailed personal interviews of a sample of farmers in the state.

The population list from which the sample was drawn was developed from the list of farms maintained by county offices of the Agricultural Stabilization and Conservation Service (ASCS). This list purported to include all cropland within the state. Farms on this list were identified by the name and address of the operator; but the same name often appeared more than once, and similar names and identical addresses were prevalent. By combining those names which appeared to represent unified operations, a single list of farms for each study area was compiled. This list for all areas included approximately 2,300 farm operations and provided the frame from which a sample was chosen.

Several requirements were deemed necessary in selecting the sample. All of the geographical areas within the major irrigated areas of the state should be represented. A cross-section of farm sizes should be obtained. Because larger farms represent a greater proportion of total cropland and hence weigh more heavily in the aggregate, these should represent a larger proportion of the sample. Randomness in drawing was necessary in order to eliminate selection bias.

The sample was drawn as follows: first, the list of farms for each farming area was arrayed according to the number of cropland acres reported in the records of the local offices of the ASCS. Those farms having fewer than thirty acres of cropland were excluded on the grounds that they did not represent bona fide full-time farming operations, nor were they of sufficient importance in the aggregate to warrant the cost of gathering data which would yield only minor refinements. Then, depending on the number and size of farms in each area, every nth farm on the list was selected after a random start.

The state was divided into six major areas encompassing 97 percent of all cropland in Arizona and almost all irrigated cropland. These divisions were made on the basis of irrigation water sources, geographical location within the state, and acres and types of crops grown. The six major areas are: Yuma County, Maricopa County Surface Water, Maricopa County Pump Water, Pinal-Pima Counties, Graham-Greenlee Counties, and Cochise County. Gross geographic outlines of the study areas are shown in figure 4-2. Detailed maps of the study areas and their subareas within Maricopa, Pinal, and Pima counties are shown in Appendix A, figures A-1, A-2, and A-3. Approximately 100 detailed personal-interview questionnaires were completed for each area for a total of 600 questionnaires; about a 25 percent sample of all farm operators with

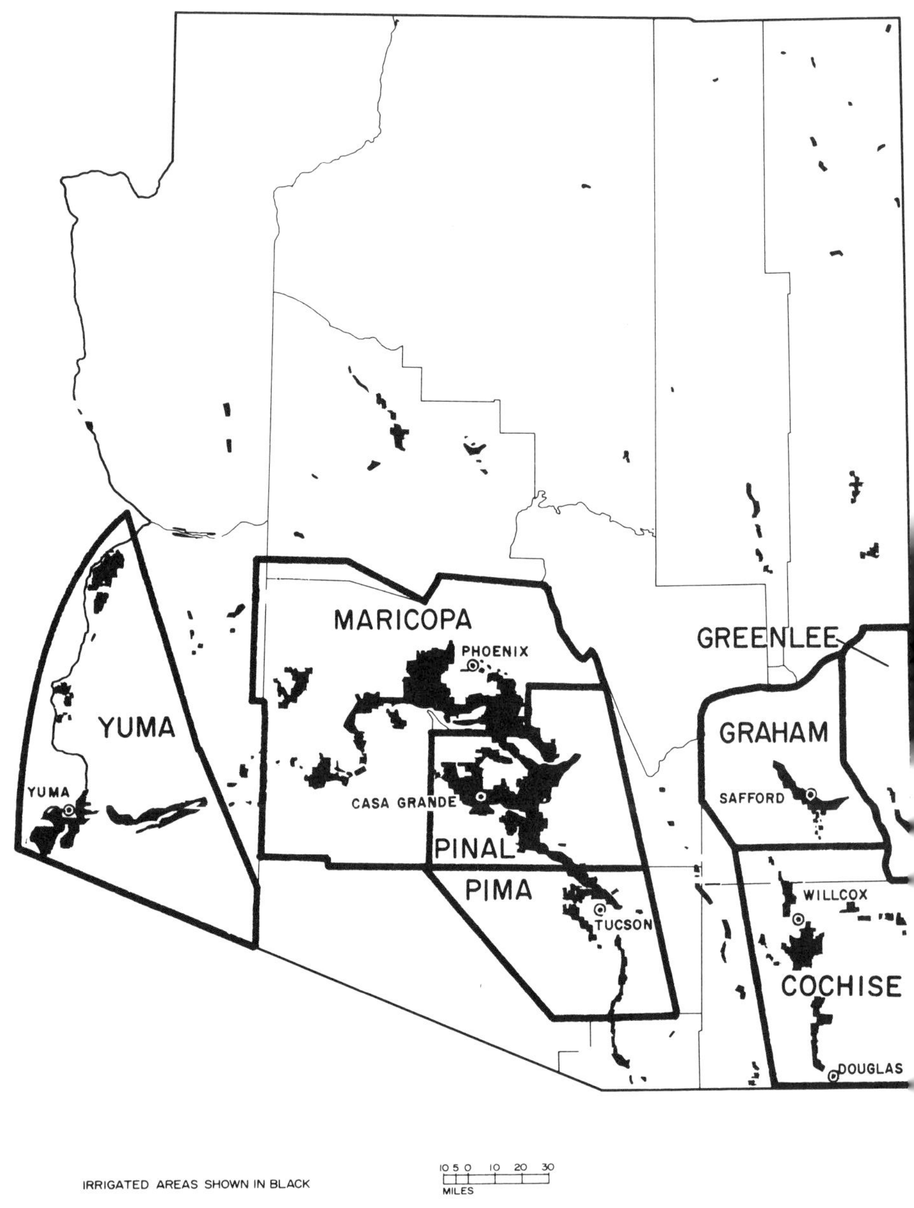

Fig. 4-2. *Major study areas and irrigated land in Arizona. (Fig. 8.10, from* Arizona: Its People and Resources, *ed. 2., University of Arizona Press.)*

farms of above thirty acres in size. Because a larger proportion of large sized farms was sampled, the sample covered about 40 percent of the irrigated field crop acreage.

Description and Location of Irrigated Agriculture

Before the representative-farm linear-programming models could be constructed, a detailed description of the irrigated crop farm economies of each area in the state was necessary so as to provide a base for the analysis. We provide brief descriptions of Arizona agriculture by area in the following sections. Then, the results of our projections of agricultural adjustment over the coming fifty years are reported. The details of our representative-farm models used in making the projections are included in Appendix A.*

General Description — All Areas

Most of irrigated agriculture in Arizona is located in what is known as the Desert Lowlands Province. Elevations at which irrigation is practiced range from about 300 feet to 4,000 feet above sea level. Although this area comprises only about 45 percent of the total area of the state, it contains more than 95 percent of the irrigated land and about 85 percent of the population.

Irrigated areas in the state are shown in figure 4-2. The major concentrations of irrigated area are in the central part of the state in Maricopa and Pinal Counties and in Yuma County along the Gila and Colorado Rivers. Other concentrations are in Cochise, Graham, Greenlee, and Pima Counties. The remaining three percent of Arizona cropland, mostly in the northern counties of Mohave, Coconino, Gila, Navajo, and Apache, is of small consequence in terms of total state crop output because of the short growing season and the type of low-value crops produced.

Total acreage cropped has remained quite constant over the decade of the 1960s. There have been substantial changes in the acreage mix of various crops, but total acreage has varied by less than 150,000 acres, as shown in table 4-1. The largest acreage in the decade was in 1969.

The distribution of major crop acreages by county is shown in table 4-2 for the latest year available, 1970. All counties in the state with their acreage of agricultural crops are listed in descending order of total acreage. Primary producing counties in descending order of acreage are Mari-

---

*Data used in the analyses of this and later chapters, and elaboration of the analytical techniques employed, are included in Appendixes A, B, and C at the end of this book.

TABLE 4-1

Acreage of Arizona's Principal Crops, 1960 Through 1970

Year	Alfalfa	Citrus	Cotton	Grains	Vegetables	Other	Total
1961	227,000	29,335	392,000	368,000	99,500	94,000	1,209,835
1962	210,000	31,025	405,000	301,000	96,650	129,000	1,172,675
1963	193,000	33,165	387,000	333,000	101,635	118,000	1,165,800
1964	201,000	34,785	375,000	365,000	104,540	73,675	1,154,000
1965	191,000	38,975	339,000	408,000	101,000	82,025	1,160,000
1966	200,000	42,260	251,260	369,000	103,050	121,930	1,087,500
1967	196,000	41,335	245,000	589,000	93,750	56,915	1,222,000
1968	202,000	49,545	296,000	501,000	91,280	64,175	1,204,000
1969	188,000	49,740	309,000	452,000	89,800	133,560	1,222,100
1970	205,000	50,050	274,800	485,000	85,900	118,280	1,219,030

Source: Arizona Agricultural Experiment Station and Extension Service (1961 through 1970). Arizona Crop and Livestock Reporting Service (1971).

copa, Yuma, Pinal, and Cochise. Over one million acres of the 1.2 million acres of cropland in the state are located in these four counties. The same acreage information is given in table 4-3 for the year 1966, the base year of our study. In the intervening period, 1966 to 1970, total acreage in the state again rose from its low year of the 1960s, 1966. The order of importance of several counties changed slightly during this time period, but all major producing counties actually increased their acreage in spite of rising irrigation water costs in counties such as Pinal, Cochise, and parts of Maricopa.

This phenomenon illustrates the point that water scarcity is not critical, as well as drawing attention to a basic facet of our representative-farm linear-programming projection technique. As will be shown, using 1966 as our base year, our projections show acreage in certain of these major counties declining over the period 1966 to 1975. These projections are made holding most variables constant at their 1966 levels and changing only water costs, factors that would accompany rising water costs, and the level of urbanization. This procedure is followed in order to sort out the effects on the economy of rising water costs. Because certain other variables, including the government price and allotment programs for cotton, increased in the intervening years, it is not surprising to find actual acreage increases in the face of rising water costs.

These circumstances point out the difference between a prediction of what will actually happen and a projection of what will happen given certain specific occurrences. Our analysis is a projection of what would happen in the face of rising water costs, given that economic and technological conditions remain about as they were in 1966. If economic or technological conditions improve over the fifty-year projection period, the observed effects of rising water costs on the Arizona economy will be less than shown because the negative effects will be masked by offsetting positive effects. If economic conditions deteriorate over the projection period, effects of rising water cost might appear to be greater than we show. But, of course, not all effects would be due to rising water costs. (Technology would not be expected to deteriorate. New technologies are not adopted unless they improve on the current situation.)

Descriptions of cropping patterns, irrigation water situations, and the number and types of farms in each of the individual major irrigated cropfarm areas follow.

Yuma County Study Area

Number and Types of Farms. There are approximately 350 commercial farms with over thirty acres of irrigated cropland in the Yuma County study area, exclusive of specialized citrus farms which occupy approximately 24,000 acres. These general crop farms are diversified, typically using a cotton-alfalfa and small grain or vegetable-melon rotation.

Major field crops in descending order of acreage are alfalfa, short-staple cotton, lettuce, cantaloupes and other melons, grain sorghum, barley, Bermuda grass seed, and wheat. Other field crops grown in lesser amounts are Sudan grass and miscellaneous hays and grasses for pasture, and various types of winter vegetables. Small acreages of seed crops, particularly lettuce, beets, onions, sugar beets, and carrots are also raised. In the past safflower, long-staple cotton, and flax have been grown successfully.

Because of the generally mild winters and the rapid maturity of many of the crops to which the area is suited, there is considerable double-cropping in Yuma County, and occasionally three crops can be harvested from the same land within a year. Barley or wheat and grain sorghum, and lettuce and cantaloupe, are often double-cropped in this way.

In addition to field crops, there is substantial acreage of citrus within the county. Much of this citrus acreage has been developed within the past seven or eight years and has not yet achieved its full productive potential. Estimates for 1969 indicate about 31,100 acres of citrus in Yuma County with about 60 percent of this acreage producing harvestable fruit.

Water Supply. The major portion of Yuma County cropland is

TABLE 4-2 — Estimated 1970 Acreage by Coun

1970 Crop	State Total	Counties Included In This Study			
		Maricopa	Yuma	Pinal	Coc
Alfalfa (acres cut for hay)	205,000	94,800	56,000	18,000	8
Hay production (tons)	1,230,000				
Cotton (upland, acres harvested)	242,000	87,500	29,900	88,500	1:
Bales (500 lb. gross wt.)	460,000				
American-Egyptian, acres harvested	32,800	11,700	2,060	6,800	1
Bales (500 lb. gross wt.)	29,000				
Barley (acres harvested for grain)	140,000	67,000	8,700	37,000	5
Grain production (tons)	255,360				
Corn (acres harvested for grain)*	14,000	0	1,500	100	
Grain production (tons)†	9,410				
Sorghums (acres harvested for grain)*	181,000	47,000	18,000	19,200	5
Grain production (tons)†	354,760				
Wheat (acres harvested for grain)	150,000	46,400	43,800	32,900	2
Grain production (tons)	310,500				
Vegetables (acres harvested)‡	85,900	34,520	32,265	13,600	[illegible]
Production (commercial cwt)	15,501,000				
Grapefruit (total acres)	7,450	5,000	2,000	430	
Production, 1969-70 crop (cartons)	6,298,000				
Oranges (total acres)	28,100	9,750	17,750	570	
Production, 1969-70 crop (cartons)§	9,888,000				
Lemons (total acres)	14,500	2,000	12,500	0	
Production, 1969-70 crop (cartons)	5,626,000				
Other crops (acres harvested)¶	118,280	57,040	22,520	14,350	
Total Acres	1,219,030	462,710	246,995	231,450	11

*Includes acreage harvested for grain.
†Does not include grain from acreage harvested for silage and forage.
‡Year ended August 31, 1970. County acreages based on data from Arizona Fresh Fruit and Vegetable Standardization Service and County Agents.

irrigated from surface waters of the Colorado River. A complex of six irrigation districts in the southwest corner of the county encompasses approximately 145,000 acres of irrigable cropland. In one of these districts a small amount of irrigation water is obtained from shallow wells. Some of this pumped water is reclaimed percolating water which is diluted with surface water in order to maintain the salinity content within tolerable limits. In each of the other five districts, all water supplies are

Total State Production of Principal Arizona Crops

unties Included (continued)			Counties Excluded From This Study						
m	Pima	Greenlee	Navajo	Apache	Mohave	Coconino	Yavapai	Santa Cruz	Gila
0	2,100	1,900	4,400	2,600	4,200	800	3,000	1,200	400
0	13,830	1,420	0	0	246	0	13	32	24
0	2,280	0	0	0	0	0	0	0	0
0	10,500	300	0	0	500	200	200	500	0
0	0	0	4,300	3,600	0	3,100	100	0	100
0	16,600	1,000	100	300	100	100	100	200	0
0	2,500	200	600	100	400	100	400	700	0
0	2,390	0	0	0	0	0	0	0	0
0	20	0	0	0	0	0	0	0	0
0	30	0	0	0	0	0	0	0	0
	0	0	0	0	0	0	0	0	0
	5,250	500	3,380	1,620	2,270	570	1,020	990	680
	55,500	5,320	12,780	8,220	7,716	4,870	4,833	3,622	1,214

des tangerines and tangerine types.
not include pasture.
: Arizona Crop and Livestock Reporting Service (1971)

obtained by surface diversions from the Colorado River. These districts contract with the United States Bureau of Reclamation for their water deliveries.

The Colorado River Indian Reservation Project, located in the northwest corner of the county, has a recent history of about 32,000 acres of irrigated cropland annually; however, this project has sufficient arable land and water rights to allow for expansion to about 100,000 acres.

TABLE 4-3 — Estimated 1966 Acreage by Coun

1966 Crop	State Total	Counties Included In This Study				
		Maricopa	Yuma	Pinal	Cochise	Gra
Alfalfa (acres cut for hay)	200,00	98,100	52,300	20,600	7,200	5
Hay production (tons)	1,040,000					
Cotton (upland, acres harvested)	217,200	78,800	24,400	83,500	8,570	6
Bales (500 lb gross wt)	468,000					
American-Egyptian (acres harvested)	33,800	14,000	190	7,200	197	9
Bales (500 lb gross wt)	37,000					
Barley (acres harvested for grain)	110,000	58,700	8,200	26,000	2,600	5
Grain production (tons)	176,880					
Corn (acres harvested, all purposes)*	30,000	5,600	600	400	2,000	
Grain productions (tons)†	18,100					
Sorghums (acres harvested, all purposes)*	206,000	55,900	18,400	32,000	58,000	24
Grain production (tons)†						
Wheat (acres harvested for grain)	23,000	9,000	4,700	7,300	1,300	
Grain production (tons)	27,600					
Vegetables (acres harvested)‡	103,050	52,500	36,300	7,500	4,300	
Production (commercial, cwt)	17,163,000					
Grapefruit (total acres)§	7,150	5,200	1,930	0	0	
Production (1965-66 crop, ctn)	6,100,000					
Oranges (total acres)§	26,390	10,660	15,600	100	0	
Production (1965-66 crop, ctn)¶	5,200,000					
Lemons (total acres)§	8,720	2,000	6,720	0	0	
Production (1965-66 crop, ctn)	3,940,000					
Other crops (acres)#	122,190	58,165	23,700	20,240	5,590	
Total acreage cropped	1,087,500	448,625	193,040	204,840	89,757	5

*Includes acreage harvested for grain, silage, and forage.

†Does not include grain from acreage harvested for silage and forage.

‡Year ended August 31, 1966. County acreages based on date from Arizona Fresh Fruit and Vegetable dardization Service and County Agents.

§Source: County Agricultural Agents.

Total State Production of Principal Arizona Crops

…unties Included (continued)		Counties Excluded From This Study						
…a	Greenlee	Navajo	Apache	Mohave	Coconino	Yavapai	Santa Cruz	Gila
…0	1,400	3,000	2,500	1,300	2,300	3,600	800	400
…0	1,280	0	0	263	0	7	125	25
…0	0	0	0	0	0	0	0	13
…0	700	0	30	0	50	0	320	0
…0	200	10,800	4,900	0	2,200	2,000	100	50
[illegible]	1,150	300	100	250	100	200	700	500
…0	70	300	50	0	100	0	0	0
[illegible]	100	400	50	150	0	400	0	0
[illegible]	0	0	0	0	0	0	0	0
[illegible]	0	0	0	0	0	0	0	0
[illegible]	0	0	0	0	0	0	0	0
[illegible]	620	1,000	720	3,020	3,050	1,615	500	290
[illegible]	5,520	15,800	8,350	4,983	7,800	7,822	2,545	1,278

…des tangerines and tangerine types.

… not include pasture. Data from Arizona Crop and Livestock Reporting Service and from County Agricul- … Agents.

…: Arizona Agricultural Experiment Station and Extension Service (1967). Includes both irrigated and …d crops.

This project receives administrative and supervisory support from the Bureau of Indian Affairs and is authorized to enter into development leases for as long as twenty-five years. If reclamation and development of these additional lands proceed according to present plans, the entire 100,000 acres should be under cultivation by 1975.

Additional irrigation diversions from the Colorado River have been made by farmers who pump directly from the river, or in the absence of a clearly defined water right, from shallow wells adjacent to the river. Lands irrigated in this manner are concentrated in two areas; along the left limit of the Colorado River adjacent to the Yuma Valley Irrigation Project but outside of the Project itself; and in the Cibola area located about twenty miles downstream from Blythe, California, on the eastern bank. Both of these areas lie adjacent to the meanders of the Colorado River. As a by-product of attempts to regulate the flow of the river in the past three decades, considerable land has been created along the present river channel through the processes of accretion or avulsion. Some of this has been brought into cultivation and has been irrigated directly from the river. Other land more distant from the river bank is irrigated from shallow wells which are recharged from percolations from the river flow.

Ownership of some of these lands, resting on color-of-title claims or on claims to accreted land, is presently in doubt and has been the subject of considerable litigation between private claimants and the United States government through its Department of Interior agencies. Other privately owned land has been irrigated by pumping directly or indirectly from the river without proper authorization – clearly cases of water trespass. Because of the unclear status of ownership of some of these riparian lands and the equally questionable status of some water rights, it is difficult to estimate the acreage of irrigable lands of this type.

In the past as much as 15,000 acres has been reported under cultivation on nonproject-riparian land; however, more informed estimates by U. S. Department of Interior employees and County Extension Service personnel suggest that privately held lands subject to irrigation and with a potentially valid water right do not exceed more than about 10,000 acres at the present time.

The remaining cropland in Yuma County is in small widely-scattered areas in the eastern and northeastern section of the county where water supplies are pumped from groundwater basins. Costs and returns and cropping patterns in this area are similar to those found in adjacent areas of Maricopa County directly to the east. These small isolated areas were not covered in our representative-farm linear-programming models.

Therefore, our projections identified as for Yuma County include only those lands in Yuma County which are irrigable with surface waters of the Colorado River (figure 4-2).

Water Rights. The nature of water rights and water availability varies among the several irrigation districts within the study area. In the earlier organized districts, the doctrine of beneficial use determines the water right, and water availability may be limited only by the capacity of the diversion facilities and not by any institutional or contractual restriction. In other cases the water right is specified in terms of a maximum aggregate flow rate (for example, not to exceed so many second feet) to the district as a whole without regard to its distribution to specific lands.

In some instances water rights take the form of contracts between water user groups and the United States, through U.S. Department of Interior agencies. These may call for the delivery of a specified volume of water annually to the irrigation districts. In these cases, the districts themselves are able to specify how water may be allocated to users through the rate structure of water delivery charges or by specifying other limitations on delivery. As the land-use pattern changes from agricultural to nonagricultural uses (which tend to use less water per acre), the amount available for agricultural use may be increased. Water availability for a given area of land for agricultural use, therefore, may vary from year to year, and the combination of land and water does not necessarily occur in a fixed ratio over time.

The legal status of water rights for the nonproject-riparian lands is even more nebulous. Here, land owners are not under contract with the U.S. Department of Interior for water deliveries nor do they have a legal and enforceable right under state law. They must depend for their water supplies on the flow of the river and on the confused status of their rights.

Past experience, however, has shown that water supplies are generally adequate for the amount of irrigable and developed land in each district in the area even though problems of timely delivery sometimes occur during peak water using periods.

The agricultural potential of this area, therefore, is limited not by water availability so much as by the amount of land which has a water right associated with it.

Water Drainage Problems. In past years some areas within the county have been subjected to severe subsurface drainage problems. Application of large amounts of irrigation water in these areas has resulted in raising the level of the groundwater table to within a few feet of the surface. Because of the effective leaching properties of the surface water as it is applied for irrigation purposes and the high salinity levels of the area soils, groundwater has a relatively high salt content. If subsurface drainage is inadequate, saline groundwater may move into the plant's root zone, and reduction of the water content of the upper layers of soil either through plant use or evaporation may result in the build-up of alkaline soil conditions which are unfavorable for production of most crops.

These problems have been rather severe in some areas in the past; however, in most of these areas extensive drainage and pumping facilities have been constructed to lower the groundwater level and halt any further advance of this salinity condition. As these facilities continue to operate and as the associated lands continue to be irrigated with "sweet" surface water, residual salts will be leached out of the upper soil strata and carried downward and into the drainage system. Over a period of several years soil salinity conditions may be expected to improve. Therefore, salinity problems may be considered to be of temporary duration and of minor importance in terms of agricultural adjustment over the long run.

Maricopa County Study Area

The Maricopa County study area embraces all of the irrigated land in Maricopa County. For purposes of our representative farm analysis, this aggregate area was subdivided into sixteen subareas. These subareas are defined and delineated in detail in Appendix A. Though the patterns of operation and enterprise make-up of the agriculture in these subareas are similar throughout, the projected responses of their agriculture to changing water conditions over the next fifty years will differ; thus our projections of their future land and water use and income production also will differ. However, in reporting the results of our analysis of Maricopa County, in most instances we aggregate into only two areas. These are (1) the Salt River Project (SRP) and its associated Roosevelt Water Conservation District (RWCD), which rest principally on surface water from the Salt-Verde River system supplemented by groundwater, and (2) the rest of the irrigated land in the county which is dependent on groundwater with some supplementation from surface water in local situations. We refer to these two areas respectively as the Salt River Project and the Maricopa County groundwater areas.

The first modern irrigated agriculture in central Arizona began along the Salt River in the vicinity of Phoenix about 1869 when only a few hundred acres were under cultivation. The first irrigation facilities were owned and operated by private companies that supplied water directly from the surface flow in the River to the land. In 1910 approximately

151,000 acres were being actively farmed under irrigation. Since that time the number of acres of irrigated cropland in this area has increased with some fluctuations to about 462,700 acres in 1972.

Number and Type of Farms. The Maricopa County study area has approximately 900 commercial farms with 30 or more acres of cropland. Of these 900, approximately 295 are located in the Salt River Project (surface water) area and 510 in the predominantly groundwater area.

Most farms in the study area are diversified in that they raise a combination of cotton, alfalfa, and small grains. Barley and sorghum may be double-cropped in some instances; in other cases, two crops of sorghum may be harvested from a single acre in one year. Alfalfa, due to mild winters and low altitudes, may be harvested throughout the entire year. This is typically practiced by using alfalfa land for sheep pasture during winter months. A small number of operations are speciality farms in that they produce only vegetables, citrus, or flowers. Vegetable acreage is primarily spring and fall lettuce. Farms in certain isolated areas are restricted as to kinds of crop options available to them due to agronomic soil-type or water-quality conditions.

General Water Supply Situation. Irrigated agriculture in the Maricopa County study area has two water supply sources: surface flows and groundwater stocks. Surface supplies are developed or distributed to users through several irrigation districts. Groundwater is pumped both by self-supplying private firms and by irrigation districts for their members. Generally the water table has been declining and pumping lifts increasing throughout the county, but these changes have halted or reversed slightly in some parts of the study area between 1968 and the early 1970s.

Surface water supplies for the Maricopa County study area are obtained almost exclusively from the Salt and Verde rivers. A series of six dams impound water for controlled use by the organizations that have claims on this surface water. This water, or its equivalent in Salt River Project (SRP) pump water, is delivered through the conveyance system of the SRP, which itself uses the largest quantity, to the lands of the Fort McDowell, Gila, and Salt River Indians, and to the Roosevelt Water Conservation District, St. Johns Irrigation District, Buckeye Irrigation District, and the Peninsular-Horowitz Ditch Company. The only other source of surface water to this study area is Lake Pleasant on the Agua Fria River, which provides a small, rather unstable quantity of water to the Maricopa County Municipal Water Conservation District No. 1.

In addition to district-developed-and-distributed pump and surface water, individual-farmer-owned pumps also operate in most districts, as well as, of course, in areas not covered by any district. The number of wells and the quantity of water obtained from them vary considerably among districts. In several districts, private pumps provide the only source of water. Table 4-4 summarizes selected irrigation district data for the Maricopa County study area.

Cities and towns also operate and maintain pumping units in the study area, and several of them also receive some surface water through the Salt River Project. The cities of Phoenix, Mesa, and Tempe are the three largest municipal water users in the area. The cities of Phoenix, Tempe, Gilbert, Glendale, and Peoria have domestic water contracts with the SRP under which Project water deliverable to Project lands within the service area of each city's water company may be delivered instead to the city's water plant for delivery through its system to those lands the uses of which are, generally, nonagricultural. Water delivered under these contracts may be from either surface or ground sources. The City of Phoenix has, in addition, a claim to some surface water from Horseshoe Dam, referred to as "gatewater" and delivered to it through the SRP by virtue of an investment made by the city that increased the dam's reservoir capacity. Several other smaller municipalities are located in the area, but their combined total water use is less than five percent of the total municipal use in the area.

Salt River Project. This Project was authorized for construction in 1903 and was the first project undertaken under the National Reclamation Act of 1902. The Salt River Valley Water Users' Association operates the irrigation system and acts as an agent for the Project.

The service area of this Project includes 238,250 acres in central Maricopa County surrounding the City of Phoenix, Arizona. The irrigated lands lie north and south of the Salt River in the triangles formed by the intersection of the Salt-Gila Rivers and the Salt-Agua Fria Rivers. Elevation of the irrigated lands range from 900 to 1,300 feet above sea level. At the present time, approximately 80,000 acres of the total area are devoted to residential, commercial, or industrial use. As the municipal areas grow, the land and its associated water transfers from agricultural to urban-industrial use.

Two rivers are the source of surface water. A series of four dams and reservoirs on the Salt River and two on the Verde River supply approximately two-thirds of the present water distributed by the Project. The remaining one-third of the water supply available to the Project is obtained from approximately 250 Project owned and operated pumps.

TABLE 4-4

Selected Irrigation District Data for the Maricopa County Study Area

Irrigation District	Active	Inactive	Power Generation	District Sources: Ground-Water	District Sources: Surface Water	Private Pumps	Acreage
aman Mutual Water Company	X			X			2,493
uila Irrigation District		X				X	42,240
ington Canal Company	X			X		X	4,800
ckeye Water Conservation and Drainage District	X			X	X	X	20,465
ndler Heights Citrus Irrigation Districts	X			X			1,380
quahala Valley Irrigation District	X					X	60,000
icopa County Municipal Water Conservation District No. 1	X			X	X	X	35,000
Micken Irrigation District	X					X	45,000
State Irrigation and Drainage District	X					X	2,400
insula Ditch Company	X					X	2,262
sevelt Irrigation District	X			X		X	38,152
sevelt Water Conservation District	X			X	X	X	39,425
River Indian Irrigation Project	X			X	X		46,619
River Project	X		X	X	X	X	240,000
ohns Irrigation District	X			X	X	X	2,960
en Creek Irrigation District		X				X	9,600

ce: United States Department of the Interior (1965).

Water is distributed by the Project under several classes and priorities of rights.

Normal flow water rights are those that were established by the Kent Decree (*Hurley vs. Abbott et al,* 1910). This right related to water that would be carried by the rivers if their flows were not restricted by dams. These rights to "natural flows" of the river existed prior to the development of the Project and give their holders first claim on diversion and use of surface water "flowing" in the river at any and each point in time. Lands entitled to this water must have been in continuous cultivation beginning sometime between 1869 and 1909. Land cultivated and irrigated in the earlier years of this time period has a greater probability of obtaining water under this normal flow right than lands continuously cultivated toward the end of the period. This water is delivered to its claimants on demand through the district's system.

During periods of less than adequate flow, many lands with priorities near 1909 do not receive any water under this right. Much of this water right goes unclaimed because it must be used at the time it would theoretically flow if not held in reservoirs. Also, most of the flow of the rivers takes place in the winter and early spring months when there is little demand for water. This normal flow water right is applicable to 151,083 acres of the 238,252 acres of the Project area.

Water in the rivers over and above that covered and claimed under the normal flow right as well as unclaimed "normal flow" water is stored in the Project's system. This water is called stored and developed water. Rights to this water are held equally by all lands originally agricultural having capital stock in the association. After payment of an annual assessment, the Project allocates this water equally among project lands. In some instances, excess or floodwater becomes available and is also allocated on an equal basis.

Rights to Project-developed pump water are held by Project lands for which they were purchased by Project members, beginning in 1948. This right was purchased from the association in one-half acre-foot per acre increments up to two acre-feet per acre. This right, when purchased, is a permanent right to buy pump water from the Project if and when needed. These are available for sale by the Project for an indefinite period. As of 1967, 163,580 acres of Project land (or about 70 percent of the eligible acres) had purchased 242,376 acre-feet of this pump water right.

A final water right is that entitled "townsite rights." These rights provide for the delivery of water to cities and towns within the Project. This right is granted under the Reclamation Act of April 16, 1906, allowing the Project to deliver water to land designated "Townsite Lands" by the Secretary of Interior.

In addition to, and in conjunction with its irrigation operations, the SRP maintains and operates an extensive electrical power producing system. Generating capacity is composed of both hydro and thermal plants. These facilities have grown tremendously over the years and revenue obtained from the electrical plant has been used in support of the water production and delivery operations. Because of these revenues, and the fact that the Salt River Project operates as a "user cooperative" for its members, irrigation water costs to its farmer-members are not expected to rise over the projection period of this study in spite of expected increases in the cost of producing and delivering the water.

Roosevelt Water Conservation District. This district, covering an area of 39,425 acres in southeast Maricopa County, delivers the next greatest quantity of surface water after the SRP. A part of this area, 2,544 acres, is owned by the district, and water rights have been withdrawn from it. All other lands within the district boundaries have equal rights of access to district water. District water supplies are derived from both surface and underground sources. The district operates approximately sixty wells, from which two-thirds to three-fourths of its water supply is produced. Typically, one-quarter to one-third of its supply is obtained from the Salt and Verde rivers and the balance from project wells. During the late spring and summer months, the project wells are unable to furnish enough water to meet the demand of users. Surface water impounded in the SRP's system, to which the RWCD has a claim, is then used to help meet these peak demands. The source of this water is a 1924 agreement whereby the district contracted with the SRP to pay the cost of lining certain portions of the SRP's major canals. In return, the RWCD was granted the right to use 5.6 percent of SRP diversions for agricultural purposes at Granite Reef diversion dam. This water is stored by the SRP and delivered to the RWCD on demand.

In order to apportion the water supply throughout the year and to insure a more equitable distribution, the district has established a seasonal "prorate" or limitation on water deliveries to individual district members. At the beginning of each year, the board of directors sets the amount of water that will be available to each acre of project land during the prorate period. This quantity typically varies between two and three acre-feet per acre, depending upon the anticipated supply for the year. The prorate is generally in effect from early March to about October 1.

Individual members in this district can transfer water rights from one account to another, either under the same or different ownerships.

Any member having a surplus of prorate allotment water may give or sell his right to that water to any other member. The transferred water is then added to the buyer's account and handled in the same manner as his original account. Payments made to the selling member for this water are in addition to the charge made for the water by the district.

Other Maricopa County Irrigation Districts. In addition to those two irrigation districts discussed above, which distribute relatively large quantities of surface runoff water, there are several districts which supply agricultural users primarily with pump water, plus small quantities of surface water. Table 4-4 presents general features of several districts. Of those presented, five major ones are discussed below.

Roosevelt Irrigation District. This irrigation district was organized in 1923 for the purpose of conveying drainage water from the Salt River Project lands to agricultural land lying to the west of the Salt River Project. The service area of the district is approximately 38,000 acres with 144 farm units.

The district operates 55 "drainage" wells within the bounds of the Salt River Project. Due to heavy pumping in this area, the previously high water table has been lowered to the point where drainage is no longer a problem. A shortage of water now exists, and an agreement was signed limiting the amount of water pumped from within the Salt River Project into the district to a maximum of 155,000 acre-feet per year. In addition to these "drainage" wells, the district operates 46 wells within its own boundaries. There are also approximately 70 privately owned wells within the district.

Buckeye Irrigation District. This district ,as presently organized, was established in 1907. It serves a total of 150 farm units on approximately 20,000 acres. The area is entitled to normal flow of the Gila and Agua Fria rivers of up to 80 miner's inches per quarter section (3.9 acre-feet per acre per year). The district operates a diversion dam with no storage capacity below the junction of the rivers.

A contract with the Salt River Project provides water in the amount of 1.1 percent of Salt River Project diversions for agricultural purposes at Granite Reef Dam on the Salt River. Water from this source is supplied upon demand to the district.

Most of the district's water (approximately 80 percent) is supplied from underground sources. The district operates 48 wells with an average pumping depth of 60 feet. In addition to these district wells, individuals within the area operate 20 wells. The major problem with the pumped water, both district and private, is its high salinity which averages approximately 3,600 ppm.

Adaman Mutual Water Company. This company was established in 1943 to supply groundwater to a service area of 2,493 acres in central Maricopa County. All wells within the service area are owned and operated by the company. Annual net water deliveries total approximately 11,500 acre-feet.

Maricopa County Municipal Water Conservation District No. 1. This district's service covers 33,666 acres in central Maricopa County northwest of Phoenix, serving 55 farm units.

Two sources of water supply are available to the district. The portion of the water developed by the district is pumped from underground sources. Surface supplies, which vary widely and average about 20 percent of the total annual supply, are obtained from Lake Carl Pleasant.

The district operates 60 wells with an average static pumping level of 405 feet. In addition to these, most individual farms in the area operate their own private wells to supply needs in excess of the district water.

Arlington Canal Company. This company's service area covers 4,800 acres in southwestern Maricopa County. The major proportion of the water delivered by the district is obtained from nine wells operated by the company. Some additional water may be obtained from the Gila River. This river water is normally return flow from the Buckeye Irrigation District which lies directly above it on the Gila River. Total annual water deliveries by the Company average approximately 10,000 acre-feet. This is supplemented by water from privately owned wells.

Pinal County Study Area

Number and Types of Farms. There are approximately 400 general crop farms above 30 acres in size in Pinal County, plus a few specialized operations. Short-staple cotton, barley, sorghum, and alfalfa comprise the greater portion of cropped acreage. Vegetables and citrus comprise less than five percent of the total acreage. Cotton is the major crop with acreage fluctuating in response to government price and acreage allotment programs. Cotton acreage has decreased since 1952, when it reached a record high of 261,000 acres. As cotton acreage has declined, acreage of other crops such as alfalfa, barley, and sorghum have expanded. Overall cropped acreage has, however, decreased since its record high of 315,000 acres in 1952. Little double-cropping is practiced in the county.

Water Situation. Pinal County is primarily a groundwater county but has one surface-water area. The San Carlos Irrigation Project, completed in 1928, was to provide for irrigating 100,000 acres – 50,000 on the Indian Reservation of Sacaton and 50,000 on privately owned land in Pinal County. The total acreage has never been placed under irrigation because San Carlos Reservoir, which supplies the Project, has never reached expected capacity. While maximum capacity of this reservoir is 1,300,000 acre-feet, deliveries from it average only about 90,000 acre-feet per year. This surface supply is about 17 percent of total irrigation water use in the county.

Major development of irrigation from wells in Pinal County began in the 1930s. Beginning in 1941, large acreages of pump-irrigated land were added each year for several years. Since little recharge of the groundwater supply occurs in Pinal County, an overdraft resulted which led to a rapid drop in the water table. Depending on the area of the county, the rate of decline has ranged from zero to over 20 feet per year. Pumping lifts have been increasing until, by the early 1970s, some farmers were pumping from a depth of more than 600 feet.

The extent of the stock of groundwater in Pinal County has never been fully determined. Investigations indicate that in most of the irrigated areas water-bearing strata extend far below current pumping depths. Although there are questions as to the quality of water and the yield of the aquifer as depth increases, there is not enough evidence to determine whether water quality or yield will improve, remain about the same, or deteriorate as depth increases. It is probable that irrigators in Pinal County will face a declining water table rather than a physical shortage of water and that the quality of water and yield of the aquifer will remain about as in the 1960s.

Pima County Study Area

Number and Types of Farms. Pima County has approximately 60 general crop farms. Of these, an estimated 50 are commercial farms of 30 acres and over, with gross sales exceeding $10,000. A cotton, small grain, alfalfa, or vegetable rotation is a typical cropping pattern. Some speciality operations of citrus and especially pecans have entered the county in recent years.

Agriculture in Pima County is quite similar to that in Pinal County. Agricultural land is located in the upper part of the Santa Cruz Basin and in an area adjacent to this basin in Avra Valley. Total cropland is approximately 60,000 acres, with total acres cropped in 1970 estimated at 55,500. Short-staple cotton and grain sorghum are by far the dominant crops in the county. Barley, long-staple cotton, and alfalfa occupy cropland in descending order. There is little double-cropping of field crops. Lettuce, which is a short-term crop, may be double-cropped with an alternate season crop.

Water Situation. Irrigated agriculture in Pima County has three sources of water as distinguished by cost. All water, however, is obtained initially from the groundwater aquifer. The three sources are private pumped, irrigation district pumped, and sewage effluent from the city of Tucson treatment plant.

Private wells provide the largest single water source producing approximately 130,000 acre-feet annually. Pumping levels range from as little as 100 feet to slightly over 400 feet, with an average pumping lift of approximately 300 feet. The annual rate of decline in the water level throughout the county varies considerably, depending on the concentration of wells in any one area and the amount of water pumped. Annual groundwater decline rates varied during the five-year period prior to 1967 from less than one foot to nearly six feet per year.

Irrigation water is also supplied to users in the county through the Cortaro Water Users Association. This association serves an area of 14,600 acres in the north central part of the county. This area is served by pump-water produced by 42 district wells. The well field is divided into two parts by a natural fault. Those wells in the Marana area have a 150 feet deeper average static water level than do those near Cortaro. All rights to underground water in the project boundaries are held by the association, with the exception of 50-gallon-per-minute wells for domestic use. The average annual water production of the district is 32,500 acre-feet. A basic assessment of $12.00 per acre is levied against each project acre. Water users are entitled to one and one-half acre-feet of water per acre for this payment. Additional water is priced at $8.00 per acre-foot.

A third source of irrigation water in Pima County is Tucson city sewage effluent. As of 1970, only about one-half of the total production of the plant was being utilized in agriculture. In the future it is expected that this water source will be fully employed. The exact use to which it will be put has as yet to be determined. The present contract with agricultural users, which is to expire in 1975, provides for the water to be purchased at $1.00 per acre-foot. A re-negotiation of this contract at its termination date will obviously place the water at a considerably higher price.

Graham and Greenlee County Study Areas

Number and Types of Farms. Graham and Greenlee are bordering counties located in southeastern Arizona containing approximately 64,000 acres of cropland. In both counties, the agricultural producing areas are located along the Gila River, which supplies water for use in irrigation.

These two counties have an estimated 230 commercial farms with cropland acreage in excess of 30 acres. Of this number, 195 are in Graham County and the remaining 36 are in Greenlee. Farms in both counties are generally diversified, with few specialized operations. Typical is a cotton, alfalfa, small-grain rotation. Small grains include barley, wheat, and sorghum. Long-staple American Egyptian cotton is grown only in Graham County. Cotton yields are generally lower than those experienced in the central and western parts of the state, due to higher elevations resulting in shorter growing seasons. In recent years, a limited acreage of sugar beets has been grown on the larger farms in Graham County. Vegetable acreage is of little significance in farm operations of either county.

Water Situation. Irrigation water in Graham and Greenlee counties is obtained both from surface and ground sources by both irrigation districts and private pumpers.

Graham County agriculture is serviced by the Safford Valley Irrigation District, which serves as a central clearing agency for the thirteen separate irrigation companies that supply water in the Safford Valley. The area with water rights totals 32,512 acres. Water for irrigation is obtained from the flow of the Gila River as allocated by a Water Master and from wells operated by individual companies. Prices for water range from $10.00 per acre for 2.3 acre-feet to a high of $20.25 per acre for 2.7 acre-feet.

Pumping depths generally range from 50 to 70 feet, with little if any change in the water level from year to year, due to adequate natural recharge of the groundwater aquifer. Total water deliveries by all irrigation districts in the valley are quite variable but average approximately 90,000 acre-feet per year.

Greenlee County irrigators obtain water from the Duncan Valley Irrigation District. This district was formed as a central agency for 15 separate companies in the valley. A portion of the service area is in New Mexico, with 4,736 of the total 8,061 acres in Greenlee County.

Surface water supplied by the district is diverted from the Gila River. This water is supplemented by groundwater pumped by the individual canal companies comprising the district. Total net diversion is variable, depending upon the river flow. In a period from 1960 to 1964, it ranged from 8,448 to 20,894 acre-feet. Average per-acre diversion during this same period was 1.88 acre-feet. The average charge for this quantity of water was an assessment of $6.00 per acre. Additional water for irrigation is obtained by irrigators from their private wells which have average pumping lifts ranging from 50 to 80 feet.

Cochise County Study Area

Number and Types of Farms. Estimated cropland acreage in Cochise County and the irrigated portion of the Sulphur Springs valley in Graham County is approximately 125,000 acres, most of which is in Cochise County. There are an estimated 350 farms with 30 acres or more of cropland. Of these, approximately 275 are "established" diversified farms, with the remainder being "new" farms developed since 1962 and specializing in grain sorghum.

Water Situation. Irrigated agriculture in this study area is completely dependent on water obtained with private pumps from groundwater aquifers. There are four distinct groundwater basins within the county. These are the San Simon, Willcox, Douglas, and San Pedro basins, with the Willcox basin containing the major share of the total irrigated cropland.

Water levels throughout the entire county have been declining over time. The range in depth to groundwater and rates of decline are extremely variable, depending upon localized conditions. Changes in the groundwater levels have ranged from small increases to declines of as much as 30 feet within the period 1962 to 1967. Pumping lifts generally range from a low of approximately 150 feet to an estimated high of 300 feet.

Projections of Direct Agricultural Adjustments to Changing Water Costs

Crop Acreage Adjustments, 1966–2015

Projected changes in individual crops and total state crop acreage over the fifty-year time span developed from our representative-farm linear-programming models, are shown in table 4-5 and illustrated in figure 4-3. Projections by crop by time-period for each study area, from which table 4-5 is derived, are presented in Appendix B, table B-1.

Four major Arizona crops – vegetables, cantaloupes, cotton, and bermuda grass – are projected as remaining at their 1966 acreage levels throughout the projection period. These crops are of such high value per acre that they remain the most profitable choices in the face of increasing water costs. Although rising water costs will affect total net income derived from these high-valued crops, water costs do not reach high enough levels over the projection period to affect acreage grown in any of the study areas of the state. A particular crop's acreage will not be adjusted downward as long as the gross revenue per acre derived from growing that crop is larger than its variable cost of production, including the cost of irrigation water.

TABLE 4-5 — Projected Individual and Total C

Time Periods	Total Acres of Crops	Long Staple Cotton	Short Staple Cotton	Sugar Beets	Alfalfa
Acres in 1966	1,067,462	26,145	217,104	17,416	184,57
% of 1966	100	100	100	100	10
% of total	100	2.45	20.3	1.63	17.2
Acres in 1975	991,103	26,122	217,104	17,416	173,77
% of 1966	92.43	100	100	100	94.1
% of total	100	2.64	21.91	1.76	17.7
Acres in 1985	931,381	26,126	217,104	15,416	156,89
% of 1966	87.25	100	100	88.52	85.0
% of total	100	2.81	23.31	1.66	16.8
Acres in 1995	852,033	26,126	217,086	15,416	127,32
% of 1966	79.81	100	100	88.52	68.9
% of total	100	3.07	25.48	1.81	14.9
Acres in 2005	788,850	26,127	217,103	15,416	114,81
% of 1966	73.90	100	100	88.52	62.2
% of total	100	3.31	27.52	1.95	14.5
Acres in 2015	773,310	26,127	217,120	13,416	104,5
% of 1966	72.44	100	100	77.03	56.6
% of total	100	3.39	28.08	1.73	13.5

Table 4-5 and figure 4-3 show that high-value crops remain at 100 percent of their 1966 acreages but become an increasingly larger percent of total cropped acreage in each succeeding projection period. Long-staple cotton increases from 2.45 percent of cropped acreage in 1966 to 3.39 percent in 2015; short-staple cotton increases from 20.3 percent in 1966 to 28.08 percent of cropped acreage in 2015; and vegetable acreage is 6.04 percent of the total in 1966 and 8.34 percent of the total in 2015. Bermuda grass and cantaloupe acreages increase as a percentage of cropped acreage from 0.89 and 1.5 percent in 1966 to 1.23 and 2.07 percent, respectively, in 2015.

Sugar beets, a crop of medium value per acre, exhibit only a modest net decline (about twenty-three percent) in projected acreage between 1975 and 1985 and between 2005 and 2015. Appendix table B-1 shows that this projected net decline in sugar-beet acreage occurs in the Cochise

eages in Arizona by Time Periods, 1966 Through 2015

Barley	Wheat	Sorghum	Bermuda Grass	Safflower	Cantaloupes	Vegetables
10,811	26,186	268,965	9,500	26,300	16,000	64,480
100	100	100	100	100	100	100
18.91	2.45	25.2	0.89	2.46	1.50	6.04
89,432	21,406	237,402	9,500	18,463	16,000	64,480
89.80	81.75	88.27	100	70.20	100	100
19.11	2.16	23.95	0.96	1.86	1.61	6.51
71,438	17,030	224,129	9,500	13,261	16,000	64,480
81,32	65.03	83.33	100	50.42	100	100
18.41	1.83	24.00	1.02	1.42	1.72	6.92
46,176	16,744	211,270	9,500	1,909	16,000	64,480
69.33	63.94	78.55	100	7.26	100	100
17.27	1.97	24.80	1.11	0.22	1.88	7.57
32,812	10,902	180,714	9,500	979	16,000	64,480
63.00	41.63	67.19	100	3.72	100	100
16.84	1.38	22.91	1.20	0.12	2.03	8.17
31,853	10,022	180,095	9,500	192	16,000	64,480
62.55	38.27	66.96	100	0.73	100	100
17.05	1.30	23.29	1.23	0.02	2.07	8.34

County study area where the smaller size farms that characterize the area have relatively higher water and other production costs than do the larger sized units of other areas. Although sugar beet acreage declines absolutely over the projection period, its acreage relative to total acres cropped increases from 1.63 percent in 1966 to 1.73 percent in 2015.

Projected acreages of alfalfa, barley, wheat, sorghum, and safflower all decline significantly over the projection period. Alfalfa acreage declines by slightly more than one-half (56 percent) between 1966 and 2015, while barley and sorghum acreages decline by about one-third (38 and 33 percent respectively) over the same period. Wheat acreage declines by almost two-thirds (62 percent) over the fifty-year projection period. Safflower acreage shows the largest relative change over the projection period in that it almost completely disappears, declining from 2.46 percent of total cropped acreage in 1966 to a projected 0.02 percent in 2015.

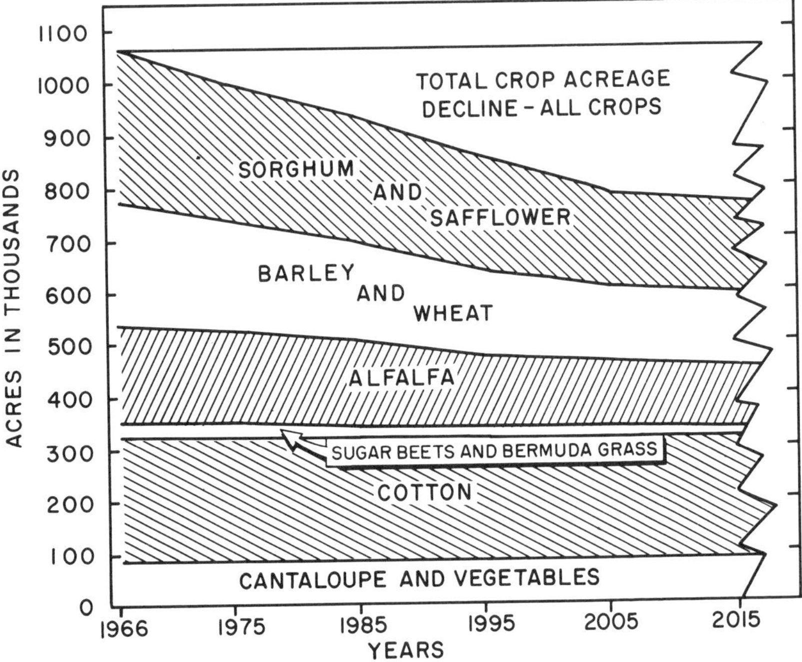

Fig. 4-3. *Projected acreage adjustments by crop, Arizona, 1966–2015.*

Acreage Adjustments by Study Area, 1966–2015

Study of Appendix table B-1 shows that all declines in irrigated crop acreage take place in Pinal, Pima, Cochise, and Maricopa Counties. No effects on acreage related to water cost are expected for Yuma, Graham, and Greenlee Counties. These acreage adjustments by area are summarized in table 4-6 and figure 4-4.

The projected decline of 75 percent in agricultural acreage in the Salt River Project area between 1966 and 2015 is not related to rising water costs but to projected urban growth. Although groundwater is expected to increase in cost due to a declining water table, we assume SRP power revenue will continue to subsidize water production and distribution to agriculture. Farmers will not be faced with higher water costs over time, hence the decline in cropped acreage in the SRP over time will not be the result of water cost changes.

Urban growth in the Salt River Project contributes to the total decline of low valued crops (grains and forages) in the state, but will not affect total acreage of the high-valued crops. Where high-valued

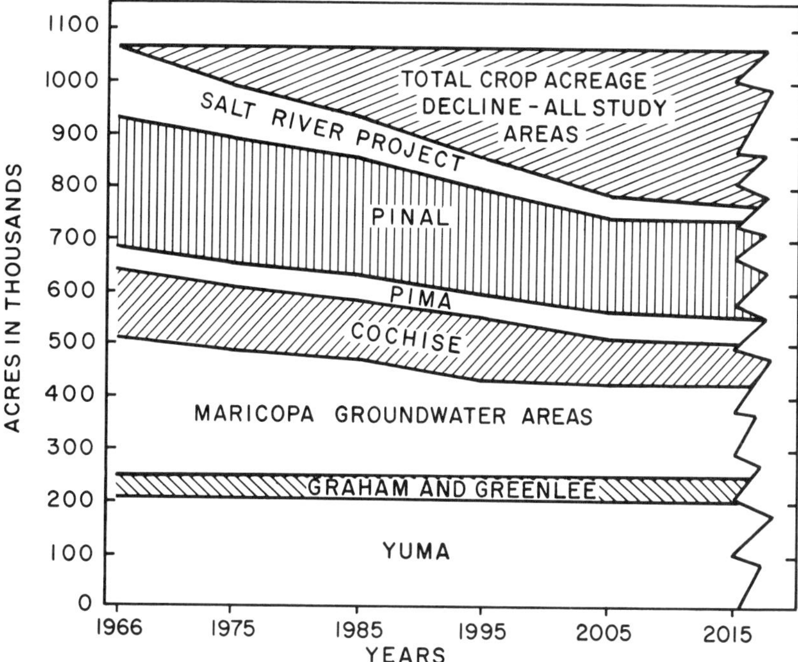

Fig. 4-4. *Projected crop acreage adjustments by study area, 1966–2015.*

crops are displaced by urban growth, their acreage will simply move to other areas where low-valued crops had previously been grown. Displaced cotton acreage was projected as moving into the groundwater areas of western Maricopa County. Sufficient cropped acreage will remain within the Salt River Project, at least until 2015, to permit enough citrus and vegetables to be produced to meet that area's share of market demand. Thus, we projected no transfer from SRP of acreage devoted to these high-valued crops.

The groundwater areas of Maricopa County will experience a 32 percent decline in net cropped acreage over the 50-year projection period, even though cotton acreage from the Salt River Project was assumed to transfer into these areas. Note, however (figure 4-4), that cropped acreage in these areas almost stabilizes by 1995, indicating that increases in cotton acreage in these areas will thereafter be almost exactly offset by decreases in acreages of other lower valued crops. Projections of the distribution among particular crops of these offsetting declines in the acreages of low-valued crops were not derived in our analysis. However,

TABLE 4-6 — Projected Arizona Crop Acreage Adjustme

Year	Yuma	Graham	Greenlee	Maricopa SRP	Maricopa Groundw Areas
1966	207,946	37,562	4,957	131,244	262,4
1975	207,946	37,562	4,957	97,722	239,1
1985	207,946	37,562	4,957	71,707	221,2
1995	207,946	37,562	4,957	56,232	183,0
2005	207,946	37,562	4,957	42,127	178,6
2015	207,946	37,562	4,957	33,146	178,9
Decline between 1966 and 2015	0	0	0	98,098	83,5

cotton acreage displaces acreage previously devoted to low-valued crops or to fallow; it also uses water which has an effect on groundwater levels and water costs. Higher water costs force low-value crops to become unprofitable and be discontinued, thereby causing a decline in cropped acreage devoted to their production. Therefore, although cotton acreage transferred into this area does keep acres in crops (cotton), it may force other crops to be discontinued at earlier points in time than they otherwise would have been, because of an acceleration in the rate at which groundwater costs increase. Alfalfa, barley, sorghum, and safflower are the low-valued crops that account for the downward acreage adjustments in these study areas.

Cropped acreage in the Cochise County study area is projected to decline by about 40 percent between 1966 and 2015. This decrease in acreage is a result only of increasing water costs in the area. Crops which produce low amounts of net revenue per acre-foot of water used are discontinued over time as water costs rise. Decreases in cropped acreage in this area stem primarily from fewer acres of alfalfa, sorghum, and barley. Wheat and sugar beet acreages are discontinued altogether. Cotton and vegetable acreages remain constant.

In the Pinal County and Pima County study areas, more detailed

Study Area and Time Period, 1966 Through 2015

hise	Pima	Pinal	State Totals	Decline in State Totals	State Total Excluding SRP Decline	Decline Excluding SRP Decline
,872	48,503	246,916	1,067,462		1,067,462	
				76,359		42,837
,560	48,475	237,707	991,103		1,024,625	
				59,722		33,707
,708	48,531	224,767	931,381		990,918	
				79,348		63,873
,606	48,503	197,202	852,033		927,045	
				63,183		49,078
007	48,503	185,145	788,850		877,967	
				15,558		6,577
764	47,814	185,145	733,292		871,390	
108	689	61,771		294,170		196,072

projection models were used than elsewhere; in these areas, adjustments in the quantity of water applied per acre with resulting adjustments in yield per acre were allowed in addition to adjustments in cropped acreage itself. In Pima County cropped acreage is projected to decline by only one percent, all of which is in alfalfa acreage. Most of the adjustments related to water cost in Pima County are made by applying smaller quantities of water at the sacrifice of obtaining lower yields per acre rather than by abandoning cropland altogether. Cropped acreage in Pinal County declines by approximately 25 percent in response to increasing groundwater cost, in addition to the decrease in water applications and in yields per acre that also occur on the cropped acreage that remains in use. Acreage adjustments in this area take place in crops of low value per acre-foot of water used such as alfalfa, barley, and grain sorghum. Cotton and vegetable acreages remain unaffected by rising groundwater costs, although water inputs per acre of cotton decline with a sacrifice in per acre yields.

As shown in table 4-6 and figure 4-4, total projected cropped acreage in the state declines by 27.6 percent between 1966 and 2015. This decline includes both the effects of increasing water costs as well as the effects of acreage absorbed into urban and industrial uses in the

SRP area of Maricopa County. An approximation of water-cost effects alone can be made by excluding from the projections the decline in cropped acreage occurring in the Salt River Project, all of which is due solely to urbanization. These estimates are shown in the last two columns of table 4-6. Thus, over the fifty years, a decline of only 196,072 acres, or 18.4 percent of the 1966 base acreage, may be attributed to increasing irrigation water cost in agriculture.

Agricultural Water Use Adjustments, 1966–2015

Total water use of 4,790,000 acre-feet in 1966, as shown in these projections, is the total quantity used on the farms described by the representative-farm models – not the total diversion and pumpage by all irrigated agriculture. Some of the high-valued crops that will not be affected by increasing water costs were not included in the models, nor were distribution losses between gross diversions and the farm headgates. It is the change in water pumpage that is important to the analysis, not the total absolute quantity of use.

Total agricultural water use on all crops included in the representative-farm linear-programming models for each study area of the state is shown in table 4-7 and figure 4-5 for the base period and each future projection point over time.

Water use in three of the areas studied, Yuma, Graham, and Greenlee counties, is projected as remaining constant just as was acreage in these areas. Yuma County, which is supplied with irrigation water from the Colorado River, will experience no major changes in its irrigation water situation. Graham and Greenlee counties are both located along the upper part of the Gila River and obtain irrigation water from both surface and groundwater sources. Although there is fluctuation in the annual availability of surface water to farmers in these two areas, average total water used is relatively constant. Groundwater aquifers in these two areas have remained quite stable; as a result, there is no foreseeable reason to expect the cost of obtaining groundwater to change over time. Given no change in its acquisition costs, there is no reason to expect the quantity of irrigation water used in these two areas to change over the projection period.

Annual agricultural water use in the Salt River Project (SRP) is projected to decline from 641,000 acre-feet in 1966 to 178,000 acre-feet in 2015. This 72 percent decline in agricultural use of water over the projection period is in no way related to changes in water costs. It is likely that the SRP, operating as it does as a user cooperative, will continue to subsidize irrigation water production from its power revenues, thereby preventing increases in irrigation water cost. Therefore, increasing water cost will not be a factor in agricultural adjustment in this area.

Agricultural water use in the SRP decreases only as agricultural land is transferred to urban and industrial uses. As land transfers from agricultural to these nonagricultural uses, appropriated water rights and access to groundwater also transfer to the new uses, with consequent decrease in agricultural water use. Projected land and water thus *available* for agricultural use after urbanization in the SRP are shown in Appendix table B-2.

Though projected reductions in water use in all other study areas (table 4-7) may be interpreted to result in net savings in the groundwater stock, this cannot be the interpretation in the SRP area, because here it is projected that the water not used in agriculture is used in its entirety in municipal-industrial uses. Though consumptive use of water in municipal-industrial uses is less than in agricultural uses, we made no allowance for possible saving in groundwater withdrawals attributable to this factor.

Total water use projections in the groundwater areas of Maricopa County as a whole exhibit a decline only until 2005. Counterbalancing effects to decline in groundwater use begin early in the projection period.

Annual water use in the subareas of Maricopa County designated as Maricopa A in the Appendix declines only through the 1985 projection period. Beginning with the 1995 period, an increase in annual water use is projected in this subarea. This increase in water-use stems from the transfer of cotton allotments out of the Salt River Project, which is being urbanized, onto available land within the same county. Water use increases because some of this land previously will have been idled as low-value, high-water-using crops were phased out of production.

Projected agricultural water use in the Cochise County study area is shown as declining from 475 thousand acre-feet in the 1966 base period to a projected 300 thousand acre-feet in the final 2015 period. The decline in projected water use in this area is due entirely to increasing irrigation water costs, resulting in fewer irrigated acres.

Agricultural water use in the Pima and Pinal County areas will decline steadily between 1966 and 2015. In these two areas, a more detailed projection procedure was used (see Appendix A) involving water-yield relationships where the amount of water applied per acre is allowed to vary and the level of yield per acre is dependent on the amount of water applied. Therefore, the declining annual water use projections stem from two sources. First, as the water table declines and per acre-foot pumping costs increase, water use per acre on any one crop will be lowered. Physical product produced will also be lower, but that acre will remain in crop use so long as it remains economically rational

TABLE 4-7 — Projected Arizona Agricultural Water

Year	Yuma	Graham	Greenlee	Maricopa	
				SRP	Groundw Area
1966	879	175	26	641	1,40
1975	879	175	26	543	1,28
1985	879	175	26	416	1,12
1995	879	175	26	313	1,02
2005	879	175	26	235	1,01
2015	879	175	26	178	1,02
Decline between 1966 and 2015	0	0	0	463	38

*Figures within table are in units of 1000 acre-feet.

to continue growing that acre of crop even at the lesser yields. Second, as water costs increase, and after water-yield adjustments have taken place, the acreages of lower value crops such as feed grains and forages will decline, and some cropped acres will go out of crop use entirely.

Total annual agricultural water use will decline by 1,369,000 acre-feet or 28.6 percent over the 50-year projection period; that is, on an annual basis, agricultural water use will be 1,369,000 acre-feet less in 2015 than it was in the base period of 1966. The annual yearly decline in total agricultural water use will take place gradually over this time period, as indicated in the column headed "Decline in State Totals" in table 4-7. Over the nine-year period from 1966 to 1975, total annual irrigation water use will have declined from 4,790 thousand acre-feet in 1966 to 4,480 thousand acre-feet in 1975, or a decline of 310 thousand acre-feet used annually in 1975 compared to 1966 or an average annual decline of 33,300 acre-feet per year during this nine-year period. Average annual decrease in water use will be larger (35,800 acre-feet) during the ten-year period from 1975 to 1985 decreasing from 4,480 thousand acre-feet in 1975 to 4,122 thousand acre-feet in 1985 or by 358,000 acre-feet during the ten years. In all following projection periods, water-

Study Area and Time Period, 1966 Through 2015*

chise	Pima	Pinal	State Totals	Decline in State Totals	State Total Excluding SRP Decline	Decline Excluding SRP Decline
75	210	976	4,790		4,790	
				310		212
43	210	921	4,480		4,578	
				358		231
38	201	864	4,122		4,347	
				312		209
45	181	765	3,810		4,138	
				263		185
26	181	714	3,547		3,953	
				126		69
00	179	663	3,421		3,884	
75	31	313		1,369		906

use decreases will occur at a declining rate. As marginal agricultural lands are taken out of production, less water will be pumped each year. As less water is pumped each year, the groundwater level will drop more slowly. As the groundwater level drops more slowly, decline in acres of crops will occur more slowly and there will be less decrease in water use. One could project that at some time beyond 2015 when somewhat more adjustment in agriculture will have taken place, an equilibrium will be reached where no further decrease in acreage or water use will occur. Note the slowing rate of decline as shown in figure 4-6.

The change in total agricultural water use over time stems both from the effects of increasing groundwater costs with the resulting decrease in acres of low-value crops and from the encroachment of urban and industrial activities onto Salt River Project farm land. Since change in land use is independent of water conditions in the Salt River Project, water-use declines in the SRP area are subtracted from total changes by time period to obtain the effect of increasing water costs on agricultural water use. Agricultural water use adjusted to eliminate the effects of urban and industrial expansion in the SRP are shown in the last two columns of table 4-7, where projected changes in water use in the Salt

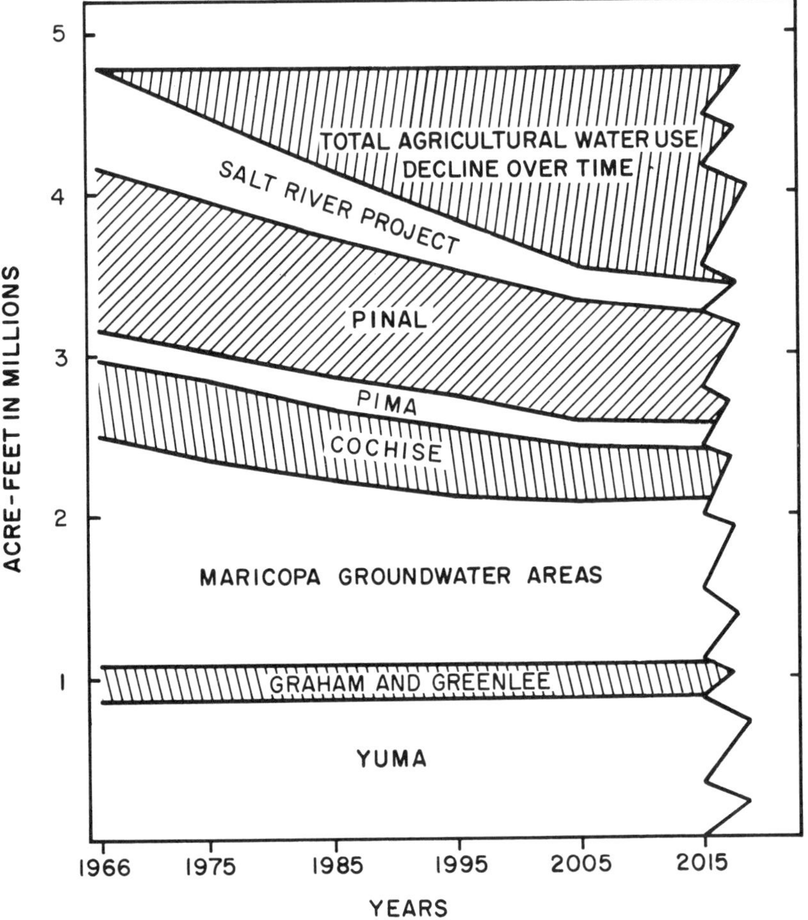

Fig. 4-5. *Projected agricultural water use by study area by time period, Arizona, 1966–2015.*

River Project have been excluded. These adjustments show that with urban and industrial influences excluded, annual agricultural water use would decline only by 906 thousand acre-feet over the fifty-year period, or that annual water use in agriculture in 2015 would be 81.1 percent of what it was in the 1966 base period. We may conclude that if Arizona wished for some reason to maintain its agricultural sector of the economy at its 1966 level, excluding the effects of projected urban growth, an additional 906 thousand acre-feet of water would need be developed over the coming fifty years, *at a price low enough to permit its use in the irrigation of low-valued grains and forages.*

Agricultural irrigation water use and changes in quantity used over the projection period are depicted graphically in figure 4-6, both with and without urban and industrial effects. The vertical distance between the two graphed functions at any point over the projection period represents water use transferred out of agriculture by urban and industrial expansion onto agricultural land. We repeat that our analysis of the effects on agricultural water use caused by urban-industrial expansion onto agricultural land in the Salt River Project assumes that an urban-industrial acre will use the same quantity of water that was used when the acre was farmed. Available studies suggest that this assumption may over-estimate the quantity of water transferred out of agriculture in that, when land is transferred from rural to urban uses, water used decreases (Smith, 1968; Corollo, 1968).

If less water is used as land moves from rural to urban use in the SRP, the groundwater table under the SRP will decline less rapidly than we have projected. Though this slower decline in the SRP water table will have no effect on projected agricultural water use and income in

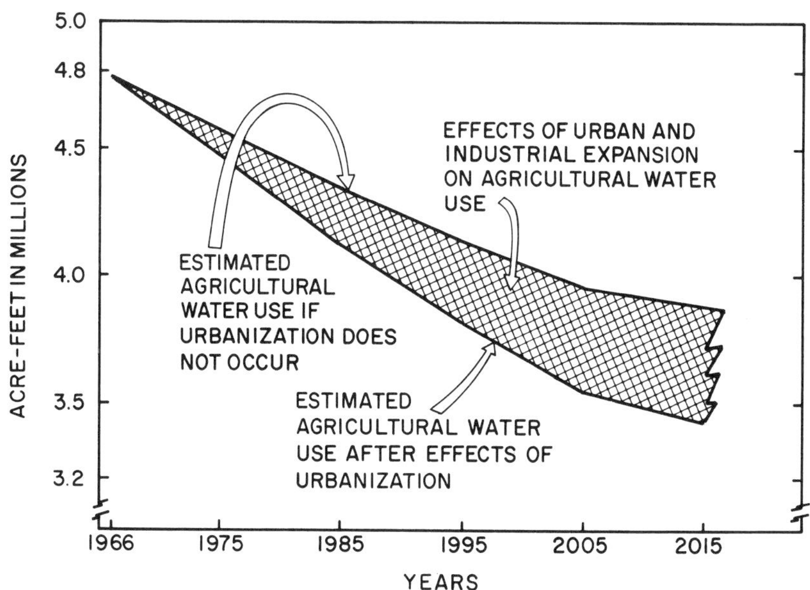

Fig. 4-6. *Projected agricultural water use showing effects of urban expansion, Arizona, 1966–2015.*

TABLE 4-8 — Projected Arizona Gross Farm Revenu

Year	Yuma	Graham	Greenlee	Maricopa	
				SRP	Groundwa Areas
1966	60.8	7.9	0.9	33.9	76.9
1975	60.8	7.9	0.9	31.0	74.0
1985	60.8	7.9	0.9	27.5	71.9
1995	60.8	7.9	0.9	23.5	69.6
2005	60.8	7.9	0.9	20.0	69.3
2015	60.8	7.9	0.9	17.1	70.6
Decline between 1966 and 2015	0	0	0	16.8	6.3

*Figures within table are in units of one million dollars.

the SRP due to our assumption that the Project will insulate its farmer members against changes in groundwater costs, it will bring about a slower decline in the water table underlying agricultural areas surrounding the SRP because of hydrologic linkage among aquifers of the area. Thus, pumping costs in these surrounding groundwater areas will rise less rapidly than we have projected, allowing more water to be used in the production of low-valued crops such as forages and grain than we have projected. However, selection of the assumption of a one-to-one relationship between agricultural and urban use follows our basic rule to select the assumption that most enhances the estimated value of additional water if one assumption is not clearly more correct than the other.

Gross and Net Farm Revenue Adjustments, 1966–2015

Water cost increases over the projection period are reflected not only in a decline in quantities of water used, agricultural crop acres, and physical output, but also in a decline in both gross and net farm revenues. Gross farm revenues are defined as the total dollar returns accruing to

tudy Area and Time Periods, 1966 Through 2015*

ise	Pima	Pinal	State Totals	Decline in State Totals	State Total Excluding SRP Decline†	Decline Excluding SRP Decline
	12.4	60.3	273.2		273.2	
				8.4		5.5
	12.4	58.5	264.8		267.7	
				7.9		4.4
	12.3	56.5	256.9		263.3	
				10.3		6.3
	12.2	53.4	246.6		257.0	
				7.9		4.4
	12.2	52.2	238.7		252.6	
				2.6		+0.3
	11.9	52.2	236.1		252.9	
	0.5	8.1		37.1		20.3

column is interpreted as the projected gross farm income that would exist if urbanization did not take within the boundaries of the Salt River Project.

the farm operators of the area from the sale of their products plus any government payments. Net farm returns are gross farm returns less operating costs. (These measures are discussed in detail in Appendix A.) Projected gross and net farm revenues by study area and time period are shown in tables 4-8 and 4-9, respectively. Total projected gross and net farm revenues by time period are graphed in figures 4-7 and 4-8.

In those areas of the state where no relative changes in water costs are foreseen, no change in either gross or net farm revenues are projected as stemming from changes in water costs. Though changes surely will occur in the next fifty years which will influence farm revenues in these areas, these changes will stem from sources other than the water input. These areas are the study areas of Yuma, Graham, and Greenlee counties.

Salt River Project gross and net farm revenue projections show a decline of approximately one-half between 1966 and 2015. This area is being absorbed by urban and industrial expansion, and projected revenue changes reflect this transfer of land out of agriculture. Both gross and net farm revenue are declining relatively and absolutely faster than in

TABLE 4-9 — Projected Arizona Net Farm Revenues Over Varia

Year	Yuma	Graham	Greenlee	Maricopa SRP	Maricopa Groundwa Area
1966	24.6	4.0	0.35	15.6	21.7
1975	24.6	4.0	0.35	14.6	20.5
1985	24.6	4.0	0.35	13.5	19.4
1995	24.6	4.0	0.35	11.7	19.1
2005	24.6	4.0	0.35	10.1	19.0
2015	24.6	4.0	0.35	8.6	18.8
Decline between 1966 and 2015	0	0	0	7.0	2.9

*Figures within table are in units of one million dollars.

any of the other study areas where the decline is caused by rising water costs.

In the areas of Maricopa County served primarily by pump water, gross and net farm revenue decline through the 2005 projection year. Beginning with the 1995 projection period, however, the decline is almost negligible and by 2015 gross farm revenue actually rises slightly. This relative stability in revenue after 1995 results from the transfer of cotton allotment acreage out of the Salt River Project, where agricultural acreage is absorbed by urban and commercial interests, to the Maricopa groundwater areas — especially the subareas that are designated as Maricopa A in the Appendixes.

Another factor contributing to the small relative change in either gross or net farm revenues in the Maricopa groundwater areas is that the RWCD irrigation district obtains approximately one-third of its water through contractual agreements with the Salt River Project. This is surface runoff from the Salt-Verde River watershed. Water obtained from this source is assumed to remain at its 1966 base year price and thereby

duction Costs by Study Area and Time Period, 1966 Through 2015*

hise	Pima	Pinal	State Totals	Decline in State Totals	State Total Excluding SRP Decline†	Decline Excluding SRP Decline
8	5.8	29.8	108.7		108.7	
				3.6		2.6
2	5.6	29.2	105.1		106.1	
				3.9		2.8
5	5.4	28.4	101.2		103.3	
				4.2		2.4
8	5.1	27.3	97.0		100.9	
				2.9		1.3
3	4.9	26.8	94.1		99.6	
				2.3		0.8
9	4.7	26.8	91.8		98.8	
9	1.1	3.0		16.9		9.9

column is interpreted as the projected net farm revenue that would exist if urbanization did not take within the boundaries of the Salt River Project.

not cause agricultural adjustment. As water pumped by the RWCD becomes more costly due to a decreasing groundwater level, the proportion of surface runoff water used to groundwater used increases. The net effect of this change in proportions of surface versus groundwater will be to slow down the rate of decline in the pumping levels and thus increase the length of time at which adjustments in cropping patterns will take place. Resulting gross and net farm revenue changes are also spread out over much longer periods of time.

In the Cochise County study area gross farm revenues decline 5.3 million dollars and net revenues decline by 2.9 million dollars over the fifty-year period. These declines occur at relatively constant rates over the projection period. The decrease in gross farm revenue follows from the total elimination of some crop activities due to increasing water costs, whereas the decline in net farm revenue results in addition from lower returns on all remaining crop activities due to projected water cost increases. Revenue changes result only from declines in acreages of low-value crops, primarily alfalfa, wheat, barley, and sorghum, and in acreage

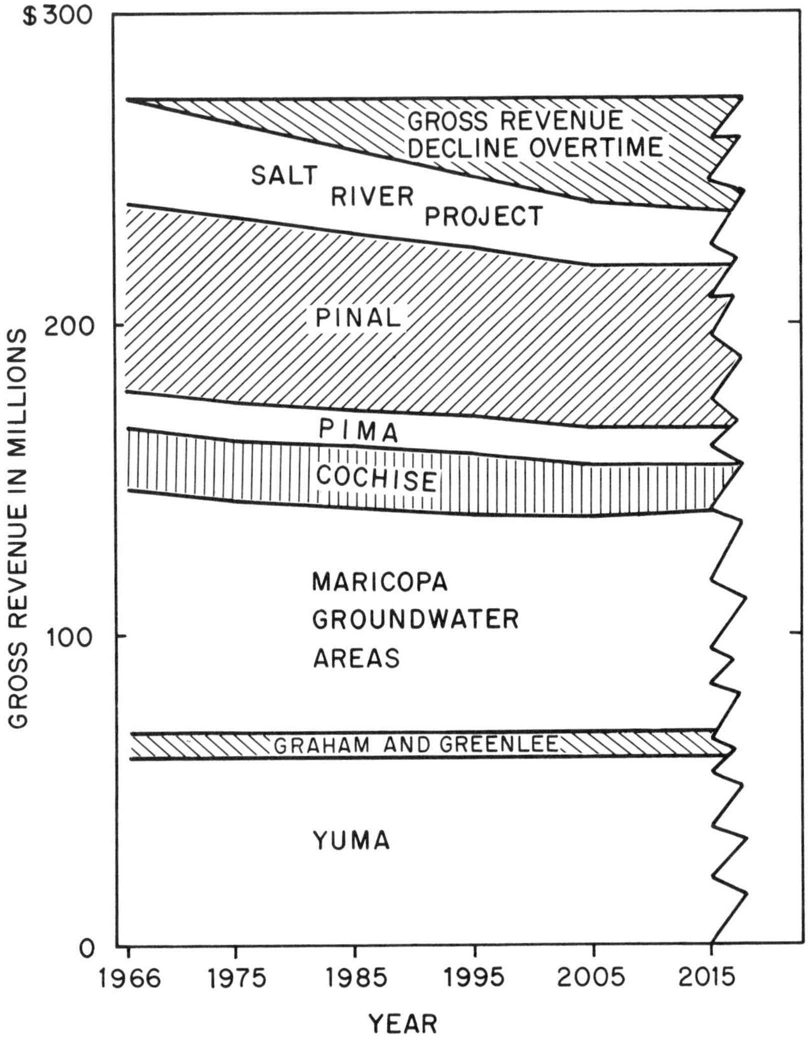

Fig. 4-7. *Projected gross farm revenue by study area by time period, Arizona, 1966–2015.*

of sugar beets. Only wheat and sugar beets disappear completely, and then toward the end of the projection period. All other low-value crops continue to be grown though at reduced acreages.

Revenue decline in the Pinal and Pima county study areas also occurs uniformly over the period 1966 to 2015. Gross farm revenue

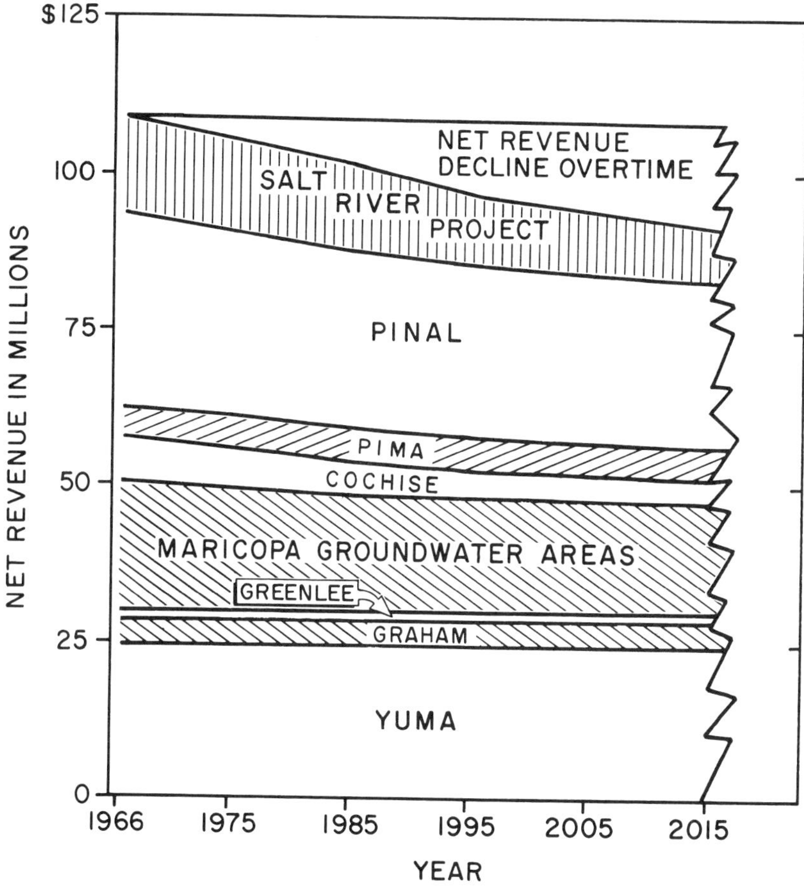

Fig. 4-8. *Projected net farm revenue by study area by time period, Arizona, 1966–2015.*

declines by 3.5 and 1.1 million dollars respectively. Projected net farm revenue declines in these two study areas by 9.3 million dollars in Pinal County and 500,000 dollars in Pima County. Changes in revenue in these two counties result from three separate but related factors. First, projected increases in water costs per acre-foot will cause net revenues to decline irrespective of cropping activity. Second, smaller quantities of water will be used on each acre as water costs increases. As quantities of water used per acre are reduced, physical output per acre will also fall accompanied by a decrease in gross revenue. Finally, as water costs rise to certain

TABLE 4-10

Projected Declines, Including SRP Declines, for Cropped Acreage, Water Use, and Farm Revenues, 1966 to 2015

Projection Period	Adjustments (%)			
	Cropped Acreage	Water Use	Gross Farm Revenue	Net Farm Revenue
1966 to 1975	7.2	6.5	3.1	3.3
1975 to 1985	6.0	8.0	3.0	3.7
1985 to 1995	8.5	7.6	4.0	4.2
1995 to 2005	7.4	6.9	3.2	3.0
2005 to 2015	2.0	3.6	1.1	2.4
Total change 1966 to 2015*	27.6	28.6	13.6	15.5

*Percent changes between periods do not sum to total percent change because each percentage is computed from a different base.

levels, crops that use large amounts of water per dollar of output will be discontinued.

Comparisons of Adjustments in Acreage, Water Use, and Revenues

Major variables affected by increasing water costs and by urbanization and the magnitude by which they have been projected to change have been discussed in immediately preceding sections. Cropped acres, water use, and gross and net farm revenues are all affected. The relative total magnitudes for the state by which each of these four factors decline are shown in table 4-10.

Through the period 1985-1995 the relative rate of decline for all variables except water use continues to increase. The rate of decline in water use starts to decrease one period earlier. After the period 1985-1995, the rate of decline in all variables begins to and continues to decline.

The total percentage change over the entire fifty-year projection period for each of the four variables is shown in the bottom line of table 4-10. Total state agricultural cropped acreage and total irrigation water use decline by approximately the same percentages, 27.6 and 28.6, respectively. Gross and net farm revenues also decline by the approximately equal percentages of 13.6 percent and 15.5 percent respectively.

Projected total cropped acres fall entirely due to rising water costs and urbanization of agricultural lands rather than due to any physical shortages of water. Fewer acres of the low-valued crops are grown. Acreage of high-valued crops, including cotton, vegetables, and citrus, are not affected.

Water use decreases slightly faster than acreage because less water is used per acre as water costs rise and as farms become larger and more efficient water users. Use would fall even faster except that the high-valued, high-water-using crops occupy a larger percent of total cropped acres.

Net farm incomes and gross farm revenues both decline at only about one-half the rate of declines in water use and cropped acreage over the projection period. There are several reasons. Adjustments in total acreages are due entirely to decreases in acreages of low-valued crops which are even presently contributing little to gross and net incomes. In 2015, a much larger proportion of the farms are large farms with lower costs of production. Finally, an increasing proportion of total water use in the state will be drawn from low-cost surface supplies.

Analogous percentage comparisons among rates of decline in agriculture in the state, excluding the decline in agriculture within the Salt River Project, are given in table 4-11. These percentage declines exclude effects of urbanization in the SRP and thus are due only to adjustments caused by rising water costs. These percentage adjustments over the entire fifty-year projection period are only one-half to two-thirds as large

TABLE 4-11

Projected Declines, Excluding SRP Declines, for Cropped Acreage, Water Use, and Farm Revenues, 1966 to 2015

Projection Period	Adjustments (%)			
	Cropped Acreage	Water Use	Gross Farm Revenue	Net Farm Revenue
1966 to 1975	4.0	4.4	2.0	2.4
1975 to 1985	3.3	5.0	1.6	2.6
1985 to 1995	6.4	4.8	2.4	2.3
1995 to 2005	5.3	4.5	1.7	1.3
2005 to 2015	0.7	1.7	+0.1†	0.8
Total change 1966 to 2015*	18.4	18.9	7.4	9.1

*Percent changes between periods do not sum to total percent change because each percentage is computed from a different base.

†Projected gross revenue increases in this period.

as those shown for total change in agriculture, including the effect of SRP urbanization.

Are the Projected Adjustments Large or Small?

Empirical estimates of agricultural adjustment over the period 1966 to 2015 have been presented in terms of absolute magnitudes of change (in constant 1966 dollars) and in terms of percentage change from the 1966 base year. But, from the material presented thus far, we cannot judge whether these adjustments are large or small, important or unimportant. To do so, we must convert our estimates of change occurring because of rising water costs into estimates of the value of additional water that, if available and developed, would make these adjustments unnecessary. In doing so, we must also consider the fact that declines in gross and net farm revenue and in water use and cropped acres in agriculture will not only directly affect the agricultural economy but will have both direct and indirect effects on other sectors of the economy. Closely related industries such as agricultural input suppliers and the processors of agricultural products will be affected. Other industries supplying the agricultural product processors and input suppliers will be indirectly affected. The magnitudes of these indirect effects must be estimated and added to the direct effects on crop agriculture before the judgment of importance or unimportance can be made.

These relationships, their magnitudes *and the implications thereof* on the value of additional water for the Arizona economy over the fifty-year projection period are taken up in the following chapter. Before doing so, however, in the remainder of this chapter we outline the static marginal demand for irrigation water in Arizona agriculture in the 1966 to 1975 planning period in order to obtain precise estimates of the per acre-foot values of alternative quantities of water in irrigation in the early 1970s.

Derived Marginal Demand for Irrigation Water in Arizona

In our preceding analysis, we developed the demand for particular quantities of irrigation water over time given the cost of water at those same points in time. But this analysis showed only the particular quantities of water that would be demanded *given* our particular assumptions as to water cost. As outlined earlier in our conceptualization of the water problem, alternative quantities of water would be demanded in each study area at any alternative irrigation water cost. In the economist's language, these relationships are short-run derived *marginal demand curves* for irrigation water. Thus far in the chapter, we have essentially presented estimates relating to *one point* on each marginal demand curve. Now we present the marginal demand curves themselves. The curves presented are developed to reflect conditions only in the year 1966; they are static. However, given the basic assumptions of our study, that cost-price ratios of producing crops in Arizona will not change greatly over time, the marginal demand curves derived should closely approximate marginal demand curves for water in following periods. The major exception would be for the Salt River Project where conversion of agricultural land to urban and industrial use would lower the demand for irrigation water for agriculture over time. In the other, non-urbanizing areas, the major difference between curves for 1966 and for following periods would be that following curves would be slightly higher because the larger, more efficient, farms of future years will be better able to afford irrigation water at slightly higher prices.

How Marginal Demand Curves for Irrigation Water Are Derived

Our derived marginal demand curves are obtained through the use of the variable resource procedure of linear programming. In this procedure, all variable factors of production other than the quantity of water applied are held constant in the representative-farm models. The quantities of water available for use are varied in small increments. At each quantity of water a new optimum linear-programming solution is generated. With each new solution, a "shadow price" or "marginal value product" of an additional acre-foot of water is also determined. (For a comprehensive treatment of the "pure theory" of this technique, see Appendix A of Bain et al., 1966.) That is to say – what would an additional quantity of irrigation water produce in terms of net revenue to the representative-farm model? Or, to say the same thing in another way, what is the maximum amount of money that a farm operator could pay for one more additional acre-foot of water in the short-run? The phrase, "in the short-run," indicates that for this additional acre-foot of water, only the variable cost of production would be covered at that water cost. In the long-run, farmers could not afford to pay that much for additional water because in the long-run the fixed costs of real estate and depreciable capital would also need be covered.

Empirical Marginal Demand Curves

Individual representative-farm marginal-demand functions and the aggregate function for irrigation water are presented here for only two of the study subareas, the Salt River Project (SRP) and the Roosevelt

Water Conservation District (RWCD). Estimates from the aggregate derived marginal-demand functions for water for all other areas studied are listed in Appendix table B-3. The SRP and RWCD derived marginal demands are shown in detail to illustrate how the aggregate functions are derived and to show how each step in the farm models, as well as in the aggregate, is developed. We also relate the cost of water, that is, the marginal cost of presently available water supplies to the aggregate derived marginal demand functions in the two subareas.

Figures 4-9 and 4-10 present derived marginal demand functions for irrigation water for each of the sizes of representative-farms as of 1966. The breaking points of these discontinuous functions represent quantities and prices at which water use will shift among enterprise combinations. The horizontal portions of these functions over a range of water quantities indicate expansions of water inputs to a single crop enterprise.

In both figures, values for water above $56.75 per acre-foot result from its use in producing vegetables. Vegetables are grown only on SRP farms in Size Groups II and III, and RWCD farms in Size Group II.

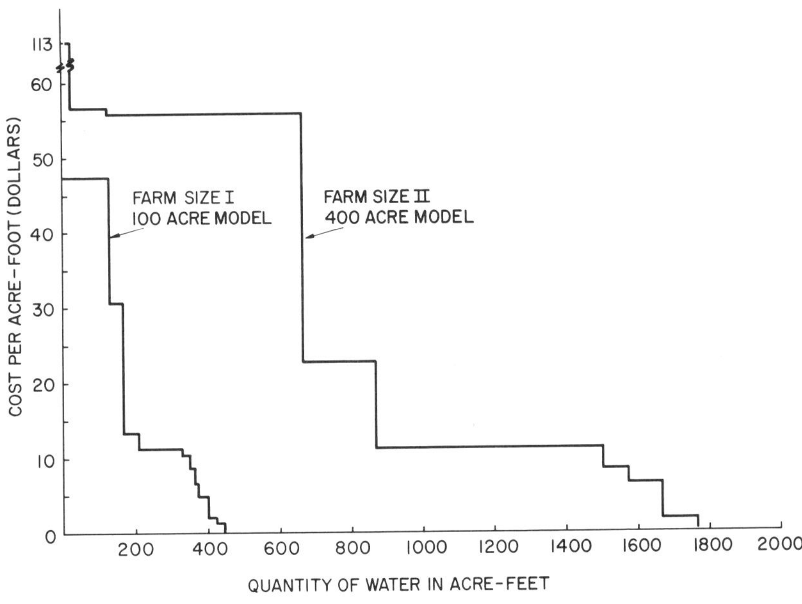

Fig. 4-9. *Individual representative-farm derived marginal-demand curves for irrigation water, Roosevelt Water Conservation District, 1966.*

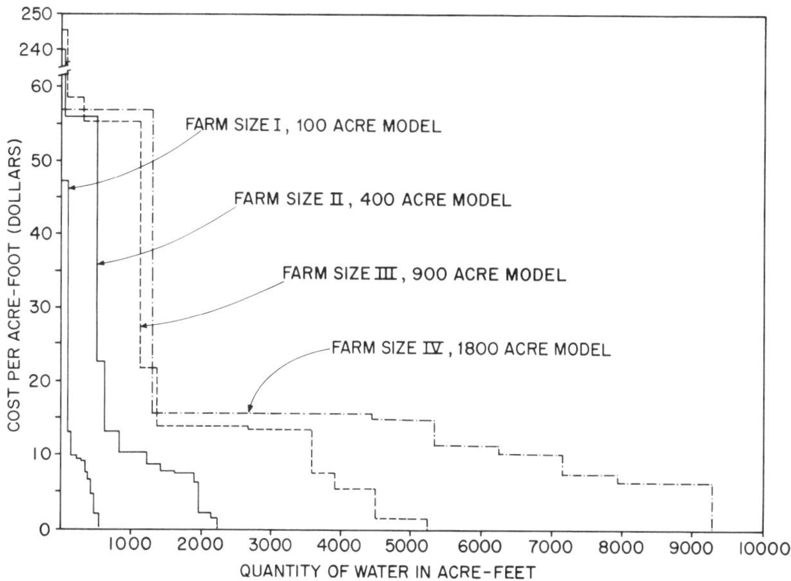

Fig. 4-10. *Individual representative-farm derived marginal-demand curves for irrigation water, Salt River Project, 1966.*

All values for water between \$56.75 and \$30.26 per acre-foot result from its use in cotton production. Sugar beet production demands water on SRP farm Size Groups II, III, and IV, and RWCD farm Size Group II at water values between \$30.26 and \$21.90 per acre-foot. Alfalfa competes for water in all farm models at water costs between \$15.42 and \$9.38 per acre-foot. Barley can compete for water at water values between \$14.66 and \$11.18 per acre-foot. Wheat becomes a competitor for water at costs between \$13.93 and \$13.08 per acre-foot. Early-planted grain sorghum can afford to use water at a range of water values between \$11.23 and \$1.36 per acre-foot. Late-planted sorghum and barley-sorghum double-cropped become effective demanders for water at water costs between \$7.38 and \$1.36. At the approximate quantity where the demand function meets the horizontal axis in the graphs, no more irrigation water could be used on farms of that size in that area even if the cost of additional water dropped to zero.

Figures 4-11 and 4-12 show the aggregate quantities of water which would be demanded at irrigation water costs between zero and \$247.99 per acre-foot and between zero and \$113.00 per acre-foot in the SRP and RWCD respectively. Tables 4-12 and 4-13 show the water quantity and cost data from which the individual representative-farm and aggregate irrigation district water marginal demand functions were constructed.

In the SRP, at water costs of $15.42 per acre-foot and below, relatively large increases in water use occur, as shown in figure 4-11. At this cost of water and below, crops requiring relatively large quantities of water per unit of net revenue produced enter into the optimum farm solutions. At prices above $15.42 per acre-foot, only vegetables, sugar beets, and cotton return sufficient revenue to command water on any SRP farm-size group. At this price for water, only 248,000 acre-feet would be used. At water prices between $15.42 and zero per acre-foot, rapidly increasing quantities of water up to a total additional quantity of 568,000 acre-feet of water are employed in growing alfalfa and small grain crops. No more than 817,000 acre-feet of water would be used in agriculture in the Salt River Project even if the cost of additional water were zero.

In the RWCD, as shown in figure 4-12, relatively large increases in water use occur at water costs of $11.20 per acre-foot and below. At water costs above $11.20, only vegetables, cotton, sugar beets, and barley can afford its cost. At costs of $11.20 and below, alfalfa, sorghum, and double-cropped barley-sorghum become water users.

Empirical Marginal Supply Curves

Aggregate water supply conditions based on conditions that existed in 1966 in the SRP and RWCD are also shown in figures 4-11 and 4-12. Aggregate water supply in the SRP is a composite of quantities available at different prices. The first 288,000 acre-feet are received after a fixed per-acre assessment has been paid. The *variable* cost of this water is zero. A second aggregate quantity of 216,000 acre-feet can be obtained at a cost of $2.00 per acre-foot. The next most inexpensive source of water is private pump water at $6.44 per acre-foot. In 1966, on SRP Farm Size Groups II, III, and IV, 126,413 acre-feet of private pump water were used. A final source of water is from project pumps. A total agricultural supply of 288,000 acre-feet of this water at $7.50 per acre-foot is available. Of the total amount available, only 10,147 acre-feet were used in the 1966 projection. This water was used exclusively on Farm Size Group I farms which have no private wells.

The intersection of the 1966 marginal demand and supply functions, as shown in figure 4-11, projects the use of 640,560 acre-feet of water in the SRP at a marginal water cost of $7.50 per acre-foot. The normal average cost concept does not apply in this area since water is supplied on a marginal rather than an average cost basis.

TABLE 4-12

Derived Marginal Demand for Irrigation Water, in Acre-Feet, at Various Prices by Farm-Size Group and by the Aggregate of All Farms, Salt River Project, 1966*

Price per Acre-foot	Farm-Size Group I (100 acres)	II (400 acres)	III (900 acres)	IV (1800 acres)	Total
$247.99		0	3,500		3,500
240.15		2,100	3,500		5,600
58.94		9,354	13,004	0	22,358
56.75		9,354	13,004	30,516	53,874
55.75		53,813	13,004	30,516	97,333
55.41	0	53,813	48,558	30,516	132,886
45.47	25,390	53,813	48,558	30,516	158,277
22.80	25,390	63,900	48,558	30,516	168,364
21.90	25,390	63,900	56,592	30,516	176,398
15.42	25,390	63,900	56,592	102,960	248,842
14.66	25,390	63,900	56,592	123,552	269,434
13.93	25,390	63,900	113,184	123,552	326,026
13.52	25,390	63,900	150,912	123,552	363,754
13.08	33,480	63,900	150,912	123,552	371,844
13.03	33,480	85,536	150,912	123,552	414,072
11.23	33,480	85,536	150,912	144,144	414,072
10.03	33,480	128,304	150,912	164,736	477,432
9.67	55,800	128,304	150,912	164,736	499,752
9.38	66,900	128,304	150,912	164,736	510,852
9.13	78,120	128,304	150,912	164,736	522,075
8.53	78,120	149,688	150,912	164,736	543,456
7.65	78,120	172,072	150,912	164,736	565,840
7.50	88,197	203,861	164,498	184,004	640,560
6.43	91,758	203,861	164,498	184,004	644,051
6.37	91,758	203,861	164,498	214,822	674,939
6.27	91,758	208,811	164,498	214,822	679,889
5.44	91,758	208,811	188,732	214,822	704,213
4.80	105,930	208,811	188,832	214,822	718,295
2.00	122,690	227,379	188,732	214,822	753,623
1.36	122,690	235,224	207,504	214,822	780,240
0	128,852	251,278	220,739	216,004	816,873

*An example of the interpretation of the table is as follows: If all water were priced at $247.99 per acre-foot, only 3,500 acre-feet would be used in total (all on the size III farms). If all water were priced at $240.15 per acre-foot, 5,600 acre-feet would be used in total. However, 5,600 acre-feet would also be used if the original 3,500 acre-feet were priced at **no higher than** $247.99 and only the marginal 2,100 acre-feet were priced at $240.15. Any quantity of water available at **less** than the given price of $240.15 would need be subtracted from the total 5,600 acre-feet that would be purchased at the single price of $240.15.

TABLE 4-13

Derived Marginal Demand for Irrigation Water, in Acre-Feet, at Various Prices by Farm-Size Group and by the Aggregate of all Farms, Roosevelt Water Conservation District, 1966*

Price per Acre-foot	Farm-Size Group I (100 acres)	Farm-Size Group II (400 Acres)	Total
$113.35		1,000	1,000
63.16		5,610	5,610
55.75	0	30,135	30,135
47.57	12,285	30,135	42,420
30.26	14,742	30,135	44,877
22.80	14,742	39,290	54,032
13.08	18,925	39,290	58,215
11.20	29,741	39,290	69,031
11.18	29,741	68,005	97,746
10.03	32,242	68,005	100,247
8.50	33,100	71,064	104,164
6.43	33,818	75,234	109,052
4.80	37,115	75,234	112,349
2.00	38,678	79,359	118,037
1.64	40,050	79,359	119,409
0	40,778	89,560	130,338

*An example of the interpretation of the table is as follows: If all water were priced at $113.35 per acre-foot; only 1,00 acre-feet would be used in total (all on the size II farms). If all water were priced at $63.16 per acre-foot, 5,610 acre-feet would also be used if the original 1,000 acre-feet were priced at **no higher than** $113.35 and only the marginal 4,610 acre-feet were priced at $63.16. Any quantity of water that is available at **less** than the given price of $63.16 would need be subtracted from the total of 5,610 acre-feet that would be purchased at the single price of $63.16.

Water supply conditions in the RWCD, based on conditions of 1966, are shown in figure 4-12. In this district, there is but one price for district water to all members. In 1966, that price was $8.50 per acre-foot. At that price, 104,164 acre-feet were projected to be used. (See the intersection of the marginal supply and demand functions in figure 4-12.) All water projected by the analytical model to be used on the model farms in 1966 is shown as purchased from the district. Although some farms in Farm Size Group II have private wells, these wells do not pump water in the model projections. In reality, some water is pumped by these private wells because of timing problems in obtaining water from the district.

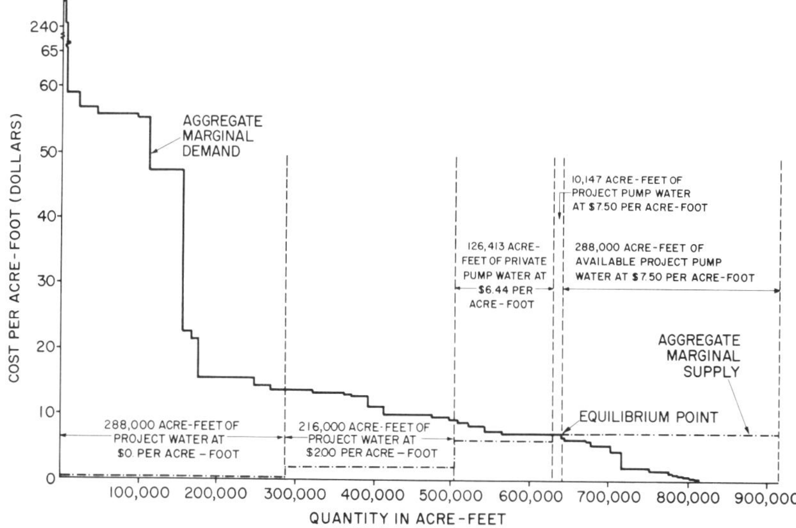

Fig. 4-11. *Aggregate agricultural derived marginal demand for and marginal supply of irrigation water, all farms, Salt River Project, 1966.*

A comparison of the actual quantity of water supplied in 1966 by the irrigation districts and water use projected by the representative-farm models for 1966 in each district shows a high degree of similarity. Comparisons are discussed below for the RWCD and SRP districts.

Water produced by the RWCD in 1966 totaled 126,144 acre-feet. Of this amount, 90,215 acre-feet were pumped by the project, and the remaining 35,929 acre-feet came from surface sources. Project records show that 108,312 acre-feet were actually delivered to water users. Thus, 17,832 acre-feet, or 14 percent, was system loss. The representative-farm model projects a 1966 RWCD water use by farmers of 104,164 acre-feet. The difference in these quantities (4,148 acre-feet) is remarkably small and is accounted for by crops not included in the models, such as citrus and grapes, of which there are approximately 4,000 acres. (These crops are also a source of demand for water supplies from private pumps.)

The SRP produced 1,108,000 acre-feet of water for irrigation use in 1966. Of this amount, 709,000 acre-feet were from surface sources and 395,000 acre-feet were pumped. The relative surface and groundwater percentages fluctuate from year to year; however, 1966 was a historically typical year.

SRP irrigation deliveries for agricultural uses in 1966 totaled

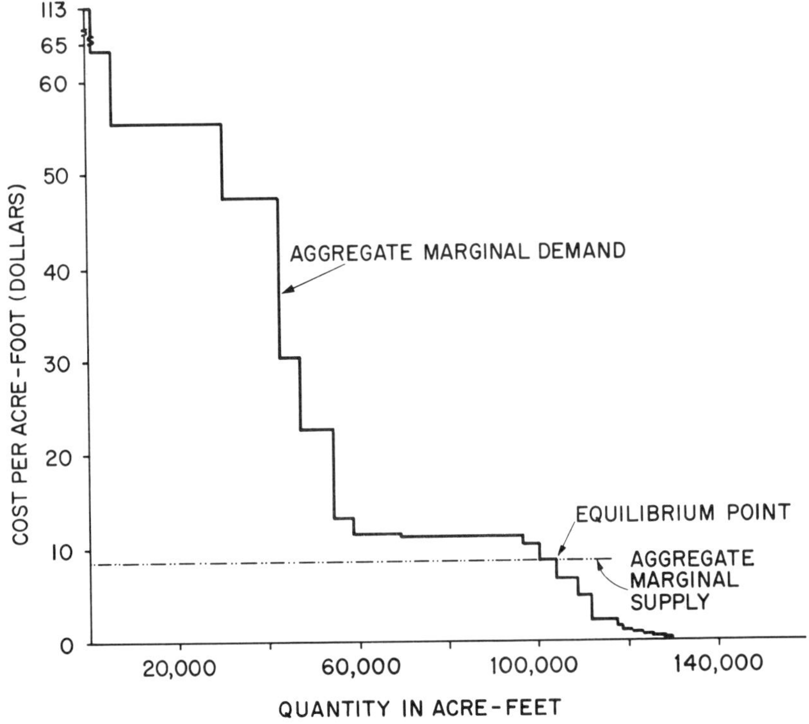

Fig. 4-12. *Aggregate agricultural derived marginal demand for and marginal supply of irrigation water, all farms, Roosevelt Water Conservation District, 1966.*

541,167 acre-feet on 160,000 acres. Other project deliveries, such as subdivision irrigation, domestic contracts, and other municipal and industrial uses totaled 179,228 acre-feet. Thus, total deliveries were 720,395 acre-feet. Compared to 1,108,000 acre-feet produced, this leaves 377,605 acre-feet unaccounted for or as system loss. Smith (1968:92) estimates that approximately 15 percent (56,640 acre-feet) of this unaccounted for water is actually delivered to farm water users. Adding 56,640 acre-feet of the 541,167 acre-feet reported as delivered to farms gives an estimate of total water use of 597,807 acre-feet on 160,000 project acres.

Total water use in the SRP projected for 1966 by the representative-farm model was 640,575 acre-feet on 144,000 acres. Private pumps provided 126,368 acre-feet of this total amount. The project supplied the remainder, or 514,207 acre-feet. Water in the amount of 597,807 acre-feet was estimated to have been actually delivered by the SRP to 160,000 acres in 1966: the analysis reported herein projected that project supplied water in the amount of 514,207 acre-feet would be delivered to 144,000 acres. The difference between the actual and predicted figures is 83,600 acre-feet of project water available for use on 16,000 acres not included in the representative-farm models. These acres were used for crops considered as exogenous to the model such as sugar-beet seed, fruits and nuts, garden crops, and pasture. Average water use per acre on these 16,000 cropped acres was approximately five acre-feet per acre; thus, essentially all the apparent discrepancy between the actual and projected water deliveries in the SRP is accounted for.

Aggregate marginal supply functions for water are not as easily constructed in other study areas as they are in the SRP and RWCD, the Yuma study area excepted. These three areas have integrated distribution facilities and centralized control over the production, pricing and distribution of irrigation water. Although several smaller irrigation districts in the state do have centralized control and integrated distribution facilities, these small districts were not modeled separately but were analyzed as integrated overlapping subareas of larger study areas. Thus, it is not possible to separate these smaller districts from the larger study areas in terms of derived marginal demand functions to which district water supply functions might be related, as is done for the SRP and RWCD.

These other study areas, where the major quantity of water is supplied from privately owned and operated wells by water users themselves, have several water supply situations. Individual supply conditions depend upon size and type of equipment used, source and cost of energy to power the equipment, and depth to water. In areas such as these, supply functions more properly exist for individual farms or relatively small groups of farms rather than as a single aggregate function for the entire study area. However, the demand functions (shown in Appendix table B-3) may be related to the cost of water if the interpretation of water supply is as follows. If all water used were available to all farms in the area at the listed price per acre, the maximum quantity of total water use is given. For example, if a surface irrigation system were developed for the farms of Pinal County and water was supplied through that system at a single price of $18.39 per acre-foot (as in the RWCD), a maximum of 712,328 acre-feet of water would be purchased for use, assuming *no* water was available at a lower cost, including water from privately owned wells (see table B-3). Any quantity of water that would be available at a lesser price than $18.39 would need be subtracted from the 712,328 acre-feet that would be sold at the single price of $18.39.

5. Costs of Agricultural Adjustment to the Arizona Economy and Its Individual Members

Thus far we have focused on the *direct* adjustments in gross agricultural output that we project will take place in Arizona agriculture in response to rising irrigation-water costs. While doing so, we were also able to estimate the short-run derived-demand functions for irrigation water and thus the direct short-run value of an additional acre-foot of water to the farmer, the individual who would directly use the water. This is the maximum amount that the farmer would rationally pay in the short-run for an additional acre-foot of water in order to grow and sell farm products.

We recognize that in addition to the direct value of an acre-foot of water to the farmer, there are indirect benefits accruing to the rest of the economy which interrelates with irrigated agriculture. These indirect benefits must also be estimated. There is an additional problem, however. One may distinguish between the amount that individuals would rationally pay for the direct and indirect benefits of an additional acre-foot of water and the *total value* of that acre-foot of water to the aggregate economy of the state. The two concepts are quite different. The total value of the acre-foot of water to the aggregate economy is considerably larger than the amount of the sum of individual rational payments for direct and indirect benefits received. There is a further problem of what is the rational short-run payment, and what payment could one afford to make on a continuing long-run basis? This chapter attempts to make each of these distinctions.

We first estimate the *total costs* (direct and indirect) of agricultural adjustment under two alternative assumptions about the extent of the effects of adjustment on the state's entire economy. Total costs to the aggregate economy are exactly equal to the *total value* of water to the aggregate economy in the sense that costs of agricultural adjustment are a measure of the value of the acre-feet of water that would make the adjustment unnecessary. These estimates may be referred to as the gross costs of adjustment or the gross value of water. We conclude by relating the total cost estimates to other estimates of rational payments by individual groups which are really the net costs of adjustment to the people of which the economy is composed.

"Value Added" as an Estimator of Total Adjustment Costs

"Value added" is a measurement of the additional value added to a set of resources because of additional processing. It may be thought of as the residual return to labor, management, and the owners of capital and land resulting from the production process after other inputs have been paid for at their market prices. Total value added for a nation is one way of measuring gross national product (GNP); that is, it is the total value of the production process after subtracting out purchased inputs so as to avoid double counting. Total value added for the state, therefore, may be defined as "gross state product" (GSP). Thus, we define the total cost of agriculture adjustment as the decline in total value added that is associated, both directly and indirectly, with the projected decline in agricultural output. Since this projected decline in agricultural output is occurring as less water is used in agriculture, total value added may be divided by the acre-feet of water no longer used to obtain the total value of a replacement acre-foot of water to the Arizona economy. The gross value of a marginal acre-foot of water is the total value added (GSP) that is associated with the use of a replacement acre-foot of water in Arizona agriculture.

Direct and Indirect Costs

Direct Costs. Value added *directly* associated with the decline in agricultural output includes the return to owners of capital and land and to management and all agricultural labor (both hired and family labor) that will no longer be generated in agriculture because of rising irrigation water costs. This direct loss is a real loss to the state to the extent that undepreciated capital is abandoned, land is not transferred to other uses, and labor and management do not find alternative employment within the state. (We hereafter include all agricultural labor with direct effects. They were excluded in the direct effects on the farmer described in the preceding chapter.)

Indirect Costs. Value added *indirectly* associated with the decline in agricultural output includes the return to the owners of nonagricultural capital and land and to management and labor that would no longer need to be generated in support of agriculture because agricultural output had declined. Most nonagricultural sectors would not experience an absolute decrease in output because of this indirect effect, since much of the nonagricultural economy is growing independently of the farm sectors. Thus, the effect would be one of not growing as fast as "might have been" rather than being an absolute loss.

Indirect effects on the economy may be classified as two separate types.

First, there are those effects on economic sectors which provide agricultural inputs (including the labor employed by these sectors). These effects are called "backward linkages" to agriculture. They precede agriculture in the input-output chain. The way in which these effects are spread backward into the economy may be described by quoting from Tijoriwala et al. (1968), the study that is used in this chapter to quantify these effects.

> For example, because of rising water costs due to declining water tables, the cropping pattern in Arizona has changed during the last five years. In Pinal County, at least partially because of these increasing water costs, alfalfa acreage decreased from 32,000 acres in 1957 to 18,500 acres in 1963. Such a reduction in alfalfa acreage in Pinal County could start a chain of reactions. First, the farmers may demand fewer machines and implements because of reduced alfalfa production. This, in turn, could decrease the demand for services and products of industries supplying machinery manufacturers, and so on. In some cases, effects of a single change in output (or demand) may complete a circle within the economy and further change the demand for the product that began the cycle.

Secondly, there are those effects on economic sectors which purchase agricultural output to process into more finished products (including the labor employed by these sectors). These effects are called "forward linkages" to agriculture. They succeed agriculture in the input-output chain. These forward-linked industries would, of course, have backward linkages with all industries which supply them with inputs, including agriculture itself.

Measurement of Direct and Indirect Effects

In order to quantitatively measure these direct and indirect effects, an Input-Output (Interindustry) model was constructed of the entire Arizona economy for the base year 1958. This model, described in detail elsewhere (Tijoriwala et al., 1968), enables us to obtain empirical estimates of the indirect and circular effects as well as the more easily observed direct effects.

We have summarized in table 5-1 the information from the Input-Output model that will be used in estimating the direct and indirect values

TABLE 5-1

Direct and Indirect Multipliers for the Arizona Agricultural Sectors Responding to Changing Water Cost (Backward Linkages)*

Agricultural Sector	Adjusted Direct & Indirect Gross Output Multipliers†	Direct Value Added Multiplier‡	Adjusted Indirect Value Added Multiplier§
Food and feed grains	1.205	0.568	0.125
Cotton	1.229	0.733	0.150
Forage	1.087	0.842	0.050
Miscellaneous agriculture	1.171	0.761	0.128
Livestock products processing	1.946	0.200	0.432
Miscellaneous agricultural processing	1.444	0.515	0.240

*Derived from data in Tijoriwala et al. (1968). "Adjusted" multipliers differ from standard input-output model multipliers in that they relate to per-dollar changes in output rather than per-dollar changes in final demand.

†One dollar of direct output change for the sector listed plus induced changes for requirements for output from the rest of the economy.

‡Direct value added per dollar of output for the sector listed.

§Change in value added in the rest of the economy induced by a one dollar change in output for the sector listed.

of an acre-foot of water used in agriculture. Included are adjusted direct and indirect gross output multipliers, the proportion of gross output that is composed of value added, and the indirect value added that would be generated throughout the economy per dollar of gross output in specific agricultural sectors. ("Adjusted" direct and indirect gross output multipliers differ from standard input-output model multipliers in that they relate to per dollar changes in output rather than per dollar changes in final demand. See Martin and Carter (1962) for their derivation.)

For example, the first entry in column one of table 5-1 (1.205) shows that a one-dollar decrease (or increase) in gross output of food and feed grains in Arizona would tend to induce a total of $0.205 of decrease (or increase) in gross output in the other sectors of the Arizona economy. Of the one dollar of gross output of food and feed grains, $0.568 was value added generated directly in the food and feed grain sector (entry one of column two). For every one dollar of gross output in the food and feed grain sector, $0.125 of value added were induced in the other sectors of the economy (entry one of column 3). Identical interpretations are given to the other entries of the table in relation to the gross outputs of the sectors listed.

Cotton, food and feed grains, forages, and miscellaneous agricultural crops (including sugar beets, safflower, and bermuda grass) are those crops that we projected (chapter 4) would be affected substantially by rising water costs. The multipliers are applied directly to our estimates of output change derived from our representative-farm linear-programming models to obtain backward-linkage estimates to agricultural adjustment. Livestock Products Processing and Miscellaneous Agricultural Processing are sectors which are forward linked to the three agricultural sectors. The multipliers shown give the complete backward linkages of these two sectors, once the gross output changes of these two sectors, based on changes in the agricultural sectors, have been estimated.

A simplified model of this system is given in figure 5-1. Backward linkages are described by dotted lines, while forward linkages are described by continuous lines. The crop sectors are those whose gross output is originally affected by rising water costs. These are the direct effects. Indirect backward linkages from the crop sectors work through the agricultural input sectors and then reverberate throughout the rest of the economy. Forward linkages to the crop sectors are the livestock sectors and the agricultural processing sectors. Then, backward linkages from the agricultural processing sectors work back through the livestock sectors, the crop sectors, and the rest of the economy.

The model shown in figure 5-1 is simplified in that it shows only the major avenues of linkage. In the real economy almost all sectors

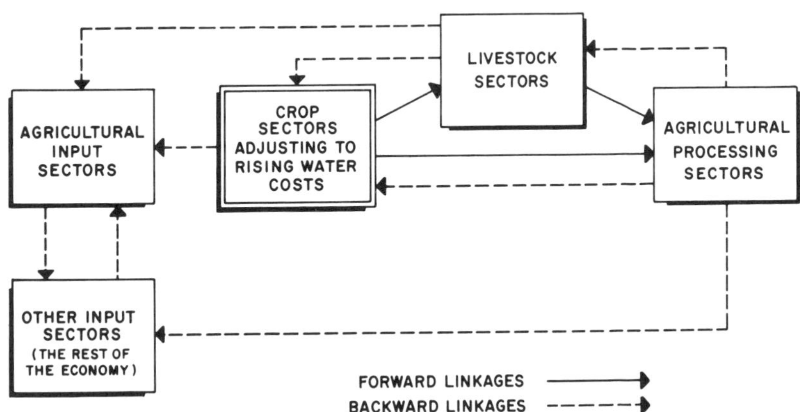

Fig. 5-1. *Backward and forward linkages between sectors responding to a changing water cost.*

are linked both backward and forward to every other sector, if only slightly. All of these linkages are accounted for in the mathematical model (Tijoriwala et al., 1968). The most important simplification, however, is that the possibility of imports and exports is not shown. Any of these linkages may be weakened or broken entirely by importing inputs from out-of-state or exporting output to out-of-state. It is the alternative assumptions relative to exports and (especially) imports that greatly affect our estimates of the total direct and indirect value of additional water to Arizona; that is, the cost of Arizona agricultural adjustment stemming from the increasing cost of water.

Empirical Estimates of Direct and Indirect Effects

Gross-Output Effects

The projected (see chapter 4) gross values of output in 1966 prices (total output, not just the associated value added) for Arizona for the agricultural sectors that will be affected substantially by rising water costs are shown in table 5-2. Value of gross output declines over time in these sectors for three reasons.

TABLE 5-2

Projected Gross Values of Output for Arizona for Selected Agricultural Sectors*

Agricultural Sector†	Gross Values (in thousands of dollars) of Output in Year					
	1966	1975	1985	1995	2005	2015
Food and feed grains‡	48,275	43,619	40,762	37,367	32,430	32,104
Cotton§	118,117	117,128	116,183	115,159	114,457	113,464
Forages¶	29,729	28,073	24,726	20,340	18,613	16,940
Miscellaneous agriculture#	10,533	9,418	8,466	7,189	7,085	6,996
Total	206,654	198,238	190,137	180,055	172,585	169,504

*Derived by aggregating the results of the representative-farm linear-programming models. All outputs are expressed in terms of 1966 prices.

†Aggregated to be consistent with the sectors of the Arizona input-output model (Tijoriwala et al., 1968).

‡Includes barley, wheat, and sorghum.

§Short-staple and long-staple.

¶Comprised entirely of alfalfa hay, seed, and pasture.

#Includes safflower, sugar beets, and bermuda grass seed.

First, output per acre decreases over time as farmers cut back on water use per acre in response to rising water cost.

Second, the number of acres of each crop except cotton declines when it no longer pays to grow that crop even with reduced water use. It always pays to grow cotton, so cotton acres remain constant; only output per acre declines. The net return per acre on cotton, a relatively high valued crop, is so high that it always pays to grow the maximum number of acres allowed, but as water cost increases, adjustments are made in gross output per acre. Acreage would also be unaffected for very high valued crops, such as vegetables and citrus. In addition, adjustments in gross output per acre would be so small as to be negligible. Therefore, the value of gross output of very high valued crops is assumed to be independent of rising water cost.

Finally, some crop acres go out of production because of urbanization – especially in the Salt River Project area. Obviously, this last reason has nothing to do with water cost or even with water scarcity. The Salt River Project is a definitely bounded area. If an acre of urbanization occurs within it, an acre of crop production must go out. (An acre of cotton allotment would transfer to another area of the state so that total cotton acres would be unaffected.)

In table 5-3 we present our estimates of the average annual decline in gross value of crop output, during each of five decades, that occurs

TABLE 5-3

Projected Annual Decline in Gross Value of Agricultural Output for Arizona Occurring Because of Rising Water Costs*

Agricultural Sector Decreasing Output	Annual Decline in Value (in thousands of dollars) of Output During Decade				
	1966 to 1975†	1975 to 1985	1985 to 1995	1995 to 2005	2005 to 2015
Food and feed grains	254.8	185.5	326.7	510.2	29.9
Cotton	109.9	94.4	102.4	104.6	64.9
Forages	120.3	90.5	232.7	32.8	79.0
Miscellaneous agriculture	112.7	95.2	127.7	10.5	8.9
Total	597.7	465.6	789.5	658.1	182.7

*The differences in output levels shown in table 5-2 include the effects of urbanization as well as those of rising water costs. Table 5-3 shows only those changes resulting from rising water costs that occurred after adjustments due to urbanization.

†1966 to 1975 is a 9-year period.

because of rising water costs. The differences in output levels as shown in table 5-2 include the effects of urbanization. Table 5-3 shows only those changes resulting from rising water costs occurring after crop adjustments because of urbanization. Effects of urbanization by decade vary from about 20 percent to a high of 44 percent of the total output changes.

Direct-Value-Added Effects

It is not the gross value of output decline that is important but only that portion of output which is value added. To consider the value of gross output decline would involve much double counting. Thus, the data of table 5-3 are multiplied by the direct-value-added multipliers from table 5-1 to obtain the value-added estimates of table 5-4. These estimates show the annual value added that would not be produced in the agricultural sectors of the economy because of the decreased output in the agricultural sectors due to increasing irrigation water costs.

The cumulative effect of these estimates of decrease in direct value added are illustrated by graphing the data of table 5-4 in figure 5-2. For example, our average of $412,400 of decline in direct value added is applied to the Arizona economy in each of the first nine years, 1966 to 1975. This is shown in figure 5-2 as a cumulative decline in direct value added starting from the base point of zero decline and reaching a

TABLE 5-4

Projected Annual Decline in Direct Value Added Occurring Because of Rising Water Costs*

Agricultural Sector Decreasing Output	Annual Decline (in thousands of dollars) in Direct Value Added in Decade				
	1966 to 1975†	1975 to 1985	1985 to 1995	1995 to 2005	2005 to 2015
Food and feed grains	144.7	105.4	185.6	289.8	17.0
Cotton	80.6	69.2	75.0	76.7	47.6
Forages	101.3	76.2	195.9	27.6	66.5
Miscellaneous agriculture	85.8	72.4	97.2	8.0	6.8
Total	412.4	323.2	553.7	402.1	137.9

*The annual value added that would not be produced in the listed agricultural sector because of decreased output due to increasing irrigation water costs.

†1966 to 1975 is a 9-year period.

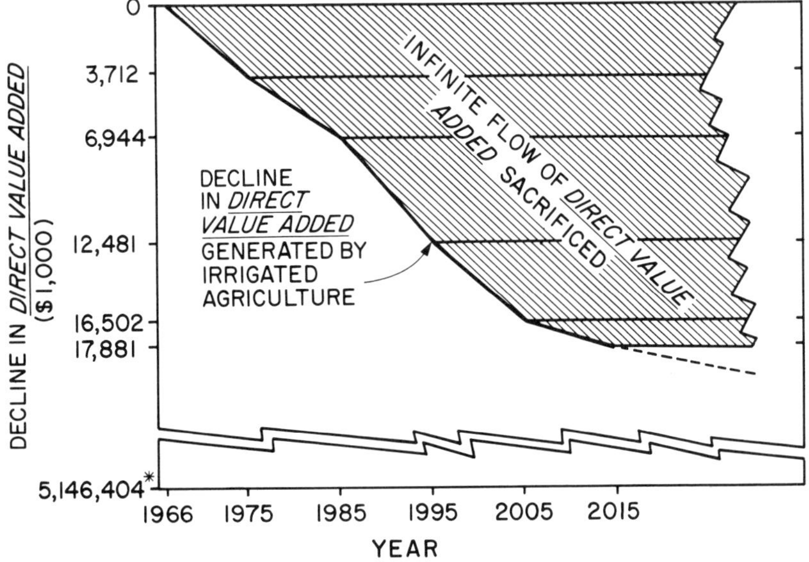

Fig. 5-2. *Decline in direct value added, generated by irrigated agriculture. The total estimated direct value added, produced in Arizona in 1966, is indicated by the asterisk.*

total of $3,712,000 of decline by 1975. Measuring from the base point of zero, $412,400 of decline will occur in 1966 and be repeated every year thereafter for an infinite number of years. Then, in 1967, an additional $412,400 of decline will occur which also will be repeated every year thereafter, and so on for each of the first nine years. Thus, an infinite flow of value added sacrificed is shown in figure 5-2 as emanating from each year's additional decline. A different average rate of decline is shown for each of the following ten-year periods.

The rate of decline in direct value added slows from 1975 to 1985 and then increases from 1985 to 1995. The rate slows again after 1995. After 2005, most adjustments have already taken place in agriculture, and the decline rate slows down considerably. This is illustrated by the shallower slope of the decline curve and the much smaller and narrower decline in infinite flows emanating from the 2005 to 2015 time period.

During this same 49-year period of time, 1966 to 2015, less and less water is being used in agriculture. Figure 5-3 illustrates this occurrence in a similar fashion to the illustration of figure 5-2. Starting from a base of zero in 1966, by 1975 approximately 212,000 fewer acre-feet of water would be used in agriculture each year because of rising water costs (the water data are listed in table 5-6). (Chapter 4 shows that additional water would also no longer be used in agriculture, but this additional water is transferred out of agriculture because of urbanization in the Salt River Project area and is independent of water cost.)

Each year there is an infinite flow of irrigation water no longer used in agriculture emanating from the year of original decline in water use. Total water use is projected to decline in an almost linear fashion until about 1995. Thereafter, the rate of decline in water use slows down, and one might project an equilibrium of water use in agriculture sometime after 2025. As shown in table 5-6, the total decline in water use per year over the decade 2005 to 2015 is only 69,000 acre-feet, or an average decline in use of only about 7,000 acre-feet in each year as compared to an average decline of nearly 24,000 acre-feet per year in the first period, 1966 to 1975. At the end of the 49-year period, 1966 to 2015, a total of 906,000 fewer acre-feet of irrigation water are being used in agriculture each year because of increased water costs.

Our objective in this section is to obtain an estimate of the direct drag on the economy in terms of dollars of value added that will be sacrificed *per acre-foot* of water as water is abandoned from use in agricultural production between 1966 and 2015. To do so, one must first convert the infinite flows of value added that will not be produced, shown in table 5-4 and figure 5-2, into *present (that is, 1966) values.*

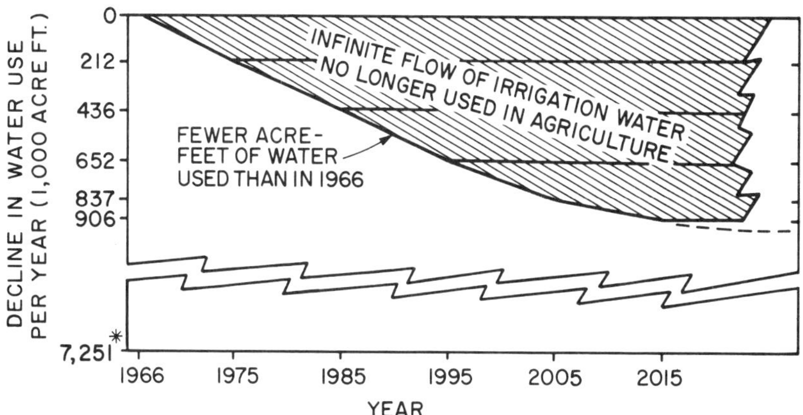

Fig. 5-3. *Decline in acre-feet of water per year used by irrigated agriculture. The total acre-feet of water pumped and diverted in Arizona in 1966 is indicated by the asterisk.*

These values are the amounts that one rationally should pay for additional supplies of water at the *present time* in order to produce the infinite flows of income that will be sacrificed in their absence. Then, these present-value estimates may be divided by the corresponding estimates of irrigation water not used to obtain the present value of the decline in direct value added that is associated with each acre-foot of water as it is abandoned from use in agriculture.

The magnitude of the present-value estimates are substantially affected by the discount rate chosen to convert the flow estimates to present values. Much has been written on the subject of the "proper" discount rate for water resource development analysis without the experts coming to complete agreement (see Committee on the Economics of Water Resources Development, 1968). We hedge our analysis by using two alternative discount rates and letting the reader choose between them, although the higher rate shown seems, to us, the more reasonable.

Our alternative discount rates are 5 and 8 percent. We consider 5 percent to be a reasonable long-term opportunity interest rate as an earnings demand on investments. We consider it highly dubious, however, that the expected earning capacity of assets (especially the wages of labor) should be capitalized at this rate to planning horizons as distant as infinity, due to risks and uncertainties inevitably involved in such long-run expectations.

Thus, we offer the alternative time discount rate of 8 percent to adjust for risk and uncertainty. It is unlikely that Arizonans would be willing to invest at lower rates than 5 percent due to available riskless alternatives (for example, savings and loan deposits). Higher rates than 8 percent might well be necessary to make such a long-term investment attractive.

Our 5 percent and 8 percent discounting factors have this relationship: 8 percent in perpetuity is (approximately) mathematically equivalent to a 5-percent discount within a 20-year planning horizon. Thus both of our discount rates could be considered as relating to a 5-percent opportunity earning rate on capital, whereby the 8-percent rate embraces risk and uncertainty by presuming a demand that the capital be recovered in 20 years at a 5-percent earning rate. Higher rates than 8 percent have the following time-related interpretations. A 12-percent discounting factor is equivalent to an 11-year planning horizon, a 15-percent factor to an 8-year horizon, and a 20-percent factor to a 6-year horizon. In these days of rapid technological change, most business firms tend to demand recovery of their capital in about 10 years, which is approximately at the 12-percent rate.

The results of the discounting analysis are shown in table 5-5. For example, if Arizonans generally demand a "net" return of 5 percent on their investments and do not discount for risk and uncertainty, the present value of the infinite flow of direct value added that will be sacrificed during the 9-year period 1966 to 1975, would be $58,625,000 in total for Arizona at the present (that is, 1966) time. Since the expected loss in value added for the 10-year period 1975 to 1985 is 9 to 19 years away, the present value of that future decline in direct value added would be only $32,175,000. The total present value of the 49 years of projected decline in direct value added would be $142,902,000 if evaluated at the discount rate of 5 percent.

If an 8-percent discount rate is required to cover risk and uncertainty in addition to a 5-percent earnings demand, the present value of the sacrificed flows drops dramatically. For example, the first 9-year period would be worth $32,203,000 rather than $58,625,000. The value of the total 49 years of projected decline in value added would drop to $60,719,000, down from $142,902,000.

To convert these totals to values per acre-foot, one need only divide the total values by the number of acre-feet of water that will no longer be used in agriculture after each relevant time period. These estimates of the decline in water use and the estimates of the present value of sacrificed value added expressed in dollars per acre-foot of water not used in agriculture are displayed in table 5-6. For example (using the five percent discount rate) $58,625,000 (from table 5-5) is divided by 212,000 acre-feet of water to yield an estimate of $276.53 per acre-foot as the present value of the direct value added that will be sacrificed during the first 9-year period, if that 212,000 acre-feet of water abandoned from use in agriculture were never replaced.

The value of investment in water development to stave off decline

TABLE 5-5

Present Value of Infinite Flow of Direct Value Added Sacrificed Because of Rising Water Costs in Agriculture

Sacrificed in Decade	Evaluated (in thousands of dollars) at:	
	5%	8%
1966 to 1975	58,625	32,203
1975 to 1985	32,175	13,561
1985 to 1995	33,839	10,761
1995 to 2005	15,087	3,619
2005 to 2015	3,176	575
Total	142,902	60,719

TABLE 5-6

Present Value of Infinite Flow of Direct Value Added Sacrificed Because of Rising Water Costs in Agriculture in Terms of Dollars per Acre-foot of Water Not Used in Agriculture

Decade	Total Decline (in 1,000 acre-feet) in Water-use per Year	Dollars per Acre-foot Evaluated at:	
		5%	8%
1966 to 1975	212	$276.53	$151.90
1975 to 1985	231	139.29	58.71
1985 to 1995	209	161.91	51.49
1995 to 2005	185	81.55	19.56
2005 to 2015	69	46.03	8.33
Total	906	—	—
Weighted average	—	157.73	67.02

in agricultural output drops off as we consider saving blocks of agriculture at times farther in the future. The present value of additional water to forestall decline in agricultural output during the period 2005 to 2015 is only $46.03 per acre-foot when evaluated at 5 percent. If an acre-foot of water is evaluated with an 8-percent instead of a 5-percent discount rate, the present value is $151.90 for additional water to prevent output decline during the nearest period and drops to $8.33 for additional water in the last period beginning 39 years in the future.

The weighted averages for the present value of direct value added that will not be produced expressed in terms of an acre-foot of water not used are $157.73 and $67.02 when evaluated at 5 percent and 8 percent, respectively, over the whole 49 years.

Let us emphasize that the per acre-foot values shown in table 5-6 are *present values;* that is, the lump-sum capital value per acre-foot of an infinite flow of future income not produced as a result of the rising cost of water. If Arizonans evaluated their opportunities at 5 percent, they could afford to invest $157.73 per acre-foot right now (1966) for a perpetual right to receive 906,000 acre-feet of water per year. Thereafter, the water would need be free because the value of the flow would have been capitalized into a one-lump-sum payment.

Water values are more conventionally expressed in terms of their flow values, that is, the value per acre-foot per year rather than merely as a one-lump-sum value. The lump sum estimates of table 5-6 are converted to values per acre-foot per year and displayed in table 5-7.

We find that, as viewed in 1966, the flow value per acre-foot per year of the direct value added that will be sacrificed would be $13.83 for the first 212,000 acre-feet of water if investments are evaluated at 5 percent. Similarly, as viewed in 1966, the flow value of the last increment of 69,000 acre-feet, not used during the decade 2005 to 2015, would be only $2.30 per acre-foot. The weighted average value per acre-foot per year as viewed in 1966, of all 906,000 acre-feet of water abandoned from use in agriculture between 1966 and 2015 would be $7.89 per acre-foot. If investments are evaluated at 8 percent, the weighted average value per acre-foot per year of this water would be $5.36.

In the foregoing discussions, the values of water, whether total value, value per acre-foot, or flow value per acre-foot per year, are present values of infinite flows of future value added that will be not produced. In each case, "present" has been considered to be 1966. That is, these present values in each case express the economic importance, viewed from the vantage point of 1966, ascribed to the value added that will not be produced in the future. The significance of this way of expressing the values lost is that they may be translated directly as estimates of the direct cost to the total economy in 1966 stemming from the loss of future direct value added brought about by rising water costs in agriculture. This way of looking at the matter may be further translated to be estimates of the amounts that could rationally be invested in 1966 (or annually beginning in 1966) to replace in 1966 the entire 906,000 acre-feet of agri-

TABLE 5-7

Flow Value of Infinite Flow of Direct Value Added Sacrificed Because of Rising Water Costs in Agriculture in Terms of Dollars per Year per Acre-foot of Water

Decade	Total Decline (in 1,000 acre-feet) in Water-use per Year	Direct Effects (in dollars per acre-foot per year) Evaluated at:	
		5%	8%
1966 to 1975	212	$13.83	$12.15
1975 to 1985	231	6.96	4.70
1985 to 1995	209	8.10	4.12
1995 to 2005	185	4.08	1.56
2005 to 2015	69	2.30	0.67
Total	906	—	—
Weighted average	—	7.89	5.36

culturally used water that will be abandoned from agricultural use between 1966 and 2015, a replacement which if made will prevent the future declines in the flow of direct value added that will result from that abandonment.

We later change the vantage point in time to future years from which the then "present" values of a replacement supply of 906,000 acre-feet might be viewed to determine whether delay in its provision to those later years might be economically advantageous.

To summarize: The above are estimates of the present value of value added that would no longer be produced *directly* by Arizona crop agriculture as Arizona farmers adjust to rising water costs over time. Therefore, the estimates may be considered to be the 1966 direct cost to the Arizona economy arising from future agricultural adjustments due to rising water costs. The estimates are the value of the decline in gross state product arising directly out of agricultural adjustment, regardless of who suffers the losses. Losses would accrue to owners of farm land and capital, to farm management, and to farm labor. These people in total could *afford* to pay *no more than* the total amount of these estimates if they wished to avoid this direct loss to themselves and to the Arizona economy. We will show later that as individuals they would rationally *value* their individual losses at a lesser amount.

Indirect-Value-Added Effects

To obtain the total effects on the entire Arizona economy, we must now add the indirect effects of agricultural adjustment to the direct effects estimates above. As previously discussed, the indirect effects may be "backward linked" only, or they may be both "backward and forward linked." We present estimates of adjustment cost for both possibilities.

Obviously, the assumption of both backward and forward linkages produces the largest possible estimates of indirect cost. The backward only assumption produces much smaller estimates. We tend to believe that the backward only estimate is the more reasonable choice. Or, possibly backward linkages with only some, much weaker, forward linkages would in fact occur. The reasons for our stronger belief in the backward-linkages-only assumption are as follows.

The basic assumption involved in the forward-linkage argument is that the livestock feeding industry and the livestock processing industries are directly dependent, in a constant proportional relationship, on the availability of locally produced feed grains and forages. Thus, under this assumption, the feeding and processing industries would disappear in constant proportion to the disappearance of Arizona feed grain and forage acreage. If the feeding and processing industries were to remain and grow, as we believe they would, the cost of agricultural adjustment due to rising water costs would be materially reduced.

Why would these industries remain? In Arizona, cattle feeding has a comparative advantage relative to other livestock feeding areas, which is independent of local feed production. Arizona has high efficiency of feed conversion due to the hot dry climate. Its livestock industry is near large centers of population in which to market its product. Arizona's livestock industry already imports large quantities of feed grains from the Southern Great Plains. In fact, Arizona has traditionally exported most of its local supply and imported the grain it actually feeds. Feed grain and forage prices in the state are now dominated by their price in the deficit areas of California less the cost of transportation from Arizona to these deficit areas. Forage is becoming a less important input into the feeding industry at the same time that pelleting technology is reducing its transportation and handling costs. Hence, it may be plausibly deduced that the livestock feeding and processing industry in Arizona is not dependent on locally grown feed grain and forage supplies but upon the comparative advantage of its feed conversion ratios and the existence of a deficit feed grain and forage demand in the Los Angeles basin and central California.

A further assumption involved in the forward-linkage argument is that livestock processing is tightly linked to local livestock feeding. It is probable, however, that even if livestock feeding declined in Arizona, livestock processing would not decline proportionately. Obviously, it is possible to import fed cattle.

A final assumption is that the miscellaneous agricultural processing industry is solidly built upon the miscellaneous agricultural crops (such as sugar beets, safflower, bermuda grass) which we have projected as declining in acreage over time. Again, it is unlikely that the linkage is directly proportional. It is more likely that a decline in miscellaneous agricultural crops would have some forward-linked effects, but not nearly as large as those we present below, as estimated by our input-output model.

One must distinguish between the relationship that holds between irrigation development and supportive business in an economy starting from zero irrigated land, from the relationship that holds in an already irrigated area. In the first case the multiplicative effect of irrigation development would be large because all development of supporting industries could be attributed to the increase in agricultural activity resulting from the new water. In the latter case, where a marginal quantity of water from an already irrigated and developed area is added or subtracted, there may be little multiplicative effect at all. The chain between related agricultural and nonagricultural industries is easily broken by imports from or exports to outside the immediate irrigated area. Such is the case in Arizona.

Thus, our forward-linkage estimates may be considered as the *maximum possible* indirect effects; but the backward-linkage-only estimates are more reasonable approximations. If, in fact, there were only backward linkages, the basic assumptions of the input-output model would tend to overestimate these effects to some extent also. Anytime a decrease in demand for inputs occurs in a regional economy where some of the inputs are imported and some of the inputs are produced locally, it is more reasonable to assume that the effects of the decline would impinge more on imports than on local industry. Thus, an input-output model, having the built-in assumption of fixed trading patterns, always will slightly overestimate indirect multiplicative effects.

Backward Linkages Only

The data of table 5-3 are multiplied by the relevant "adjusted indirect value added multipliers" from table 5-1 to obtain the value-added estimates of table 5-8. These estimates show the annual value added that would not need be produced in the nonagricultural sectors of the economy resulting from backward linkages to the decreased output in the agricultural sectors. Of course, total value added produced in the nonagricultural sectors will in fact be increasing rapidly because of the growing total economy. Thus, these estimates should be interpreted only as the annual additional "drag" on the economy because of declining agriculture rather than actual decreases in value added.

The cumulative effect of these estimates of "drag" could be illustrated by graphing the data of table 5-8 in the same way as direct value added was graphed in figure 5-2. For example, our average of $68,000 of additional drag on value added is applied to the Arizona economy in each of the first 9 years, 1966 to 1975. This would be shown as a cumulative decline in indirect value added starting from the base point of zero decline and reaching a total of $619,000 of decline by 1975. Measuring from the base point of zero, $68,800 of drag would occur in 1966 and be repeated every year thereafter for an infinite number of years. Then, in 1967, an additional $68,800 worth of drag would occur which would also be repeated every year thereafter, and so on for each of the first 9 years. Thus, an infinite flow of indirect value added sacrificed would be shown as emanating from each year's additional decline. A different average rate of decline is shown for each of the following 10-year periods.

TABLE 5-8
Projected Decline in Indirect Value Added Indirectly Induced Through Backward Linkages by the Decline in Agricultural Output Occurring Because of Rising Water Costs*

Agricultural Sector Decreasing Output	Annual Value (in thousands of dollars) of the Induced Change in Value Added in Decade				
	1966 to 1975†	1975 to 1985	1985 to 1995	1995 to 2005	2005 to 2015
Food and feed grains	31.9	23.2	40.8	63.8	3.7
Cotton	16.5	14.2	15.4	15.7	9.7
Forages	6.0	4.5	11.6	1.6	4.0
Miscellaneous agriculture	14.4	12.2	16.3	1.3	1.1
Total	68.8	54.1	84.1	82.4	18.5

*The annual value added that would not need be produced in the rest of the economy because of the decreased output of the listed agricultural sector. Total net value added will in fact be increasing rapidly. Thus, these estimates should be interpreted as the annual additional "drag" on the economy because of declining agriculture rather than an actual decrease in value added.

†1966 to 1975 is a 9-year period.

The rate of decline in indirect value added induced by backward linkages is fairly linear from 1966 through 2005 with minor fluctuations. After 2005, the decline rate slows down considerably. One would expect complete cessation of decline sometime after 2015.

As with the estimates of direct value added, we first convert the infinite flows of backward-linked indirect value added into present values. Then, the present-value estimates are divided by the corresponding estimates of irrigation water use to obtain the present value of the indirect value added that is associated with an acre-foot of water no longer used in agriculture. This value measures the total indirect drag on the economy that would be induced through backward linkages by no longer using an acre-foot of water in agriculture.

As before, we offer the alternative discount rates of 5 and 8 percent to convert to present values. The results of the discounting analysis are shown in table 5-9. For example, if nonfarmers generally demand a return of 5 percent on their investments and do not discount for risk and uncertainty, the value of the infinite flow of backward linked indirect value added during the 9-year period 1966 to 1975, would be $9,780,000 in total for Arizona at the present (that is, 1966) time. Since the expected loss in value added for the 10-year period 1975 to 1985 is 9 to 19 years away, the present value of that future drag on the economy is only

TABLE 5-9
Present Value of Infinite Flow of Indirect Value Added Sacrificed Because of Rising Water Costs in Agriculture

Sacrificed in Decade	Backward Linkages Only (in thousands of dollars) Evaluated at		Backward and Forward Linkages (in thousands of dollars) Evaluated at	
	5%	8%	5%	8%
1966 to 1975	9,780	5,372	314,763	172,898
1975 to 1985	5,386	2,269	165,920	69,932
1985 to 1995	5,140	1,634	164,834	52,418
1995 to 2005	3,092	742	143,631	34,462
2005 to 2015	426	77	4,489	812
Total	23,824	10,094	793,637	330,522

$5,386,000. The total present value of the total projected drag on the economy resulting from the 49-year projected decline in backward-linked indirect value added is $23,824,000 if evaluated at the discount rate of 5 percent.

If an 8 percent discount rate is required, the present value of the sacrificed flow is worth $5,372,000 rather than $9,780,000 in the first period. The value of the total 49 years of projected decline drops to $10,094,000, down from $23,824,000.

The estimates of dollars per acre-foot are shown in table 5-10. For example (using the 5 percent discount rate) $9,780,000 (from table 5-9) is divided by 212,000 acre-feet of water to yield an estimate of $46.13 per acre-foot as the present value of the backward-linked indirect value added sacrificed for the first 9-year period, if that 212,000 acre-feet of water were no longer used in agriculture for an infinite period of time.

The present value of additional water for the period 2005 to 2015 is only $6.17 per acre-foot when evaluated at 5 percent. If an acre-foot of water is evaluated with an 8-percent, instead of a 5-percent rate, the present value is $25.34 for additional water for the nearest period and drops to $1.12 for additional water in the last period, beginning 39 years in the future.

The weighted averages for the present value of indirect value added induced through backward linkages only in terms of an acre-foot of water not used in agriculture are $26.30 and $11.14 when evaluated at 5 percent and 8 percent, respectively, for the whole 49 years.

As with the lump-sum payments of direct effects, we convert the estimates of indirect effects of table 5-10 into flow values; the value per acre-foot per year for all the ensuing years. These flow values for indirect effects are shown in table 5-11. The weighted-average flow values per acre-foot per year for backward-linked indirect effects only are $1.32 and $0.89 when evaluated at 5 percent and 8 percent, respectively.

Forward and Backward Linkages

In order to estimate the value of both forward and backward linkages, it is first necessary to estimate the changes in gross output that are assumed to be forward linked to the changes in crop agriculture. Then, the backward linkages in terms of indirect value added from the most forward-linked industries are computed. Four crop sectors are affected by rising water costs. They are food and feed grains, cotton, forages, and miscellaneous agricultural crops. Estimation of forward linkages to each of these four sectors is explained below.

In terms of the input-output model used to estimate indirect linkages (Tijoriwala et al., 1968), the cotton sector has no forward linkages. Cotton, in Arizona, is harvested, ginned, and exported out of the state for further processing. Since ginning and transportation are treated as inputs to the cotton sector in the I-O model, these functions have already been considered as if they were backward linkages.

TABLE 5-10
Present Value of Infinite Flow of Indirect Value Added Sacrificed Because of Rising Water Costs in Agriculture in Terms of Dollars per Acre-foot of Water

Decade	Total Decline (in 1,000 acre-feet) in Water-use per Year	Backward Linkages Only (in dollars per acre-foot) Evaluated at		Backward and Forward Linkages (in dollars per acre-foot) Evaluated at	
		5%	8%	5%	8%
1966 to 1975	212	$46.13	$25.34	$1,484.73	$815.56
1975 to 1985	231	23.32	9.82	718.27	302.74
1985 to 1995	209	24.59	7.82	788.68	250.80
1995 to 2005	185	16.71	4.01	776.38	186.28
2005 to 2015	69	6.17	1.12	65.06	11.77
Total	906	—	—	—	—
Weighted average	—	26.30	11.14	875.98	364.81

TABLE 5-11

Flow Value of Infinite Flow of Indirect Value Added Sacrificed Because of Rising Water Costs in Agriculture in Terms of Dollars per Year per Acre-foot of Water

Decade	Total Decline (in 1,000 acre-feet) in Water-use per Year	Backward Linkages Only (in dollars per acre-foot per year) Evaluated at		Backward and Forward Linkages (in dollars per acre-foot per year) Evaluated at	
		5%	8%	5%	8%
1966 to 1975	212	$2.31	$2.03	$74.24	$65.24
1975 to 1985	231	1.17	0.79	35.91	24.22
1985 to 1995	209	1.23	0.63	39.43	20.06
1995 to 2005	185	0.84	0.32	38.82	14.90
2005 to 2015	69	0.31	0.09	3.25	0.94
Total	906	—	—	—	—
Weighted average	—	1.32	0.89	43.80	29.18

The grains and forage sectors have the major forward linkages. Both of these sectors provide inputs for the cattle, poultry, and dairy sectors. Since grains and forages are projected to decline at approximately the same rate over time, and since grains are the larger input per dollar of output in the three livestock sectors, we tie our projections of forward linkages specifically to the grain sector. If one assumes that the three livestock sectors will maintain about the same relative importance to each other over time, a weighted average estimate of 16 cents of grain input per dollar of livestock output is obtained (16.69 cents for cattle, 17.77 cents for poultry, 12.37 cents for dairy; cattle, poultry, and dairy output in Arizona is in the ratio of 83:3:14). Thus, it is implied that for every one dollar of decline in output of feed grains, there would be a $1.0 ÷ $0.16 = $6.25 decline in output of the livestock industry. This implication has the built-in assumption that no replacement supplies of grains through imports into the state are possible and thus obviously creates the maximum possible estimate of a forward linkage.

It is further estimated that a weighted average input of 51 cents of livestock products are required per dollar of output of the livestock product processing industries (56.9 cents for meat and poultry processing, 44.7 cents for dairy products processing; the two processing industries have an output ratio of 53:47). Thus, it is implied, if no imports of

TABLE 5-12
Projected Annual Decline (in thousands of dollars) in Gross Value of Output for Arizona Industries Which Are Forward Linked to Arizona Crop Agriculture

Decade	Projected Annual Decline in Grain Output*	Implied Annual Decline in Livestock Output†	Implied Annual Decline in Livestock Processing Output‡	Projected Annual Decline in Misc. Agricultural Output*	Implied Annual Decline in Misc. Agricultural Processing Output§
1966 to 1975	254.8	1,592.5	3,122.5	112.7	736.6
1975 to 1985	185.5	1,159.4	2,273.3	95.2	622.2
1985 to 1995	326.7	2,041.9	4,003.7	127.7	834.6
1995 to 2005	510.2	3,188.8	6,252.5	10.5	68.6
2005 to 2015	29.9	186.9	366.5	8.9	58.2

*Source: Table 5-3 and representative-farm linear-programming models.
†Grain output divided by 0.16.
‡Livestock output divided by 0.51.
§Miscellaneous agricultural output divided by 0.153.

livestock products as inputs to the processing industries are possible, there would be a $1.0 ÷ $0.51 = $1.96 decline in output of the livestock processing industries per dollar of decline in the output livestock products. The results of these computations are shown in table 5-12.

We also assume that the miscellaneous agricultural processing sector is forward linked to miscellaneous agricultural crops to the extent of 15.3 cents of inputs per dollar of output (as shown in Tijoriwala et al., 1968). The results are also shown in table 5-12.

We reiterate that these estimates of forward linkages are extremely tenuous and would be the *maximum* forward linkages which could possibly be experienced.

Having the projected estimates of decline in the two agricultural processing industries forward linked to grains, forages, and miscellaneous crops, and recognizing that cotton has only backward linkages, we apply the relevant adjusted direct-plus-indirect-value-added multipliers listed in table 5-1 to obtain all backward linkages from these most forward points. Because we want only the indirect effects related to the crop sectors, the direct-value-added estimates from the crop sectors are subtracted out of the results. The final results in terms of present values, present values per acre-foot, and flow values per acre-foot are presented in tables 5-9, 5-10, and 5-11, respectively.

These estimates include value added sacrificed in all the industries forward of the crop sectors and backward from the crop sectors, but not the direct value added sacrificed in the crop sectors themselves. This development and interpretation is exactly like that outlined for the estimates for direct value added and indirect value added for backward linkage only.

One is immediately struck by the greatly increased size of these estimates relative to either the direct effects or the backward only effects. For example, for the capitalized value of an acre-foot of water, if evaluated at 5 percent, weighted average direct effects (table 5-6) are 158 dollars, backward only effects (table 5-10) are 26 dollars, while backward and forward indirect effects are 876 dollars. In terms of dollars per year per acre-foot of flow, again evaluated at 5 percent, weighted average direct effects (table 5-7) are $7.89, backward only effects (table 5-11) are $1.32, whereas backward and forward indirect effects are $43.80.

If the effects are evaluated at 8 percent, the flow value of an acre-foot of water per year (weighted average) is $5.36 for direct effects, and $0.89 for backward only effects and $29.18 for backward and forward effects.

Timing Water Development to Forestall Agricultural Adjustment

All estimates of the cost of agricultural adjustment thus far presented are in terms of the cost to the Arizona economy at the present (1966) time. For example, in table 5-5, the total projected direct adjustment cost to the Arizona agricultural economy (evaluated at five percent) is $142,902,000 as of 1966. That is to say, if 906,000 acre-feet of water were developed for use in agriculture in 1966 in order to avoid projected agricultural adjustment, the total value of this quantity of water to all participants in the agricultural economy would be $142,902,000. The corresponding estimates of the flow value of water in dollars per acre-foot per year show that as of 1966, the total value of the same 906,000 acre-feet of water would have a weighted average value of $7.89 per acre-foot per year from 1966 henceforth. The first 212,000 acre-feet of water developed would have a value of $13.83 per acre-foot per year starting in 1966. But, because the next 231,000 acre-feet would not be needed until 1975-1985, these acre-feet would have a value of only $6.96 per acre-foot per year starting in 1966. The farther into the future that the need for additional water occurs, the lower the value that water has at the present time. Only a small quantity of additional water would be useful now. Water developed now for future use has little present value.

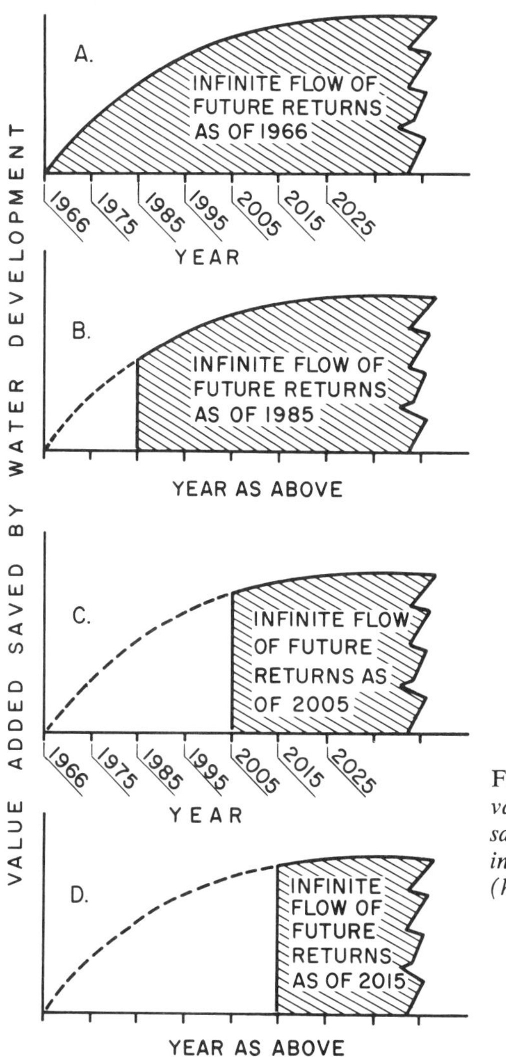

Fig. 5-4. *Infinite flow of value added that would be saved by water development in alternative years (hypothetical).*

The need for additional water increases over time. Therefore, the value of water development also will increase over time. The manner in which this increase would occur is illustrated in figure 5-4. The graph of figure 5-4A is a hypothetical illustration of the total value added that would be saved for Arizona by water development if the development occurred in 1966. Starting in 1966, during each succeeding year an increased amount of value added would be saved until sometime after 2015 when agricultural adjustment would stabilize even without water development. The graph shown is just the inverse relationship to that shown in figure 5-2. Figure 5-2 shows the decline in value added generated by agriculture that would occur if no additional water were developed. Figure 5-4A shows the gain in value added that would follow if sufficient additional water were developed in 1966. The area under the graph in figure 5-4A represents the infinite flow of future value added that would be created by such water development. (We may think of figure 5-4A as showing the sum of all direct and indirect effects whereas figure 5-1 showed only direct effects.)

If sufficient additional water were developed in 1966, as shown in figure 5-4A, the present value of the infinite flow of value added that would not be lost would be the area under the curve, evaluated at the selected discount rate. (We have already computed these values for both the direct and indirect effects and presented the estimates in tables 5-5 and 5-10.)

Because future gains occurring close to the present weigh large in the estimates of present value, and future returns more than 50 years in the future have almost no impact on the estimate, the present value in 1966 of the area under curve 5-4A is smaller than the then present value in 1985 of the area under curve 5-4B. Similarly, the 1985 present value for 5-4B is smaller than the 2005 present value for 5-4C, which is smaller than the 2015 present value for 5-4D. The area within an open-ended triangle is smaller than that of an open-ended rectangle of the same height. All we are saying is that in future years the immediate need for additional water will be greater and thus its value will be higher. One would need to compare the costs of water development with values of water development at the same alternative points in time in order to describe at what point water development would become feasible, but what this analysis shows is that the *value* of additional water may increase as its provision is delayed.

We present estimates of the projected *values* of water development over the coming 50 years in the section below.

Empirical Estimates of the Projected Values of Water Development at Future Points in Time

As we did for our base estimates for 1966, we present alternative estimates under two assumptions as to indirect linkages and two assumptions as to the discount rate. However, where the earlier estimates were displayed in three categories (direct effects, backward linkages only, and backward and forward linkages), we are now combining the estimates so

TABLE 5-13
Present Value of Infinite Flow of Future Value Added With Water Development Occurring at Alternative Points in Time*

Year of Water Development	Present Value of Future Value Added (in thousands of dollars)			
	Direct and Backward Linkages Evaluated at		Direct, Backward, and Forward Linkages Evaluated at	
	5%	8%	5%	8%
1966	166,726	70,813	936,539	391,241
1975	239,192	120,582	1,338,591	665,171
1985	315,612	176,430	1,780,495	982,007
1995	379,288	227,735	2,185,015	1,307,048
2005	410,690	254,702	2,391,484	1,490,468
2015	417,816	261,134	2,406,648	1,504,154

*For a water development of 906,000 acre-feet.

as to have only two categories, (1) direct effects and backward linkages, and (2) direct effects, backward and forward linkages. Thus, the total value of water to the economy may be shown under each of the four crucial assumptions in the same table.

Table 5-13 displays the present values of the infinite flow of total direct and indirect value added that would occur from water development in various future years. The size of the development would need to be adequate to maintain the farm crop sectors at their 1966 level through 2015 and thus also would prevent decline in the rest of the economy due to indirect effects. As estimated in the representative-farm linear-programming models, this would be a water developmentof 906,000 acre-feet.

If only backward linkages are assumed to hold, the present value of such a water development as of 1966 would be $167,000,000 if evaluated at 5 percent. If the water development were to be delayed until 1975, the present value as of 1975 would have increased to $239,000,000. If the water development were delayed clear to the year 2015, and still using the 5 percent discount rate, as of that time the present value of the investment would have increased to $418,000,000. If evaluated at 8 percent, the 1966 present value is only $71,000,000, but the rate of increase in present value over time is more rapid so that if the water development were delayed until 2015, the present value as of that time would be $261,000,000. Thus, under the assumptions of either 5 or 8 percent with backward linkages only, the total present value of added (gross state product) that would be saved in all sectors of the Arizona economy by

TABLE 5-14

Present Value per Acre-foot of Infinite Flow of Future Value Added With Water Development Occurring at Alternative Points in Time*

Year of Water Development	Present Value per Acre-foot of Future Value Added			
	Direct and Backward Linkages Evaluated at		Direct, Backward, and Forward Linkages Evaluated at	
	5%	8%	5%	8%
1966	$184.02	$ 78.16	$1,033.70	$ 431.83
1975	264.01	133.09	1,477.57	734.18
1985	348.36	194.73	1,965.22	1,083.89
1995	418.64	251.36	2,411.71	1,442.65
2005	453.30	281.13	2,639.60	1,645.10
2015	461.16	288.23	2,656.34	1,660.21

*For a water development of 906,000 acre-feet.

water resource development of 906,000 acre-feet is much smaller than any estimates of 1972 investment costs of any alternative developments, even through the year 2015. For example, the proposed Central Arizona Project, which is supposed to deliver an average of about 1,200,000 acre-feet of water per year, as of 1972 has estimated development costs of around 1.1 billion dollars, not including costs of needed distribution systems from project works to farms or any operating costs. Even if construction costs do not rise over time, costs would exceed the present value of the development as of any year in which the development was planned and evaluated.

If, however, the forward linkage assumption is accepted, with all of its rigid and questionable assumptions, the present value of an infinite flow of future value added of the sizes estimated would have a value of over 1.1 billion dollars if the water development were made in 1975 and if it were evaluated at 5 percent. The present value would exceed 1.1 billion dollars as of 1995 if the development were evaluated at 8 percent.

As briefly discussed in this chapter's introduction, we reiterate that while under certain rigid assumptions these estimates of value added are "benefits to whomsoever they may accrue," these amounts are grossly more than the sum of the amounts that all of the affected individuals could afford to pay. They are the gross costs of agricultural adjustment in the Arizona economy. In the last section of this chapter we estimate the smaller amount that actually could rationally be compared with such water development costs. Also, the construction costs mentioned above were only for the most gross comparisons. Not included, for example, were operation costs as well as additional construction costs that would be needed to get the water to the actual point of use, the farmer's headgate. The gross comparison points up the fact, however, that even the gross value of additional water to the Arizona economy is much less than any possible development costs, unless there are, in fact, rigid forward linkages based on irrigated crop agriculture.

In table 5-14, the total present values of value added to be saved by water resources development is put on a dollars per acre-foot basis. These estimates are merely the data of table 5-13, divided by 906,000 acre-feet of water. They are to be interpreted as the present value, as of the year listed, of the value added resulting from an infinite flow of one-acre foot of water per year if the water were developed in the year listed.

The present value data of table 5-14 are converted to dollars of value added per acre-foot per year in table 5-15. These are the weighted average values per acre-foot per year, beginning as of the year listed, of 906,000 acre-feet of water if that water were developed in the year listed. A maximum value per acre-foot is approached by 2015. Since by 2015 all 906,000 acre-feet would be needed, and thus are valued at their current 2015 value in use rather than being developed for future use, the discount rate chosen no longer affects the results. The only issue then, but a crucial one, is the degree of rigidity in the forward-linkage assumptions.

TABLE 5-15

Flow Value of Value Added per Acre-foot per Year With Water Development Occurring at Alternative Points in Time*

Year of Water Development	Flow Value per Acre-foot per Year of Value Added			
	Direct and Backward Linkages Evaluated at		Direct, Backward, and Forward Linkages Evaluated at	
	5%	8%	5%	8%
1966	$ 9.20	$ 6.25	$ 51.68	$ 34.55
1975	13.20	10.65	73.88	58.73
1985	17.42	15.58	98.26	86.71
1995	20.93	20.11	120.59	115.41
2005	22.66	22.49	131.98	131.61
2015	23.06	23.06	132.82	132.82

*For a water development of 906,000 acre-feet.

Value of Water to Affected Individuals and Groups

The previous sections of this chapter have estimated the gross costs to the Arizona economy of agricultural adjustment occasioned by increasing water costs in agriculture and have shown how the gross value of an increased supply of water to avoid such adjustment would change over time. We have stated, however, that the total gross costs of agricultural adjustment are much larger than the amount all individuals within the state could rationally pay in order to avoid such costs. The purpose of this section is to make estimates of the smaller rational payments both in terms of state as a whole and the individuals and groups within the state.

The Conceptual Answer

A "state" cannot rationally pay more for an additional supply of water than can the aggregate of all directly and indirectly affected persons in the state. We have estimated the sum of all the direct and indirect value added (personal income) that would be restored to these persons by a supplementary supply of water. These estimates of income restored by an additional supply of water are the *gross* benefits from that restoration. We must deduct the available alternative earning possibilities (opportunity costs) of the resources involved (labor and capital) in order to determine the *net* benefits of additional water.

For example, the gross cost estimates include the total value of wages that would be lost if there were no longer jobs for a certain given number of laborers in agriculture. But, this loss is a real loss to the laborers involved only if there are no alternative jobs available with similar earning potential. The *maximum* amount that a laborer would be willing to pay in order to keep his old job is the difference between the earnings in his old job and his next best earnings opportunity, plus a charge for the time, trouble, and wages lost while changing from one job to the other.

Owners of capital have the same conceptual problem. The maximum payment that they would be willing to make in order to restore the earning potential of their capital in agriculture would be the difference between the potential earning power of their capital in agriculture and its next best alternative use. This alternative use is termed the "opportunity cost" of using the capital in agriculture.

From the individual points of view of the laborers and capital owners themselves, it would not matter (from an economic point of view) whether these alternative earning possibilities were inside of the state's boundaries or not. It would make a difference from the aggregate view of the "state"; people and capital leaving the state would reduce the state's economy. However, the investing power of the state is made up of the sum of the individual persons within the state. It is the people who suffer any losses or make any payments to avoid loss; it is the people that "count." Therefore, if the state pays more than the difference between the earning potential of individuals' labor and capital in agriculture, less these individuals' opportunity costs in terms of alternative earning potential elsewhere, it is simply wasting that part of its available resources which it could better devote to something else for which it could obtain a positive gain.

Thus far, we have spoken only of efficiency, that is, whether it would be economically efficient for a state to invest in a water project to restore an income loss in agriculture. There is also a question of equity. To be equitable, the rational aggregate payment should be distributed among the individual or group beneficiaries in proportion to each individual's or group's share in the aggregate benefit. If not, some group will get its benefit from the supplementary water at less than its proportional share of the water's cost, and another group will be paying more for its share of the benefit from the supplementary water than its benefits are worth. It might be rational, of course, for the state to decide that one group *should* pay more than it will benefit and another group *should* pay less than it benefits on the basis of some social welfare criteria. However, if this were to be done, reason for inequitable or favored treatment of the groups involved should be carefully and clearly specified.

The "rational payments for water" estimated below show the aggregate payment the state could rationally pay for a supplementary water supply and, also, how that aggregate payment should equitably be distributed among groups of beneficiaries if no redistribution in terms of welfare criteria were to be made.

Rational Payments by the Directly Affected Farm Sector

In the preceding chapter, demand functions for irrigation water were presented which were derived from aggregating the results of representative-farm linear-programming models. In the construction of these linear-programming models, all variable production inputs except water were costed at their market prices. The linear-programming solutions gave the optimum combination of crops to be grown, the net income over variable cost that would result, and the maximum amount that could be paid for an additional acre-foot of water in the short-run if alternative quantities of water were available.

These estimates of what could be paid for an additional acre-foot of water are referred to as the marginal value product (MVP) of the additional acre-foot of water. They are estimates of the additional value of net returns above variable costs that would be earned by the farmer if he had one more acre-foot of water available to apply to his farm. Because the farmer must also apply additional other inputs in order to use the additional acre-foot of water, the additional net return is not really due only to the additional water but also to the other additional inputs. But, because the other inputs are assumed to be available at fixed prices in the market, and have been costed out, the entire excess may be "captured" by the additional acre-foot of water. (It is because other inputs are not held constant while the input being studied is varied that linear-programming MVPs are not the same as classical economic theory MVPs. Linear-programming MVPs are larger in value since the marginal productivities of the other inputs are also assigned to the input under analysis.)

In the long run, net returns above variable costs must be large enough to pay for the fixed costs of the farm, as well as for the water itself. The fixed costs include return to fixed depreciable capital, to land, and to management. But in the short-run, water could claim all of this net return since, if it were not available, there would be no additional net return at all and payments need not be made to fixed factors in the short-run. Thus, our estimates of the value of water derived from the programming models are the maximum short-run direct values of each additional acre-foot – including not only any excess value productivity actually due the other variable inputs but also any possible return to the fixed factors of depreciable capital, land, and management.

These values were estimated (depending on the particular area of the state under analysis) as roughly $6.00 to $18.00 per acre-foot for the marginal acre-foot of water supplied to farms of that area; that is, the first supplementary acre-foot of water supplied to each representative farm in the area in addition to the water it was already using in crop production (the value per acre-foot at the intersection of the supply and demand curves). Of course, these values are only for the first relatively small block of additional water supplied to each farm. For larger additions of water, the value per acre-foot for additional acre-feet would decline as the need for additional water (the derived marginal demand) becomes less and less. This phenomenon of declining values for additional blocks of supplementary water was illustrated by the downward sloping derived marginal demand curves (see figures 4-11, 4-12; tables 4-12, 4-13).

A reasonable estimate of a single weighted average value for Arizona as a whole for the MVP of an additional acre-foot of water, necessary to compare with a single weighted average estimate of value added as estimated below, is about $12.00 per acre-foot. MVPs by area vary from $6.00 to $18.00 per acre-foot. The $18.00 estimate is for a very small quantity of irrigation water for Pima County. The lowest estimates are in counties where water is plentiful and costs are not rising. Pinal County and western Maricopa County (west of the Salt River Project), the areas to experience the majority of agricultural adjustment, have MVPs for marginal quantities of water of about $12.00 per acre-foot.

The short-run marginal values (MVPs) for water used in agriculture may be compared to estimates of direct value added per acre-foot, used in this chapter as a basis for estimating the gross losses in value to the state. Estimates of direct value added are in most respects comparable to the MVP estimates, except that the value-added estimates also include the payment made to farm labor in addition to the return to depreciable capital, land, and management. Estimates of value added per dollar of crop output (Tijoriwala et al.), weighted by the amounts of crops that are projected as adjusting in the first period of the analysis (1966 to 1975), and divided by the quantity of water associated with the adjustment, give a weighted average estimate of about $17.50 of value added per acre-foot for the marginal increment of supplementary irrigation water, including the value of labor. (This estimate is the uncapitalized value of value added lost in a single year of adjustment during the first time period. It is larger than the capitalized flow value of value added per acre-foot as shown in table 5-7 because table 5-7 values assume payment begins for all 212,000 acre-feet of incremental water in 1966, while only 23,600 acre-feet (212 ÷ 9) are needed in the first year with additional increments not needed until later in the period.)

We note that for the marginal quantity of water, payments to depreciable capital, land, and management, as estimated by the linear-programming models, total roughly two-thirds of value added. The cost of labor would comprise the other third. (A wage cost of about $6.00 per acre-foot implies a wage cost per acre of $24.00. This per-acre wage cost is consistent with the data developed for the representative-farm linear-programming models and summarized in Wildermuth, Martin, and Rieck, [1969].) It seems reasonable to assume that this approximate relationship between factor shares would hold for all increments of direct water use. Thus, for example, looking at table 5-7, the weighted average value of 906,000 acre-feet of supplementary water would be somewhere between about $1.80 to $2.60 for labor's share (one-third of $5.36 or of $7.89), with about $3.60 to $5.20 assignable as the total share for depreciable capital, land rent, and management.

Of the portion of value assignable to capital, land, and management, a further reasonable approximation (derived from data in Martin and Carter, 1962; and Tijoriwala et al., 1968) is that one-half is return to depreciable capital and one-half is return to the undepreciable contribution of land. Since we are dealing with marginal changes in crops of extremely low net return per acre, occurring as intra-farm adjustments on whole farms that in general remain in business, it is reasonable to assume that return to management on these marginal acres is negligible. Thus, the weighted amount of value added on 906,000 acre-feet of additional water would also be $1.80 to $2.60 per acre-foot due to undepreciable capital and an equal amount per acre-foot because of the undepreciable contribution of the land.

Thus, our estimates of total direct value added are broken into three components, of which labor, land, and depreciable capital account for one-third each. Each of these interest groups (taken as a group) rationally could afford to pay part of their gross share to avoid loss, depending on each group's particular opportunity costs. We will examine each of the three groups in detail.

The Rational Payment by Farm Labor. Except for transfer costs, the individual laborer incurs a loss when he loses a job only if he cannot find alternative employment. Therefore, if alternative employment of equal earning potential is available (either within the state or in another state), the most that an individual laborer could rationally afford to pay in order to save his current job would be the amount of wages lost while making his job transfer, plus any other expenses involved in the move. Where alternative employment is available, the laborers' "opportunity cost" is high relative to the returns from his present job. Therefore, the net difference, the amount of money that he could rationally pay in order to retain his old job, is quite small.

As we document in the following chapter, the state of Arizona has a rapidly growing nonagricultural economy independent of marginal agricultural decline. Therefore, it is likely that jobs will be available for displaced agricultural workers within the state. Under these conditions, job transfer costs would be minimal. Where local jobs are not available, movement to jobs in the nearby Southern California area or elsewhere is possible. Thus, it seems obvious that the maximum rational payment by farm labor to avoid marginal crop adjustment in agriculture would be one small uncapitalized payment to cover the costs of moving and wage income lost during job transfer. Hartman and Seastone (1970), in a similar study of agricultural adjustment in the Imperial Valley, California, suggest "one-half a year's wages lost as a cost of movement and retraining." On the basis of the above discussion of income shares, we estimate one-half a year's wages as approximately $3.00 per acre-foot of irrigation water.

This once-only payment of $3.00 per acre-foot could rationally be made at the present time by agricultural labor only on the marginal acre-feet of water that would affect their jobs in the very near future – the next year or two. By implication, then, we are talking only about a very small quantity of additional water supply. Large quantities of water developed at the present time would not save jobs at the present time and so would not have value to labor until future time periods. However, if labor as a group were to discount future job loss, they could rationally make as much as a *single payment* of \$0.90 to \$1.30 per acre-foot for 906,000 acre-feet at the present time. These estimates are the present values of a series of one-lump-sum payments of \$3.00 per acre-foot, evaluated at 5 and 8 percent, respectively, which would rationally be paid by labor in their uncapitalized form of \$3.00 per acre-foot as additional water is needed. They are mathematically equivalent to one-half of labors' share of the weighted average gross value of 906,000 acre-feet of water, evaluated at the alternative discount rates of 5 and 8 percent, respectively (½ x ⅓ of the weighted average per acre-foot estimates of table 5-7). We emphasize that these are one-time single payments, not payments per acre-foot per year.

While as a practical matter from labor's point of view the cost of job transfer is a one-lump-sum short-run cost, we may express the one-lump-sum cost as amortized annual amounts so that they may be added to the amortized costs expressed below for other factor owners. If the one-lump-sum were evaluated at 5 percent, the rational payment in acre-feet per year for 906,000 acre-feet would be 6.5 cents. If evaluated at 8 percent, the amortized value per acre-foot per year starting at the present time, would be 7.2 cents.

How many agricultural laborers might actually be affected by the projected agricultural crop adjustment? We have projected that 196,072 acres (double cropped acres are counted twice) will go out of production over the 49-year period 1966 to 2015 because of rising irrigation water costs. The field crops affected now take about 10 labor-hours per acre to grow and harvest. Thus, we are talking about some 1,960,720 labor-hours per year (in 2015), or, if one man-year is approximately 2,000 hours, approximately 1,000 farm laborers. This attrition in farm jobs would take place over the 49-year period at a relatively constant rate (slightly higher at first, declining in later years) or at an average rate of 20 men per year. We may compare this figure with the average number of persons employed in agriculture in Arizona in 1969, that is, 37,300 people.

The Rational Payment by Owners of Depreciable Farm Capital. From the community's point of view, disappearance of depreciable agricultural capital over the 49-year adjustment period could result in reduced Gross State Product, the present value of which is roughly one payment of $22 to $53 per acre-foot (one-third of the alternative weighted average values shown in table 5-6). But this loss would be real only if as depreciable agricultural capital disappeared, a replacement investment of equal size were not made elsewhere in the economy.

From the capital owner's point of view, however, the person who would actually be taking a loss or making an investment to avoid that loss, the present value of a rational payment would be much smaller than $22 to $53.

Since agricultural water development in Arizona is necessary merely to avoid marginal changes in cropping activity in an already developed agricultural economy, capital losses in agriculture will occur only if owners are unable to salvage the value of already purchased undepreciated capital items. Because the changes projected will take place gradually over a long period of time, such losses of undepreciated capital items will be almost negligible. As our representative-farm linear-programming models have shown, attrition in cropped acreage will not occur until farmers must make a decision not to purchase a new piece of major capital equipment upon the demise of the old piece. Since the old piece would then be fully depreciated, no capital loss from abandonment of its use would occur. In terms of the concept of opportunity cost, the decision is between an investment in water to avoid a capital loss in crop agriculture, versus an investment in some alternative enterprise either inside or outside of agriculture.

The maximum rational payment to avoid loss could be no larger than the expected loss itself. Thus, from an individual farm capital owner's point of view, if he believed that he would have maximum difficulty in using up his undepreciated capital equipment over the 50-year projected adjustment period, he would pay no more than $1.80 to $2.60 per acre-foot per year for perpetual rights to an additional 906,000 acre-feet of water.

Such payments for additional water would be in the nature of maximum insurance against his inability to recover all undepreciated capital in which he had already invested. In circumstances in which all depreciable capital were recovered, either through use or through sale to another user, *any* investment in water to prevent loss of that depreciable capital would be wasted. A "most likely" insurance estimate would be somewhere between maximum and zero loss. Twenty-five percent unrecoverability of undepreciated capital would seem a fair estimate; that is, $0.45 to $0.65 per acre-foot of water per year.

The Rational Payment by Owners of Farm Real Estate. The case for evaluation of losses in farm real estate capital is more clear-cut. Any land that goes out of production because of rising irrigation water costs and does not transfer immediately to another use is a loss not only to the economy of the state but is a direct loss to the owner as well. Labor can go elsewhere to change jobs incurring only transfer losses in so doing. A large proportion (75 percent) of depreciable capital will be used up in place or through sale to another user and therefore not create a loss. The irrigated agricultural land affected by rising water costs, however, cannot go elsewhere, and most of it has little or no alternative value where it is located other than as irrigated cropland. Thus, the capital value of the abandoned acres could fall close to zero.

Most of the acres in question are located in rural desert areas where urbanization is not likely in the relatively near future. They do not include the urbanizing acres in the Salt River Valley. The only relevant alternative uses are to keep the acres as part of the fallow rotation of the whole farm, to use the acres as desert range, or simply to abandon them. Acreage maintained as part of a farm either as range or as part of the rotation system will retain a relatively low per-acre value. Some of the acreage, of course, will be urbanized over the longer term and thus may eventually prove quite valuable.

For simplicity's sake, however, and to take the position that would most enhance the value of water, let us assume that the acreage that goes out of irrigation due to rising water costs has no alternative economic use and thus that its capital value will fall to zero. Under these circumstances, a weighted average investment of up to $1.80 to $2.60 (one-third of weighted average value shown in table 5-7) per acre-foot of water per year on 906,000 acre-feet of water would be reasonable by owners of irrigated croplands whose lands are projected to "go out" of cropland use between 1966 and 2015.

Summary of Rational Payments by the Directly Affected Irrigated Agricultural Sector. Because agricultural labor is mobile and has alternative opportunities for employment, agricultural laborers could afford no more than a single payment of $0.90 to $1.30 per acre-foot if as many as 906,000 acre-feet were to be developed. Put in a form of an annuity at 8 percent and 5 percent, respectively, these payments would equal 7.2 cents and 6.5 cents per acre-foot per year. Owners of depreciable farm capital could rationally make payments of $0.45 to $0.65 per acre-foot per year on the same total quantity of water, but only as insurance against their inability to manage their capital in such a way as to avoid some undepreciated loss. Owners of agricultural land who would be forced to idle cropland acreage because of rising water prices could invest up to $1.80 to $2.60 per acre-foot per year in order to maintain the present capital value of their marginal land. The total rational payment by the directly affected agricultural sector is, therefore, ($0.072 to $0.065) + ($0.45 to $0.65) + ($1.80 to $2.60) equals approximately ($2.32 to $3.32) per acre-foot per year.

Rational Payments by Those Affected Through Backward Linkages Only

Indirect effects through backward linkages occur mostly in the nonfarm sectors of the economy, although a small amount of effects would occur in the farm economy itself through circular linkages. In the nonfarm sectors, value added is composed almost entirely of labor and management income, and return to depreciable capital. Undepreciable capital (land) is but a minor component in contrast to the agricultural sector where land area is crucial to the production process.

We will assume that value added lost through indirect linkages is composed only of two components, labor (and management) income and return to depreciable capital. Data for the United States as a whole from *The Survey of Current Business* show that labor income is approximately 60 percent of Gross National Product. Thus, we may reasonably assume that nonfarm value added in Arizona would be composed of about 60 percent labor income and 40 percent return to depreciable capital.

The argument relative to a rational payment for water by indirectly affected nonfarm labor is similar to that for directly affected farm labor. The only difference is that one would expect nonfarm labor to be even more mobile and adaptable than farm labor because of nonfarm labor's higher educational level and its physical location in urban areas. Even so, we again will assume a loss of six months wages as a reasonable estimate of transfer costs resulting from a job loss due to agricultural adjustment occurring because of rising irrigation water costs.

Thus, our estimate of a single payment by nonfarm labor per acre-foot of newly developed water for agriculture would be from 27 to 39 cents if as much as 906,000 acre-feet were to be developed at the present time. These estimates were developed by taking one-half of 60 percent of the total value added estimates shown in table 5-11. If these one-lump-sum payments are amortized at 8 percent and 5 percent, respectively, they each are worth about 2 cents per acre-foot per year.

Owners of depreciable capital could rationally make a payment in order to avoid a capital loss on the undepreciated portion of their investment. Since adjustment would take place over a 50-year period, most capital investment would likely be recovered either through use or technical obsolescence. We use Hartman and Seastone's (1970) estimate of

25 percent unrecoverable capital income for the meat processing industry as a reasonable average estimate for the other mostly nonagricultural sectors.

Since return to depreciable nonfarm capital is estimated as 40 percent of total value added, and unrecoverable capital is estimated as 25 percent of total depreciable capital, the estimate for a rational payment to avoid loss of depreciable capital would be 10 percent of total value added. Therefore, one may read our estimates of a rational payment by owners of nonfarm capital in order to avoid capital loss, as 10 percent of the estimates of total value added sacrificed because of rising water costs in agriculture as shown in table 5-11. If as many as 906,000 acre-feet are developed at the present (1966) time, these estimates would be from 9 to 13 cents per acre-foot per year.

Rational Payment by Those Affected Through Both Backward and Forward Linkages

Exactly the same reasoning holds for forward linkages as for backward linkages. Thus, estimates of rational payments by nonagricultural labor would be one payment of one-half of 60 percent of the values given in table 5-11. For a development of 906,000 acre-feet at the present time, these values are $8.75 at eight percent and $13.14 at five percent. Amortized at 8 percent and 5 percent respectively, the values are 70 cents and 66 cents per acre-foot per year. Estimates of rational payments by owners of nonfarm capital would be yearly payments of 10 percent of table 5-11 values. For 906,000 acre-feet they would equal $4.38 or $2.92 per acre-foot per year when evaluated at 5 and 8 percent respectively.

Estimates of Rational Payments Summarized

The estimates described in the preceding sections are summarized in table 5-16. We find that the directly affected persons in agriculture could rationally afford to pay, beginning in 1966, a total of $2.32 to $3.32 per acre-foot per year for a water development of 906,000 acre-feet, which would be enough water to avoid 49 years of agricultural decline because of rising water costs. Of this total payment most (78 percent) would benefit either owners of farm real estate or those creditors to whom agricultural real estate has been pledged as collateral. Twenty percent would benefit owners of depreciable farm capital, and only 2 percent would be of benefit to agricultural labor.

The estimates for the indirect effects on the nonagricultural sectors of the economy differ depending on whether one believes that only backward linkages to agriculture would be adversely affected (through the

TABLE 5-16

Rational Payments (1966) for Water Development to Avoid Agricultural Adjustment in Arizona Due to Rising Irrigation Water Costs, by Affected Group*

Affected Group	Yearly Payment in Dollars per Acre-foot Evaluated at 5%		8%	
Agriculture (direct)				
Farm labor†	$0.065		$0.072	
Depreciable farm capital‡	0.65		0.45	
General cropfarm real estate	2.60		1.80	
Total		$3.32		$2.32
Nonagriculture (indirect)				
Backward linkages only				
Nonfarm labor†	0.02		0.02	
Depreciable nonfarm capital‡	0.13		0.09	
Total		$0.15		$0.11
Backward and forward linkages				
Nonfarm labor†	0.66		0.70	
Depreciable nonfarm capital‡	4.38		2.92	
Total		$5.04		$3.62
Agricultural and nonagricultural				
Backward linkages only, total		$3.47		$2.43
Backward and forward linkages, total		$8.36		$5.94

*For a water development of 906,000 acre-feet in 1966.
†Assumes six months wages lost as the transfer cost.
‡Assumes 25 percent of capital adjustment is unrecoverable.

industries providing inputs to agriculture) or if one projects that forward linked industries would also disappear in constant proportion to agricultural decline. We have argued that backward linkages with small forward linkages is the most probable case. Therefore, the most probable rational payments would be near the lower end of the range of estimates given in table 5-16.

If only backward linkages are assumed to hold, the rational payment by nonagricultural interests in order to avoid the indirect effects of agricultural adjustment would be 11 to 15 cents per acre-foot per year. All except about 2 cents per acre-foot per year of this payment would be to the benefit of owners of nonfarm capital. Nonfarm labor would receive the benefits of the balance of 2 cents per acre-foot per year.

If rigidly proportional forward linkages do in fact hold, a large payment of $3.62 to $5.04 could rationally be made per acre-foot per year by nonfarm interests. Eighty to ninety percent of this payment would benefit capital owners; the balance would benefit nonagricultural labor.

The total rational payment by all interests in the Arizona economy would be between $2.43 and $3.47 per acre-foot of water per year if only backward linkages exist. The highest estimate of a rational payment that could be paid by all interests in the state would be between $5.94 and $8.36 per acre-foot of water per year if forward linked effects rigidly proportional to direct effects are assumed to hold. A "ball-park" judgment as a plausible compromise estimate of a total payment per acre-foot per year by all interests in the economy might be about $3.50. This amount is based on the argument that 8 percent is a more reasonable discount rate than 5 percent, and that some, but not all, forward linked nonfarm businesses would be adversely affected by the projected agricultural decline.

Who Should Pay?
The Question of Equity at the Level of the Individual

Individuals would rationally wish to pay no more for water development than an amount equal to the benefits they would expect to receive. Any payment in excess of expected benefits would be an income transfer from that individual to another; that is, a subsidy to others for which no benefit could be expected by the grantor of the subsidy.

Thus far we have identified the total rational payment by economic interests in the state and have broken the payment down into broad categories of labor, capital, and landowners of agricultural and nonagricultural interests. Even these broad categories tell us a great deal about the equity of large scale water development. Owners of farm real estate and their creditors are the largest direct beneficiaries. Owners of depreciable farm capital would benefit to a small degree while farm labor would benefit hardly at all. Owners of nonfarm depreciable capital would benefit from water development for agriculture in proportion to the degree in which they are actually linked to the level of agricultural output. Nonfarm labor has a relatively small stake in the benefits, again in proportion to its link to agricultural output.

Obviously, certain individuals within each of these categories would benefit to a greater extent than would others. Among owners of farm real estate, the greatest beneficiaries would be those owning land which would be most affected over time by rising water costs. These would be land owners in certain areas of Pinal, Pima, Cochise, and western Maricopa Counties. Among owners of depreciable farm capital, owners in the same areas would also receive the largest benefit; often land owners and depreciable farm capital owners are in fact the same individuals.

Within the category of farm labor, the greatest benefits would accrue to that labor of the owner-operator and others who are tied to the farm by virtue of their being also owners of farm real estate or depreciable capital. Hired labor would have little if any stake in the benefits.

Thus, the chief agricultural beneficiaries from the development of an additional supply of 906,000 acre-feet of water would be farm owners and farm operators dependent wholly or largely on groundwater in Pima, Pinal, and Cochise Counties and in Maricopa County outside the Salt River Project.

Nonfarm benefits would be more widely diffused over the state, but would, of course, be higher in areas nearest the areas of agricultural adjustment.

Individuals within all of the above categories would benefit more, the more closely they were associated with the grain and forage industries. For example, benefits to individuals tied directly or indirectly to citrus and vegetable production and handling would be negligible if not zero.

It is obvious that the problems involved in devising a system of equitable payment to individuals for water resources development would be difficult if not impossible to solve. Where investments in water development are made inequities are to be expected. Still, from an individual's point of view, in deciding whether to support a public investment in water development or not, it is useful to him to have some idea how large his individual subsidy to be paid or received might be.

Rational Payments for Water Development at Alternative Points In Time

In a previous section in this chapter, we explained how the value of water development made to forestall agricultural adjustment would increase over time. Empirical estimates of the total projected values of water development at future points in time were given in tables 5-13, 5-14, and 5-15. These estimates were in the form of the gross additional value added that could be created in the Arizona economy if water development occurred. As with our other estimates of gross additional value added, these amounts were much larger than the amounts that individuals and groups within the state or the state as a whole could pay in order to avoid the total loss in value.

Estimates of the way in which the smaller, rational payments for water development will increase over time are presented in table 5-17.

TABLE 5-17
Rational Payments for a Water Development of 906,000 Acre-feet Occurring at Alternative Points in Time

Year of Water Development	Yearly Payment in Dollars per Acre-foot			
	Direct and Backward Linkages Evaluated at		Direct, Backward, and Forward Linkages Evaluated at	
	5%	8%	5%	8%
1966	$3.47	$2.43	$ 8.36	$ 5.94
1975	4.98	4.14	11.95	10.10
1985	6.57	6.06	15.89	14.91
1995	7.89	7.82	19.51	19.84
2005	8.55	8.74	21.35	22.62
2015	8.70*	8.97*	21.49*	22.83*

*The two pairs of undiscounted values as of 2015 ($8.72 and $8.97; $21.49 and $22.83) are not exactly equal to each other as they were for gross value added, shown in table 5-15, because of the effects of amortizing the lump-sum payment of labor.

In table 5-16 we presented our estimates of rational payments for water development at the current (1966) time. If we assume that capital's and labor's shares of value added will not change significantly over the next 50 years, the estimates of table 5-17 result from projecting the current data of table 5-16 at the same rate as total value added was projected in table 5-16.

For example, if we assume that rigidly proportional forward linkages exist and evaluate our opportunities at a discount rate of 5 percent, the rational payment for a water resource development of 906,000 acre-feet of water is $8.36 per acre-foot per year in 1966. (It would be $5.94 at 8 percent.) If development is delayed until 2015, the usefulness of additional water for irrigated agricultural crops will have grown so that at that time a rational payment for the same quantity of water would be $21.49 per acre-foot per year in 2015 and thereafter. (It would be $22.83 if evaluated at 8 percent.)

If one assumes that only backward linked effects occur in addition to the direct effects, and if development of additional water supplies is delayed until 2015 when all of the 906,000 acre-feet of water could be used immediately (if it were available at a low enough price), the rational payment per acre-foot per year, beginning in 2015, would be slightly less than $9.00 per acre-foot per year evaluated at either 5 or 8 percent. As we have argued, the true relationship is probably closer to that of backward linkages only discounted at eight percent. Therefore, a reasonable estimate of the full value in current use that could be made as a rational payment for water beginning in 2015 evaluated at 8 percent might be about $13.00 per acre-foot per year compared to the plausible payment of $3.50 per acre-foot per year that could be paid beginning in 1966 for the same 906,000 acre-feet of additional water.

Note that even by 2015, with rigidly proportional forward linkages assumed as well as backward linkages, the rational per acre-foot per year value of water development in Arizona amounting to $21.49 to $22.83 will be still far below even current 1972 estimated costs of large-scale water-importation projects. Current 1972 costs of such development are estimated at about $35.00 per acre-foot per year at the outlets from the main importation canal. Unless significantly lower costs for large-scale water development materialize in the future, or significantly larger values for such water in the Arizona economy arises, Arizonans would be better off merely to absorb the cost of agricultural adjustment, concentrating on development of alternative nonfarm growth and the intrastate water transfers that would make that growth possible.

Furthermore, delay in entering into such development schemes has an important additional advantage. At any time, as future years unfold, should the cost of such developments decline or the value of additional water rise due to presently unpredictable technological or demand changes, decisions at those future times then may be made to proceed with development under circumstances which would be economically advantageous. Should such advantageous circumstances never arise, the Arizona economy and its citizens would then not have been committed to a schedule of wasteful and uneconomic payments, and the funds thus saved would have been available for other uses more productive to the welfare of Arizona and of Arizonans.

6. Statewide Growth and Water Use in Arizona

Previous chapters have focused on the demand for water in irrigated agriculture. Recognizing that the groundwater table is falling and that, consequently, pumping costs are rising, projections were made as to the adjustments that will take place in agriculture in response to these changes. The results of these projections, made for individual areas of the state, were aggregated into statewide projections. Then, the direct and indirect costs of such agricultural adjustment on the rest of the state's economy were estimated.

Thus, we were able to project the direct plus indirect impact on the state's economy caused by the increasing cost of the supply of groundwater over time *operating directly on agriculture only* assuming that the rest of the economy not related to agriculture would remain unchanged except for indirect effects.

This procedure permitted us to look at the value of water to two distinct sectors of the economy. First, there was the direct value to the farmer. This was estimated in terms of what he could afford to pay for an additional acre-foot of water in order to grow and sell farm products. Second, there was the indirect value of that additional acre-foot of water to the rest of the economy. This value was the amount that nonfarmers could afford to contribute toward paying for that additional acre-foot to assist farmer purchases of irrigation water so as to avoid diminishing agricultural output in the state.

The sum of these two values is the total value to the state's economy of the marginal acre-foot of water *used in agriculture*. The amount that other businesses or individuals not engaged in agricultural activities could *afford* to pay for water for their *non*agricultural purposes is irrelevant to the value of water because the value of any additional quantity of a resource is its value in its marginal use. In Arizona, agriculture (and within agriculture, particular crops) is the marginal user of water, as well as being its largest user.

These analyses of the value of water showed that the value of an additional acre-foot of water in Arizona is quite low. Without repeating exact estimates, its value was shown to be much lower than any currently proposed scheme to import water from outside the boundaries of the state.

However, while these analyses projected agricultural change over the 49-year period 1966 to 2015 and estimated the drag such change would have on the rest of the state's economy, it was not shown how the rest of the economy – the nonagricultural part – would be growing. As the total economy grows over time, the requirements for water in the nonagricultural sectors will grow. In the studies reported in the earlier chapters of this book we simply made the implicit assumption that since nonagricultural uses of water are only about 8 percent of total usage, any future requirements for water in these nonagricultural sectors could be satisfied by transferring water now used in agriculture for producing low-valued crops to the higher-valued nonagricultural uses. This transfer would take place in a natural fashion if the market mechanism was permitted to function to affect changes in water use. The transfer has been taking place already in areas such as the Salt River Valley. It could take place elsewhere, for instance in areas such as Avra Valley north of Tucson, if certain legislative restraints were lifted. It remains to show that there would, in fact, be enough water available for projected economic growth as such transfers occur over the projection period.

Balancing the State's Water Budget

The main objective of the analysis reported in this chapter is as follows: To examine how the economy of Arizona could continue to grow over the period 1966 to 2015 while remaining with several alternative posited restraints on available water. (Our analysis is based on the work of Finster (1970), including supplemental and revised analyses.) We take as given that the economy should grow rapidly; that is, for purposes of this analysis, we accept without question the goals of state and civic leaders who state that population and economic growth is both necessary and inevitable.

It is obvious that such an examination will throw considerable light on the value of developing additional water sources. The need for and value of additional water will increase over time only if its availability is restricting total state growth. Also, the rate of current water use, particularly from the groundwater stock, need not be restricted in order to save it for some future time period, unless it is shown that the value of water in the future will be much greater than its value in current use. Its future value will be much greater only if it is necessary to save it to prevent future water shortages from being a drag on high-valued agricultural uses.

Projected quantities of water demanded in the state may be more than, less than, or equal to the quantity of water available in the state. In fact, it is one of the largely unquestioned articles of faith in the conventional wisdom of Arizona water policy that the quantity available is presently less than the quantity demanded and that the deficiency will grow as the state's economy grows. Generally unrecognized in this conventional view of the water problem is an implicit assumption it contains. It assumes that the total water budget consists only of *raw water* and that, the water budget being unbalanced only by raw water deficiency, the only way to balance it is by increasing raw water supplies (by importing raw water or by producing raw water in state) or by reducing the quantity of raw water demanded. (By raw water we simply mean water in its original form – water.) Rejection of the latter alternative, that is, reducing the quantity of raw water demanded, rests on a second implicit assumption that doing so is only possible by restricting the future growth or even by reducing the present level of the state's economy, thus bringing about a reduction in population, in aggregate economic output, in per capita income, or some combination of all three. The latter being manifestly unacceptable to the state's policy makers, balancing the total water budget by increasing imports (or increasing in-state production) of raw water is the only policy alternative considered to be relevant.

The analysis we describe in this chapter is designed explicitly to examine the validity of these two assumptions, assumptions that are implicit in the conventional wisdom of Arizona water policy makers; namely, that failing to balance the water budget with raw water imports (or in-state raw water production) necessarily entails a restraint on the state's economic growth if not an outright decline in its present level.

Upon critically examining these implicit assumptions of the conventional water wisdom, we came to the recognition, seemingly obvious once one has "discovered" it, that the total water budget includes *all* water imported or exported in any form, raw water or water "embodied" in products. An obvious example of "embodied" water is that which is imported or exported in beer. Less obvious but economically more important examples are water consumptively used to produce cotton or copper for export, or that water which would have been used in Arizona to produce imported feed grains or machine tools had they been produced in state instead of imported. This leads us to see that the total state water budget need not balance the total demands for water in all its forms, raw and embodied, against in-state supplies in all its forms. It may be beneficial to the state's economic growth to *unbalance* its imports or exports of raw *and* embodied water *in order to* balance the in-state demand for raw water with the in-state supply of raw water. Our analysis reported in this chapter was directed explicitly to the validity of the second of the implicit assumptions of the conventional water wisdom; namely, can an *un*balanced *total* state water budget that embraces a *balanced* in-state *raw* water budget be achieved without any adverse effect on projected rates of population growth, aggregate economic output, and per capita personal incomes produced in Arizona?

Economic Growth With Fixed Raw Water Use

What Is Economic Growth and How May It Be Measured?

Economic growth is conventionally considered to be growth in the product of the economy. Such growth can be measured in terms of product, either on a total, a per capita, or a per worker basis, depending on the problem at hand. One wishes to measure *real* gross product rather than merely *money* gross product; however, it is impractical to add physical product data, even when available. Therefore, in order to weight the importance of goods in the total product and to make aggregation possible, dollar volume estimates are used, adjusted by price deflators which removes general price level changes from affecting the value of the output.

While real gross national product (GNP) is a significant indicator of economic growth for the nation, the difficulties in estimating real gross state product (the state's counterpart of GNP) make this measure impractical for our use (Perloff, 1957:58) (Hochwald, 1957).

However, in a complete social accounting system, each economic transaction is seen from two points of view, both as the source and the termination of a circular value flow that must be the same wherever it is measured. Such a system is exemplified by the National Income and Product accounts wherein changes in net output produced, in aggregate incomes received, and in total expenditures made, are all closely interrelated and refer to the same set of activities. Thus, the measurement of real national product can be approached either by summing real product values or by summing real income flows. These considerations give rise to the use of state real personal income as a proxy for "Real State GNP," because of the close relationships between the output produced and personal income received by the residents of a geographic region. We will project real economic growth of Arizona in terms of personal income expressed in dollars of constant (1958) value.

State personal income as a measure of economic growth has one limitation. Income received by state residents may not be the same as income produced by state residents because some of the income produced in the state is received by persons living outside the state or some of the income received in the state is produced outside of the state. Easterlin (1957) estimated that Arizona residents received about five percent less income than was produced within the state. However, our analysis focuses on the impact of *alternative* growth patterns on water use. As long as the error in estimating incomes received from alternative growth patterns is of the same relative magnitude in each case, comparisons among alternatives will not be affected by ignoring it.

Growth in Arizona Personal Income

Our 50-year projections of the growth expected in personal income in Arizona involved the following steps:

1. Aggregate real Gross National Product for the United States was projected. These projections were built by examining each of the five major components of GNP independently, and then aggregating them to obtain total real Gross National Product. The five components are government employment, agriculture and agricultural employment, nonagricultural business, nonagricultural employment, and households. These projections were based on economic trends between 1952-68 expressed in 1958 dollars (Finster, 1970).

2. Aggregate personal incomes received in the United States during the years 1952-67 were also deflated to 1958 dollars and compared to real GNP produced during those years; these relations were then applied to projected real GNP to obtain projected real personal income. Aggregate real personal income projections were divided by total United States population projections to obtain per capita real personal income projections for the United States.

3. As in the case of United States income, aggregate personal incomes received in Arizona for 1952-67 were adjusted to 1958 dollars by the United States consumption expenditures price deflator. Per capita real incomes in the state for this period were obtained by dividing state aggregate real personal income by Arizona population for the same year.

4. Arizona per capita real incomes were then related to United States per capita real incomes by least squares fitting to annual data for the period 1953-67. Arizona per capita real income was then projected

by applying this relationship to projected United States per capita income.

5. Finally, projected per capita real income for Arizona was multiplied by projected Arizona population to yield projected aggregate personal income in Arizona.

The Arizona population projections used are those agreed upon as most reasonable by the Pacific Southwest Interagency Advisory Committee on water. All state and federal agencies interested in water resources development are represented on this committee. We use these projections because we wish to consider rapid growth as given. These estimates are shown in table 6-1 along with recent actual population figures and recent and projected per capita real incomes. The resultant projections of aggregate real personal incomes in Arizona and the assumed rates of growth are given in table 6-2. Figure 6-1 illustrates the rapid projected rise in aggregate real personal income over the next fifty years.

We are projecting that all three measures of growth – population, per capita real income, and aggregate state real personal income – will increase over time at an increasing absolute rate per year (although at a decreasing percentage rate with respect to total population or income).

Given that population is to grow by as much as the projected rate and that per capita real personal income is also to increase as projected, our task is to devise several alternative, reasonable schemes of economic structure for the state whereby the raw water requirements in the state will not exceed raw water availability. To achieve this goal, the projected

TABLE 6-1

Arizona Population and Per Capita Real Income Projections

Year	Population (thousands)	Per Capita Personal Income (1958 dollars)
Actual		
1958	1,193	1,863
1960	1,321	1,974
1968	1,663	2,546
Projected*		
1980	2,143	2,915
1990	2,680	3,437
2000	3,321	4,136
2010	4,200	4,738
2020	5,003	5,402

*Source: USDA (1969).

TABLE 6-2
Arizona Aggregate Real Personal Income and Rate of Increase, 1948 Through 2020

Year	Aggregate Real Personal Income (millions of 1958 dollars)	Rate of Increase (%) in Preceding 10-Yr. Period	Average Annual Rate of Increase (%) Between Entries	Rate of Increase (%) from Base Year 1958
Actual*				
1948	1,068	—	—	—
1958	2,222	108.1	10.8	—
1968	4,234	90.5	9.1	90.5
Projected				
1980	6,246	51.8	5.2	181.1
1990	9,211	47.5	4.8	314.5
2000	13,734	49.1	4.9	518.1
2010	19,900	44.9	4.5	795.6
2020	27,028	35.8	3.6	1,116.4

*Source: United States Department of Commerce (1966b and 1968e).

demand for raw water by each alternative economic structure must remain relatively constant while the real output of the state continues to grow. It is obvious that in doing so, in-state raw water must progressively transfer over time from uses now producing low value of output to uses which will produce high value of output per unit of raw water use.

Our analytical scheme involves the use of the 1958 Input-Output model for the Arizona economy (Tijoriwala et al., 1968). As previously explained, this tool enables us to generate *consistent* estimates of production inputs and outputs for the state as a whole, given specified levels of final demand for Arizona-produced products. The chain of analysis works as follows:

(1) Given projected levels of population and aggregate and per capita real personal income, we can estimate consumer final demand by Arizonans.

(2) Total final demand for goods and services includes domestic (Arizonan) demand plus the goods and services that Arizonans export out of the state.

(3) Knowing total (domestic and export) final demand, our Input-Output model allows us to develop a consistent set of production requirements by each and for all economic sectors.

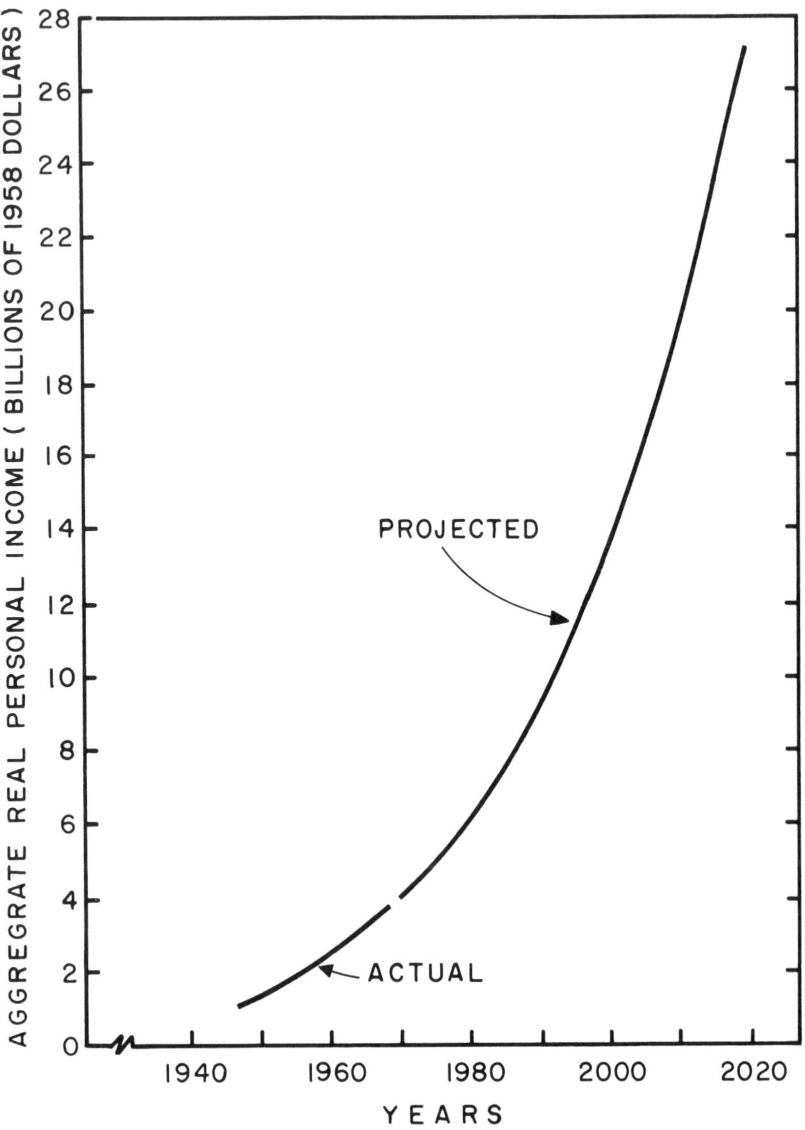

Fig. 6-1. *Aggregate real personal income in Arizona, 1948–2020.*

(4) Given the set of production requirements, we can relate these output requirements to quantities of water required in their production.

(5) If a change in raw water requirements is indicated as necessary if the economy is to live within its raw water supplies, the relative quantities of exports and imports must be changed (that is, the struc-

ture of the Arizona economy must change) since *domestic* Arizona final demand is to be held at the same level and composition for all alternative structures of the state's economy. Let us examine this system of analysis in detail.

Pattern of External Trade and Requirements for Water

We define "external trade" as trade between Arizona and the rest of the world. Thus, "exports" are those goods and services produced in Arizona and exported either to other states or outside of the United States. "Imports" are those goods and services imported either from other states or from other countries.

In the absence of external trade, all consumer demand within Arizona would have to be satisfied with "domestically" produced, that is, Arizona produced, goods and services. Under such circumstances, the productive structure of the economy would be tied directly to the structure of domestic consumer demand; raw water requirements being dependent on the productive structure, the structure of domestic consumer demand would determine total raw water needs.

This latter relationship can be severed, however, by the introduction of external trade. With external trade, Arizonans may specialize in producing one set of goods and services for which their state is especially adapted and may trade the excess of these goods and services for another set, produced outside of the state, which is needed to satisfy their in-state final demand. Obviously, if the state is short of raw water supplies, it should concentrate on producing goods and services that create high levels of income per unit of the scarce raw water used, importing products that would produce low levels of income per unit of raw water if those products were produced in state. The only restriction on such a scheme is that, on the average and over the long run, the *value* of the state's imports and exports of goods and services must be equal.

With external trade, more (or less) total water may be consumed within the state than is domestically available as raw water. Any difference between the amount of raw water domestically available and the total amount of raw water domestically consumed will be made up by water imports or exports *embodied* in the final products or services consumed. *Embodied* water is that quantity of in-state raw water required to produce \$1,000 of domestic products for final demand, including product exports, or, that quantity of in-state raw water that would have been required if \$1,000 of an imported product had been produced domestically.

Water requirements by type of product are listed in table 6-3. The

TABLE 6-3

In-state Raw Water Requirements, in Acre-feet, per $1,000 of Output and per $1,000 of Final Demand*

	Producing Sector	Direct Requirement per $1,000 of Output	Direct and Indirect Requirement per $1,000 of Final Demand
1	Meat animals and products	0.407	9.337
2	Poultry and eggs	0.008	15.803
3	Farm dairy products	0.252	17.655
4	Food and feed grains	42.087	43.630
5	Cotton	12.551	14.896
6	Vegetables	6.413	6.582
7	Fruit and tree nuts	9.950	10.227
8	Citrus fruits	11.154	11.841
9	Forage crops	46.938	47.103
10	Miscellaneous agriculture	6.408	10.307
11	Grain mill products	0.019	13.365
12	Meat and poultry processing	0.012	5.758
13	Dairy products	0.010	9.052
14	Canning, preserving, and freezing	0.043	1.016
15	Miscellaneous agricultural processing	0.020	2.140
16	Chemicals and fertilizers	0.030	0.564
17	Petroleum	0.020	0.064
18	Fabricated metals and machinery	0.003	0.131
19	Aircraft and parts	0.004	0.086
20	Primary metals	0.187	0.387
21	Other manufacturing	0.009	0.283
22	Mining	0.147	0.282
23	Utilities	0.210	0.277
24	Selected services	0.010	0.082
25	Trade and transportation	0.010	0.052
26	Unallocated services	0.010	0.122
27	Construction	0.010	0.120

*Source: Derived from Tijoriwala et al., (1968). Direct requirements are identical with their estimates. Direct plus indirect requirements are modified to reflect total requirements if Arizona did not import products.

direct water requirements are the in-state raw water that is used directly in (embodied in) the production of $1,000 of in-state output. The direct plus indirect requirements include the additional requirements for in-state raw water that are generated indirectly within the economy by the original production activity.

We may use the data of table 6-3 to illustrate the manner in which external trade can mitigate an in-state raw water supply restraint. For example, if 9.337 acre-feet of raw water are required in Arizona (direct plus indirect requirement) to produce $1,000 worth of beef cattle for final demand, then 9.337 acre-feet of raw water are "embodied" in each $1,000 worth of cattle. If the total domestic consumer final demand for beef cattle is $10,000, then the Arizona economy *consumes* 93.37 acre-feet of embodied water. If all cattle are produced domestically, then the amount of raw water needed to produce the cattle is equal to the amount of embodied water consumed. But, suppose that half of the cattle are supplied by out-of-state producers. The economy still demands $10,000 worth of cattle and still consumes 93.37 acre-feet of embodied water but now produces only $5,000 worth of cattle which require only 46.69 acre-feet (9.337/$1,000 × $5,000) of in-state raw water. However, the $5,000 worth of imported cattle must be paid for if trade equilibrium is to be maintained. Assume, for illustration, that cattle imports are "purchased" with $5,000 worth of machinery exports. Since only 0.131 of an acre-foot of in-state raw water is needed to produce $1,000 worth of machinery, only 0.66 of an acre-foot (0.131/$1,000 × $5,000) of in-state raw water is exported as embodied water in the machinery. In doing so, Arizona trades only 0.66 of an acre-foot of its scarce raw water for 46.69 acre-feet of somebody else's water. Or, to get the $10,000 worth of beef cattle to supply its final demand, it consumes only 47.35 (46.69 + 0.66) acre-feet of its scarce water instead of the 93.37 acre-feet it would consume if it produced the cattle entirely in-state.

Machinery is exported in exchange for cattle imports so that *dollar*-trade is balanced. But with 0.66 of an acre-foot of raw water exported as embodied water and 46.69 acre-feet of embodied water imported, *water*-trade does not balance. It does not need to. In effect, 0.66 of an acre-foot of Arizona's raw water exported is exchanged for 46.69 acre-feet of somebody else's raw water imported. There is a water-trade deficit in Arizona of 46.03 acre-feet, which is the difference between total water consumed in the Arizona economy and total raw water required in Arizona production. Raw water requirements in Arizona are reduced from 93.37 to 46.03 acre-feet through a change in the state's production-trade structure.

The water-trade position of a state is the difference between exports and imports of embodied water. An economy may export water or import water on a net basis, or its water-trade may be balanced; but only dollar-trade *must* be balanced over a period of time.

Terms of Water Exchange

The "terms of trade," a concept used in international trade theory, is the ratio at which commodities are traded for each other internationally. The most widely used measure of the terms of trade is the net barter or commodity terms of trade. It is an index of export prices divided by an index of import prices with the quotient expressed as a percentage [Px/Pm × 100]. A rise in the net barter index over time means that a given volume of exports will exchange for a larger volume of imports than formerly and is generally thought to indicate an increase in economic well-being. Analogously, the terms of water exchange is the average trade-price of embodied water exported divided by the average trade-price of embodied water imported with the quotient expressed as a percentage [$Pw_x/Pw_m \times 100$]. A rise in the terms of water exchange means that the state may import a larger quantity of embodied water for each unit of embodied water exported and similarly indicates an increase in economic advantage, at least for a water-scarce state.

For example, if 9.337 acre-feet of water are required to produce $1,000 worth of cattle, the trade-price (not the "value") of water embodied in cattle is $107.10 per acre-foot (1000 ÷ 9.337). In general, the more water used to produce a good, the lower is the trade-price of the water embodied in that good. Only 0.131 of an acre-foot of water is required to produce $1,000 worth of machinery. The trade-price (again not the "value") of an acre-foot of water embodied in machinery is quite high at $7,610. The terms of water exchange for these two classes of products is $7,610/$107 × 100, or 711, if cattle are imported and machinery is exported.

The higher the trade-price of embodied water exported relative to that of embodied water imported, the more favorable are the terms of water exchange and the more units of water are received per unit of water given up. If the terms of water exchange are above 100, it is a favorable exchange for a water-short state. If the terms are below 100 the water-short state is exporting more embodied water than it is gaining for an equal value of product.

The water trade-prices for the twenty-seven Arizona production sectors are shown in table 6-4. The sectors are listed in descending order of water trade-prices. The trade and transportation sector is highest with a water trade-price of $19,182 per acre-foot of water; forage crops are lowest, with a water trade-price of only $21 per acre-foot.

Final Demand Projections for Arizona

Domestic final consumer demand for Arizona was projected as the sum of four components — purchases by household, home-grown farm household consumption, state and local government purchases, and

TABLE 6-4
Water Trade-Prices by Arizona Producing Sector*

	Producing Sector	Water Trade-Price
25	Trade and transportation	$19,181.71
17	Petroleum	15,618.41
24	Selected services	12,169.89
19	Aircraft and parts	11,690.44
27	Construction	8,324.80
26	Unallocated services	8,173.27
18	Fabricated metals and machinery	7,610.29
23	Utilities	3,603.64
22	Mining	3,551.77
21	Other manufacturing	3,531.66
20	Primary metals	2,586.73
16	Chemicals and fertilizers	1,774.56
14	Canning, preserving and freezing	984.45
15	Miscellaneous agricultural processing	467.31
12	Meat and poultry processing	173.67
6	Vegetables	151.92
13	Dairy products	110.48
1	Meat animals and products	107.10
7	Fruits and tree nuts	97.78
10	Miscellaneous agriculture	97.02
8	Citrus fruits	84.45
11	Grain mill products	74.82
5	Cotton	67.13
2	Poultry and eggs	63.28
3	Farm dairy products	56.64
4	Food and feed grains	22.92
9	Forage crops	21.23

*"Water trade-prices" do not represent the economic value of water used in the production of these goods and should not be so interpreted. The concept is useful only as a means for determining the relative "terms of water exchange" in assessing the relative advantage to the state of exporting compared to importing the products of the several sectors.

federal government purchases within the state. Each component was projected separately.

Per capita consumption purchases by Arizona households were projected to rise proportionately with increases in per capita income. Total household expenditures were computed as the product of projected per capita household consumption expenditures and projected numbers of population. While total household consumption expenditures were assumed to rise proportionately to the rise in personal income, relative increases in purchases from individual sectors of the economy were adjusted to account for trends in consumer tastes and preferences. Purchases of most agricultural products, for example, will rise less than will purchases of convenience or luxury items as per capita personal income grows. The adjustments used (income elasticities) to reflect these relative differences were found in Daly (1956 and 1957) and Lee (1967). The assumption in our estimates that all additional personal income will be used for additional purchases overestimates growth in consumer demand and underestimates growth in consumer savings. The result is an overestimate of the state's real requirements for water.

Farm employment in Arizona in 1958, estimated from *Census of Population* data, was used together with total farm household consumption of home-grown food to find per capita household consumption of home-grown food for the base year, 1958. An estimate of total agricultural employment in 1975, prepared by the Arizona Employment Service (Valley National Bank, 1968:17) was used to establish the expected rate of decline in farm employment over time. The base year level of per capita home-produced farm household consumption was multiplied by projected farm employment to yield total home-grown farm household demand.

The ratio of state and local government expenditures to aggregate personal income in Arizona in the base year, 1958, was assumed to remain constant throughout the projection period. Projected aggregate personal income multiplied by this ratio yields projected state and local government demand.

Federal government expenditures in the United States (United States Department of Commerce, 1966b and 1968d) were related to aggregate GNP for the years 1952-67. This relation was used to project federal government expenditures in the United States. The base year ratio of federal government expenditure in Arizona to federal government expenditures in the United States was applied to projected levels of federal government expenditures in the United States to yield projected levels of federal government expenditures in Arizona.

Total domestic final demand projections for Arizona for the years 1980, 2000, and 2020 resulting from these estimates are shown in table 6-5, together with the base year (1958) estimates. The figures shown are the sums of projected in-state farm and nonfarm household, and in-state federal, state, and local government expenditures. Export demands for Arizona outputs are *not* included because exports are the variables to be adjusted in our analysis to reduce in-state raw water demand in order to raise the terms of water exchange for Arizona. Projected domestic

TABLE 6-5

Base Year and Projected Aggregate Domestic Final Demand, in Thousands of 1958 Dollars, in Arizona

Sector	1958	1980	2000	2020
1 Meat animals and products	2,310	2,901	3,800	5,220
2 Poultry and eggs	27,971	62,702	114,606	195,850
3 Farm dairy products	1,300	1,239	1,186	1,133
4 Food and feed grain	54	70	102	160
5 Cotton	49	138	303	596
6 Vegetables	12,353	24,209	40,089	63,620
7 Fruits and tree nuts	6,090	12,120	20,501	33,146
8 Citrus fruits	2,168	4,947	9,259	16,139
9 Forage crops	30	84	185	365
10 Miscellaneous agriculture	1,256	2,339	4,300	7,686
11 Grain mill products	11,920	19,722	29,086	42,434
12 Meat and poultry processing	85,709	185,405	329,115	549,965
13 Dairy products	48,365	91,733	148,233	231,051
14 Canning, preserving and freezing	27,580	59,710	106,082	177,408
15 Miscellaneous agricultural processing	94,464	241,875	487,108	893,279
16 Chemicals and fertilizers	54,947	141,240	285,579	525,518
17 Petroleum	42,684	176,869	521,313	1,248,950
18 Fabricated metals and machinery	97,919	302,499	704,375	1,433,515
19 Aircraft and parts	158	438	938	1,797
20 Primary metals	183	569	1,328	2,707
21 Other manufacturing	173,755	445,926	900,176	1,654,182
22 Mining	1,993	5,537	11,905	22,923
23 Utilities	76,759	281,002	760,789	1,724,632
24 Selected services	150,438	382,443	817,461	1,590,169
25 Trade and transportation	412,130	1,121,714	2,385,229	4,557,472
26 Unallocated services	600,836	1,737,695	3,891,506	7,727,915
27 Construction	181,185	486,531	1,051,134	2,052,357
Total	2,115,185	5,791,657	12,625,688	24,760,189

inal demands shown in table 6-5 are held constant throughout our ubsequent analysis so that posited changes that we introduce into Arizona's pattern of exports and imports *will have no effect on the level and pattern of products consumed by Arizonans over time,* that is, they will in no way slow down the rate of population and economic growth n Arizona over the 50-year projection period, 1970 to 2020.

Alternative Trade Patterns

The central objective of this analysis is to examine the effectiveness of changes in Arizona's external trade pattern as a means of reducing raw water requirements in Arizona without slowing down economic growth. For this purpose four alternative external trade patterns are posited for the state and introduced into the model. The results are examined for the raw and embodied water requirement associated with each. The general nature of each posited trade pattern is discussed below.

Trade Pattern I — The Naive Trade Pattern

The naive trade pattern is the same as that of the *adjusted* 1958 economy.

In any given year, some production of a state may go into inventory addition rather than be exported or consumed; or, consumption may occur out of inventory rather than from current production or imports. Also, in that given year, the value of imports and exports may not balance. However, over the long run, the value of imports and exports must balance and production cannot continually exceed demand or consumption continually exceed currently produced supplies. In 1958, Arizona produced net inventory additions and imported a greater value of products than it exported. In order to form a base from which consistent projections could be made, we adjusted the 1958 Arizona economy as described by Tijoriwala, Martin, and Bower (1968) to eliminate inventory additions or depletions and to balance the value of imports and exports.

In our projections of the naive trade pattern, the adjusted base year economy, including the adjusted base year trade pattern, grows in direct proportion with the projected rate of economic growth.

Such a projection is truly naive, for it assumes that all economic sectors will maintain their relative importance over time. It implies that agriculture, which used 92 percent of all water used in Arizona in 1958, would still use 92 percent of all water used in 2020 when the economy of the state will be many times as large. As our total water use estimates will show, such a situation would be quite impossible.

Alternative Trade Patterns II-IV

While most people would recognize the impossibility of attaining the naive pattern of growth and trade and do not propose measures aimed at holding the proportion of agricultural to industrial production constant over time, the conventional wisdom of water policy in Arizona does advocate measures which would at least prevent an absolute decline in agriculture, or, in other words, hold agricultural production constant at the current level. Thus, they advocate positive steps to mitigate changes in the pattern of water use in agriculture over time. This is shown in an appraisal report on the Central Arizona Project wherein is found the following: "The plan of development set forth in the original report on the Central Arizona Project was designed primarily to provide supplemental water for the stabilization of the existing agricultural economy of the project area." We label this view as the traditional view of the growth problem in Arizona.

The reasoning of the traditionalists is based on the fear that any absolute decline in agricultural acreage will result in a decline in the rate of development enjoyed by the state in recent years. For example, statements such as the following are common:

> Water levels are dropping progressively year by year, and unless remedial measures are taken without delay, the present economy will suffer seriously and progressively until an additional water supply can be brought into the area. (Arizona Academy, 1964:67)

> Water . . . is an inevitable limitation on future irrigated crop production, and through its effect on crop production it will have a significant impact on the state's economy . . . If the supply of water were constant, the present level of income created directly and indirectly in crop agriculture would continue indefinitely. The degree to which it will decline [as the water table declines] is the magnitude of the loss. (Arizona Academy, 1964:162, 163)

> Any shrinkage in agriculture shrinks the entire economy. (Farris and Scott, 1964:3)

Trade patterns II through IV are posited specifically to test the traditionalist point of view. Under each of these alternative trade patterns, the Arizona economy is projected to grow at the same rate in population, output, and personal income by transferring different amounts of raw water use from high-water-using agriculture to low-water-using nonagricultural industry. The alternative trade patterns differ only in the degree to which the structure of the Arizona economy is presumed to change toward nonagriculture use of raw water and resultant trade patterns emphasizing importation of agricultural products and exportation of nonagricultural goods and services in exchange.

Each of these three trade patterns is hypothetical, yet each pattern is obtainable within the basic resource restrictions of the state. Trade Pattern II reflects how we would expect the economy to change and grow if no conscious effort were made to direct its growth (and if water supplies do not prove to be truly restrictive). Trade Pattern II may be characterized as a "laissez-faire" or "do nothing" policy relying solely on general economic and market forces, reviewed in the next section of this chapter, to change and shape the Arizona economy. This pattern was developed independently of the adjustments suggested by the representative-farm linear-programming analyses of Chapter Four. Projected adjustments in Trade Pattern II are based on projections of general market trends, disregarding the effects on agriculture of possible increases in water costs. This means that in this Trade Pattern agriculture is assumed to be shielded in some appropriate way against the effects of rising water costs resulting from the inevitable groundwater depletion.

Trade Pattern III integrates the results of the representative-farm linear-programming projections of Chapter Four and the economic-trend projections of Trade Pattern II. Of the four alternatives, we view Trade Pattern III as coming closest to a prediction rather than merely a posited alternative. It shows dramatic nonagricultural growth, an economically viable agriculture remaining, and total water use well within possibilities.

Trade Pattern IV posits purposeful injection of further economic changes in the structure of the Arizona economy beyond those generated by general market trends in Trade Patterns II and III. These further economic changes were introduced explicitly for the purpose of reducing raw water use, thus improving the "water" terms of trade of the Arizona economy. Total raw water requirements in the state are reduced when the average trade-price of imported water is reduced and that of exported water is increased. To effectuate these changes, some of the agricultural sectors in the economy must decline markedly while the nonagricultural sectors grow about as in Trade Pattern III. Trade Pattern IV would be the result of a conscious effort on the part of Arizonans to modify the economic structure of their state toward a raw-water-saving policy.

Trends in Arizona's Economic Growth

The recently developed "shift" technique of regional analysis is used here to document the changing structure of the Arizona economy in recent years and to project likely future changes. The estimates for the alternative trade patterns are based on this analysis.

The shift technique is based upon a fundamental premise: A region or local area can be understood only as one views its relationships to other regions and to the nation as a whole. One must understand the role that a region plays in the total activity of the nation. The technique is built upon examining shifts in economic activity between regions. Computation is based upon the regional distribution of employment among economic sectors for different time periods. The standard of reference is the growth rate of the nation as a whole, both in total employment and in the distribution of employment within and among the various industrial sectors that compose the total economy.

An analysis of relative rates of economic development among regions reveals two reasons why some grow more rapidly than others. One stems from the fact that certain regions may have a favorable "business-mix." This means that the industrial composition of the area is concentrated in the fast-growing industrial sectors of the economy so that its growth rate will exceed that of the nation as a whole. The other reason for a rapidly expanding regional economy stems from the competitive advantages accruing to some or all of its major industrial sectors. That is, some or all of the industries of an area may be gradually improving their competitive positions relative to the same industries in other regions. A variety of factors may account for this improvement, such as (a) an increase in markets for the region's industries occasioned by the shifting regional pattern of industries and population, (b) improved access by a region's industries to important inputs because of resource discoveries or shifts in intermediate input sources, or (c) gains in relative access by a region's industries to both markets and inputs resulting from changes in technology that alter input and output requirements for the industry.

Conversely, a region may experience less rapid growth than other regions due to changes in some or all of those "shift factors" in unfavorable directions. Actual relative growth of a region is the result of the mix of favorable and unfavorable factors.

Differential Growth Measurement

Underlying the various statistical indicators of regional economic development are population magnitudes. There is, generally speaking, a correlation between increases in population and economic growth. (Correlation does not imply causation. We are talking about growth measurement only.)

An examination of census data shows the population of Arizona growing faster than that of the nation as a whole in every decade since statehood. This growth accelerated with World War II. Changes in population from the war through 1967 are presented in table 6-6. The decade 1940 to 1950 registered a 49 percent increase in Arizona's population, while the population of the United States increased by 15 percent. In the period 1950 to 1960, the increases were 75 percent and 19 percent respectively, while increases from 1960 to 1970 were 34 percent and 14 percent. Arizona's share of the nation's population increased from 0.4 percent in 1940 to 0.9 percent in 1970.

The major single factor determining the distribution of population over broad regions of the United States is economic opportunity, and

TABLE 6-6

Changes in Population of the United States and of Arizona, 1940 through 1970

Year	U.S. Population (thousands)	Change in U.S. Population (%)	Arizona Population (thousands)	Change in Arizona Population (%)	Arizona Population as % of U.S. Population
1940	131,954		506		0.4
		15.0		49.3	
1950	151,863		756		0.5
		18.6		74.7	
1960	180,684		1,321		0.7
		13.7		34.1	
1970	205,395		1,772		0.9

Source: United States Department of Commerce (1968a and 1968b).

the major single dimension of economic opportunity is employment opportunity. When the growth of employment in Arizona is compared with that of total United States employment for the period 1940 to 1970, we find Arizona's growth rate to be nearly two and one-half times the national rate for the period 1940 to 1950, about five and one-quarter times the national rate from 1950 to 1960, and again two and one-half times the national rate from 1960 to 1970. Of all fifty states, Arizona had the second fastest rate of growth in employment from 1940 to 1950 and the highest growth rate from 1950 to 1960 (table 6-7; 1970 data not yet available).

TABLE 6-7

Rate of Growth in Employment for the Fastest Growing States, 1940-1950 and 1950-1960

	Change in Total Employment (%) 1940-1950		Change in Total Employment (%) 1950-1960
United States	26.7	United States	15.5
1 Alaska	117.0	1 Arizona	81.6
2 Arizona	63.8	2 Nevada	80.6
3 California	61.4	3 Florida	70.9
4 Nevada	60.0	4 California	48.7

Source: United States Department of Commerce (1965).

TABLE 6-8

Shifts in Total Employment in Arizona, 1940-1950 and 1950-1960

Year	Actual Total Employment (thousands)*	Hypothetical Total Employment, at U.S. Growth Rate (thousands)	Shift in Total Employment (thousands)
1940	150.2		
1950	246.0	190.2	+ 55.8
1960	446.8	284.0	+162.8

*Source: United States Department of Commerce (1965).

Differential Growth Analysis

We now come to grips with the economic performance of the state as revealed by these rapid rates of growth in total employment. Table 6-7 shows the rates of growth of total employment in the United States for the periods 1940 to 1950 and 1950 to 1960. These rates are applied to recorded levels of total employment in Arizona for 1940 and 1950 to deduce what the employment changes in Arizona would have been if they had been commensurate with national growth (table 6-8). Table 6-8 reveals a substantial inward shift of total employment to Arizona during the study period. This shift is nearly three times greater during the most recent period, 1950-60, than during the earlier period, 1940-50.

We must disaggregate this shift in total employment to examine what seems to have underlain it. As stated previously, the theoretical explanation for regional growth behavior falls into two categories. First, some regions grow faster or slower than other regions because they specialize in the rapid-growth or slow-growth sectors of economic activity. Thus, there is a *composition effect* which is based upon the business-mix of the region. Second, some regions grow more or less rapidly than other regions because particular sectors of their economy are growing at different rates than are the same sectors in other regions. In classical economic terms, their comparative economic advantage in these activities is greater or lesser than the same activities in other regions. The shift in total employment attributable to a competitive advantage or disadvantage is designated as the *competition effect*. The observed shift in total employment is the net effect of combining these two elements – the composition effect and the competition effect.

The Competition Effect. Detailed analysis of the shift in total employment begins with consideration of the competition effect. Columns 1 and

TABLE 6-9

Competition Shifts in Employment in Arizona for Each Major Industrial Component, 1940-1950 and 1950-1960

	Industrial Component	1940-1950		1950-1960	
		Competition Shift (no.)	Distribution of Shift (%)*	Competition Shift (no.)	Distribu[illegible] of Shift
1	Agriculture	8,662	12.77	12,445	7.2
2	Forestry and fisheries	34		279	
3	Mining	−2,489		7,297	4.2
4	Construction	5,694	8.39	17,503	10.1
5	Food and kindred products	1,000		2,395	
6	Textiles	−678		−1,183	
7	Apparel manufacturers	279		2,059	
8	Lumber and wood products	528		657	
9	Printing and publishing	561		2,002	
10	Chemicals	271		194	
11	Machinery (electrical and other)	420		8,958	5.2
12	Motor vehicles and equipment	15		391	
13	Transportation equipment	98		5,316	
14	Miscellaneous equipment	2,266		9,850	5.7
15	Railroads	892		1,102	
16	Trucking and warehousing	340		1,513	
17	Other transportation	1,038		1,131	
18	Communications	987		2,795	
19	Utilities and sanitation	2,843		1,549	
20	Wholesale trade	1,261		4,763	
21	Food and dairy products	1,970		4,156	
22	Eating and drinking establishments	2,692		4,487	
23	Retail trade	7,693	11.34	14,872	8.[illegible]
24	Finance, insurance, real estate	3,389	5.00	10,997	6.[illegible]
25	Hotels and personal services	3,484	5.67	5,432	
26	Households	2,692		4,121	
27	Business and repair services	2,105		4,074	
28	Entertainment and recreation	304		1,435	
29	Medical and professional services	5,700	8.40	16,923	9.[illegible]
30	Public administration	2,504		9,059	5.[illegible]
31	Armed forces	3,245	4.78	4,673	
32	Other	1,340		8,250	4.[illegible]
	Total	61,504	100.00	169,495	100.[illegible]

*For emphasis and clarity only the more significant percentages are shown. (Percentages are based sum of all competition shifts added without regard to sign.)

Source: United States Department of Commerce (1965).

3 of table 6-9 show the change in employment in Arizona because of the competition effect and how the total shift was distributed among the sectors of the total economy. A positive figure in these columns means that the corresponding sector enjoyed a rate of increase in employment more marked than did the same sector in many other states and in the United States as a whole. Arizona's competitive position in that sector of its economy, as measured by employment, improved vis-à-vis other regions. When the competitive gains and losses of all sectors are added algebraically, the result is the total net competition shift for the state.

Examination of table 6-9 reveals that, with a single exception, Arizona has consistently gained in competitive position in all sectors of industrial activity during the period under study. The contribution which each sector made to Arizona's competitive performance is reflected in columns 2 and 4 in which are recorded the larger percentages of total competition shift. The greatest contributor to competitive gains in Arizona from 1950 to 1960 was construction, followed closely by medical and professional services, retail trade, and agriculture. In the earlier period of somewhat slower relative competitive growth, agriculture made the largest contribution, followed by retail trade, medical and professional services, and construction. The one sector to consistently lose competitive position was textile mill products manufacturing. While mining lost competitive position from 1940 to 1950, it recovered strongly to contribute 4.25 percent of the gain in competitive shift from 1950 to 1960. In general, Arizona is quite competitive throughout the broad range of its economic structure.

The Composition Effect. The composition element of the shift in total employment in the United States is the benchmark used for classifying the growth characteristics of each sector. The national differential growth rate for any sector is found by subtracting the growth rate of total employment in the United States from the growth rate of employment for that sector for the United States as a whole. To find the contribution of a particular Arizona sector to Arizona's total composition effect, we multiply employment in that sector by the differential United States growth rate for that sector. The algebraic sum of the components generates the composition shift for the state.

Table 6-10 reveals that during both study periods, agriculture, a slow-growth industry which was a large part of the Arizona economy, caused economic growth related to the composition shift in employment to Arizona to be much slower than that for the nation as a whole. Agriculture accounted for 34 percent of the adverse composition shift for the period 1940-50 and 30 percent from 1950-60. Three sectors – agriculture, mining, and domestic service (households) – accounted for just over 50 percent of the adverse composition shift in the earlier period while agriculture, mining, and railroads accounted for 43 percent of the adverse composition shift in the later period. The largest favorable composition effect during 1940 to 1950 was posted by construction, which accounted for 8.3 percent of the gain. From 1950 to 1960, the medical and professional services sector registered the largest share of the favorable composition shift with 16.4 percent.

In general, during the period under study, Arizona was laboring under the handicap of an adverse business-mix because, on balance over all economic sectors, the total shift of employment to Arizona due to composition effects was negative. That is, the state's employment did not grow as fast as it might have grown compared to the nation's because its business-mix was less favorable for growth than that for the country as a whole. There was considerable specialization in agriculture and mining, both of which are slow-growth or declining industries. It appears that this situation is changing, however, and at a relatively rapid rate. Bureau of Census data for 1940, 1950, and 1960 show agriculture as a share of Arizona's total employment, declining from 21.5 percent to 14.5 percent to 7.6 percent (United States Department of Commerce, 1965). A recent projection by the Arizona State Employment Service shows agriculture falling to 4.4 percent of total employment in 1975 (Valley National Bank, 1968). As agriculture declines in relative importance, Arizona should realize a larger share of the employment gains of the nation.

Recognize that we are not claiming that total economic growth in Arizona would have been more rapid in the *past* if slow-growth industries such as agriculture and mining had not been a part of the economy. Agriculture and mining were cornerstones in the development of Arizona. However, once a region reaches a certain level of development, other types of industries provide greater potential for growth. Agricultural (and often mining) development, its maturation and ultimate *relative* decline are natural phenomena in an economically developing region. In fact, copper mining in Arizona has expanded considerably in the period 1960 to 1970. Still, it has continued to decline in relative importance.

Growth of Specific Industrial Components

The analysis to this point has focused upon the broad sectors of employment activity in Arizona. Shifts in total employment resulting from composition and competition elements were disaggregated and

TABLE 6-10

Composition Shifts in Employment in Arizona for Each Major Industrial Component, 1940-1950 and 1950-1960

Industrial Component	1940-1950		1950-1960	
	Composition Shift (no.)	Distribution of Shift (%)*	Composition Shift (no.)	Distribution of Shift (%)*
griculture	−14,425	33.90	−18,987	29.92
orestry and fisheries	−34		−165	
ining	−3,242	7.62	−4,742	7.47
onstruction	3,572	8.39	−1,044	
ood and kindred products	28		528	
extiles	−443		−708	
pparel manufacturers	3		−23	
umber and wood products	1		−939	
rinting and publishing	118		435	
hemicals	91		135	
achinery (electrical and other)	244		348	
otor vehicles and equipment	16		−21	
ransportation equipment	9		126	
iscellaneous equipment	201		214	
ailroads	−270		−3,866	
rucking and warehousing	188		354	
ther transportation	244		−284	
ommunications	578		0	
tilities and stnitation	351		−60	
holesale trade	1,770		−346	
ood and dairy products	−554		−1,328	
ating and drinking establishments	1,134		−879	
etail trade	1,591		498	
inance, insurance, real estate	119		1,805	
otels and personal services	−1,248		−1,364	
ouseholds	−3,806	8.94	107	
usiness and repair services	785		496	
ntertainment and recreation	−34		−329	
edical and professional services	2,272	5.34	10,423	16.42
ublic administration	2,577	6.06	1,515	
rmed forces	2,508	5.89	3,895	6.13
ther	−96		7,495	11.80
Total	−5,572	100.00	−6,711	100.00

mphasis and clarity only the more significant percentages are shown. (Percentages are based on the of all composition shifts added without regard to sign.)

Source: United States Department of Commerce (1965).

TABLE 6-11

Distribution of Employment, in Percent, Among Industries for Arizona, 1940, 1950, and 1960, and for the United States, 1960

Industry	Arizona			U.S.
	1940	1950	1960	1960
Agriculture	21.6	14.9	8.0	6.7
Mining	8.6	4.4	8.4	1.0
Construction	6.0	8.6	9.3	5.9
Manufacturing	8.4	8.8	12.8	27.1
Transportation; communications; public utilities	7.9	8.9	6.8	6.9
Wholesale-retail trade	18.5	21.9	20.2	18.2
Finance; insurance; real estate	2.0	3.0	4.9	4.2
Services:	21.6	22.5	24.0	21.0
Business repair	2.2	3.1	2.9	2.5
Personal	9.5	8.2	7.2	6.0
Entertainment and recreation	1.2	1.1	0.9	0.8
Professional	8.7	10.1	13.0	11.7
Government	3.9	5.3	5.9	5.0
Other	1.5	1.6	4.7	4.0
Total	100.0	100.0	100.0	100.0

Source: United States Department of Commerce (1940, 1950, and 1960).

ascribed to the individual economic sectors from which they arose. In this way the unique contribution to the total result made by each sector was identified. However, the analysis has not *explained* the direction or magnitude of these individual sector shifts. In this section, we deepen the analysis by giving special attention to those individual economic sectors of particular importance.

In selecting which sectors to examine more intensively we are guided by the principal finding of a recent historical survey of regional growth in the United States by Perloff and others (1960). They found convergence of demographic, labor force, and income structures among regions of the United States. Although some regional differentials in the structure of productive activities remain, there is a tendency for the business-mix of regions to move closer to the national average. Arizona's economic experience conforms to this generalization, as shown in table 6-11. The distribution of total employment among Arizona economic sectors has tended, over time, to approach national magnitudes. As of 1960, the percentages of total state employment for most major economic sectors in Arizona were similar to the percentages of national sectors relative to total national employment with three significant exceptions – manufacturing, construction and mining. Mining would be expected to differ from the national percentage because mining is affected by the fortuities of discovery and Arizona is a "fortuitous" area. Construction is more important in developing regions than in already developed areas, while manufacturing is less important in a developing area.

While for the nation, manufacturing employment accounted for 27.1 percent of total employment, in Arizona manufacturing represented only 12.8 percent. We expect that past economic tendencies will persist and that Arizona will realize a steady growth in the manufacturing sector of its economy until the ratio of manufacturing to total employment in Arizona approximates that for the nation as a whole. Thus, two sectors command our attention: agriculture, because of its restraining effect upon the economic growth of the state, and manufacturing, because of its tremendous growth potential.

Agricultural Growth

The composition shift of agriculture accounted for 52 percent of the total adverse shift in aggregate Arizona employment for the period 1950 to 1960. While the favorable competition shift of agriculture contributed to the inward shift of total employment for Arizona, specialization in agriculture resulted in a substantial reduction in the magnitude of this shift.

One may probe beneath the shift in aggregate agricultural employment in the same way that the shift in total employment was analyzed by examining the shifts in its component sectors. Thus, employment shifts within the agricultural sector alone are composed of the two basic elements – composition effect (product mix) and competition effect (regional comparative advantage) operating differently on each separate agricultural sector.

Data on agricultural employment by commodity are not available for the various states. Therefore, our analysis uses the value of agricultural products sold rather than the number of workers employed (see Tables 6-12 and 6-13) as the indicator variable.

Table 6-13 shows that the composition effect is especially important for the period 1954 to 1964. Just as the major factor in the net outward composition shift in total Arizona employment is specialization in the slow-growth sectors of total employment, so is Arizona's specialization

TABLE 6-12

Changes in Value of Arizona Agricultural Products Sold, 1940-1954

Sector	Changes (in $1,000) Related To: National Growth	Product-Mix (composition element)	Competitive Advantage (competition element)
1 Meat animals and products	43,238	1,097	11,877
2 Poultry and eggs	2,906	−252	−461
3 Farm dairy products	8,098	−2,129	4,117
4 Food and feed grains	1,089	97	23,175
5 Cotton	35,985	2,487	114,996
6 Vegetables	6,743	−1,142	22,386
7 Fruits and tree nuts	1,443	—	—
8 Citrus fruits	3,379	615	203
9 Forage crops	4,132	−1,224	2,872
10 Miscellaneous agriculture	1,140	428	1,210
Total agriculture	108,153	−23	180,375

Source: United States Bureau of the Census (1941, 1956, and 1966).

TABLE 6-13

Changes in Value of Arizona Agricultural Products Sold, 1954-1964

Sector	Changes (in $1,000) Related To: National Growth	Product-Mix (composition element)	Competitive Advantage (competition element)	Total Arizona Change
1 Meat animals and products	31,239	10,883	54,720	96,842
2 Poultry and eggs	1,415	537	1,941	3,893
3 Farm dairy products	5,660	−540	6,866	11,986
4 Food and feed grains	10,702	−5,039	3,313	8,976
5 Cotton	72,099	+80,350	−34,521	−42,772
6 Vegetables	13,177	3,003	12,707	28,887
7 Fruits and tree nuts	623	−189	383	817
8 Citrus fruis	2,357	942	10,786	14,085
9 Forage crops	3,161	8,376	−1,740	9,797
10 Miscellaneous agriculture	1,384	1,628	4,944	7,956
Total agriculture	141,817	−60,749	59,399	140,467

Source: United States Bureau of the Census (1941, 1956, and 1966).

TABLE 6-14

Percentage Distribution Among Sectors of Total Value of Arizona Agricultural Products Sold

Sector	1940	1954	1964	1967
1 Meat animals and products	40.5	22.0	36.0	38.0
2 Poultry and eggs	2.7	1.0	1.5	1.3
3 Farm dairy products	7.6	4.0	5.4	6.1
4 Food and feed grains	1.0	7.6	7.2	6.8
5 Cotton	33.7	50.8	26.5	15.1
6 Vegetables	6.3	9.3	12.7	17.0
7 Fruits and tree nuts	—	0.4	0.5	0.2
8 Citrus fruits	3.2	1.7	4.2	5.4
9 Forage crops	3.9	2.2	3.6	4.7
10 Miscellaneous agriculture	1.1	1.0	2.4	5.4

Source: United States Bureau of the Census (1941, 1956, and 1966); United States Department of Agriculture (1968).

in slow-growth or declining sectors of agriculture the major factor in the net outward composition shift in agricultural products sold. Cotton, Arizona's major field crop, accounted for 93 percent of the total adverse composition effect on agricultural commodities sold during 1954 to 1964. Food and feed grains, another major field crop sector, accounted for 4 percent. Meat animals and products and forage crops show positive composition effects; however, these positive effects were small compared to the adverse effects of cotton.

Large positive competition effects are shown for livestock, vegetables, and citrus, but cotton again shows adverse effects. The net adverse composition plus competition effects of cotton together with a relatively slow growth rate in the food and feed grains sectors offset the net advantages in all other sectors to cause the growth rate of total agricultural products sold in Arizona to be slightly under that for the nation as a whole. (Compare the totals of columns 1 and 4 in table 6-13.)

Table 6-14 summarizes the changes since 1940 in the percentage distribution of the value of agricultural products sold in Arizona. From a high of 50 percent in 1954, cotton's share of total product has decreased markedly. The percentage share of food and feed grains has remained almost constant since 1954. Livestock and livestock products have regained the prominence they had in 1940 and again account for the largest proportion of agricultural product sales. Vegetables have shown a steady increase since 1940. Miscellaneous agriculture, while still a

TABLE 6-15

Changes in Manufacturing Employment in Arizona by Industry, 1947-196

Standard Industrial Classification	Manufacturing Sector	Changes (in number of people) Related To:				Ari Minu Gr Rat
		National Growth	Business-Mix (composition element)	Competitive Advantage (competition element)	Total Arizona Change	
201	Meat and poultry processing	105	−55	186	238	
202	Dairy products	43	369	1,148	1,560	
204	Grain mill products	87	−87	15	15	
205-8	Bakery, sugar, confectionery, and beverages	205	−231	1,095	1,069	
209	Misc. food preparations and kindred products	175	−279	219	115	
23	Apparel and finished textile products	12	—	2,568	2,580	
24	Lumber and wood products	472	−761	781	492	
25	Furniture and fixtures	49	−5	564	608	
27	Printing and publishing	289	139	2,144	2,572	
28	Chemicals and allied products	115	−13	136	238	
29	Petroleum refining	5	−12	50	43	
32	Stone, clay, and glass products	161	48	2,093	2,302	
33	Primary metals	638	−1,542	1,964	1,060	
34	Fabricated metals	91	−36	2,032	2,087	
35	Machinery	67	−87	5,432	5,412	1
36	Electrical machinery and supplies	36	136	8,765	8,937	4
37	Transportation equipment	—	—	—	—	
372	Aircraft and parts	31	315	4,804	5,150	2
38	Professional and scientific instruments	1	1	1,491	1,493	24
39	Miscellaneous manufacturing	21	−39	249	231	
Sum of listed manufacturing		2,603	−2,137	35,736	36,202	
All manufacturing		2,647			42,851	

Source: United States Department of Commerce, 1965.

TABLE 6-16
Distribution and Relative Growth of Personal Income, by Source, in Arizona, for Selected Years*

Source of Income	Distribution			Relative Growth From 1950		
	1950	1960	1970	1950	1960	1970
Farms	16.4%	7.4%	3.2%	100%	123%	131%
Mining	4.9	3.8	3.5	100	212	471
Manufacturing	5.2	10.2	12.8	100	529	1629
Government	20.7	21.7	26.8	100	286	865
All other sources	52.8	56.9	53.7	100	295	679
Total	100.0%	100.0%	100.0%	100%	273%	667%

*Calculated from table 1-1.

small sector, has increased its share sharply. In summary, of all agricultural sectors, only cotton exhibits appreciable decline in its share of total agricultural product sales.

Manufacturing Growth

Table 6-9 showed that total manufacturing – components 5 through 14 – accounted for 7 percent of the favorable competition shift in total employment in Arizona from 1940 to 1950 and 18 percent from 1950 to 1960.

When shift analysis is applied to the individual components of this sector, those components showing the largest contribution were electrical machinery, other machinery, and aircraft and parts (table 6-15). Every component of the manufacturing sector showed competitive gains, although the composition elements were mostly negative. Examination of differential growth rates (Arizona growth rate less United States growth rate) for each sector reveals an outstanding advantage for instruments and related products in Arizona, with large advantages in electronics, aircraft, and other machinery; with substantial advantages in another ten sectors; and modest advantages in the remaining six sectors.

These gains in manufacturing employment are reflected in the dramatic changes from 1950 to 1970 in manufacturing's share in the production of personal income for Arizonans (table 6-16). Manufacturing in 1950 accounted for 5 percent of Arizona personal income. This share increased to 10 percent in 1960 and to almost 13 percent in 1970. Personal income produced in manufacturing increased more than sixteenfold between 1950 and 1970, increasing more than fivefold between 1950 and 1960 and more than tripling again between 1960 and 1970. Only government and "all other sources" approached manufacturing as significant growth sectors, and they fell significantly behind manufacturing in this regard. Personal income created in government sectors increased almost ninefold between 1950 and 1970, falling just short of tripling between 1950 and 1960 and more than tripling between 1960 and 1970. Personal income generated in "all other sources" increased almost sevenfold during these twenty years, almost tripling during the first decade and more than doubling again during the second decade. The impressive growth in importance of manufacturing in generating personal income in Arizona is shown in figure 1-9.

The major area of manufacturing expansion in Arizona in recent years has been machinery production. Machinery (electrical and nonelectrical) accounts for about 36 percent of the state's value of manufacturing output. The 1968 Sales and Employment Survey of the Western Electronics Manufacturers Association indicates that sales of Arizona firms are growing at a faster rate than those of California (Modern Arizona Industry, Inc., 1969).

While growth of the electronics industry in Arizona has been exceptional and virtually unparalleled in any other part of the country, it is not the only type of manufacturing experiencing impressive growth in the state. Arizona has the largest machine job shop and production for small gas turbine equipment in the United States. Other producers manufacture aircraft and parts, aerospace equipment, water and sewage treatment equipment, guided missiles, electronic computers, construction supplies, metal and plastic extrusions, wearing apparel, food products, and process primary metals.

More than 1,200 establishments are engaged in manufacturing activity in Arizona in the early 1970s, an increase of about 500 from ten years earlier. Attracted to Arizona by high labor productivity as well as climate and markets, new manufacturers have tended to concentrate operations in the state's metropolitan centers. The situation in Phoenix and vicinity has been especially favorable. This area has emerged as a notable manufacturing center – with particular emphasis on science-oriented industries. Manufacturing employment in 1969 was estimated to average 71,500 – an increase of almost 7 percent of the state's total manufacturing employment over the previous year.

Among the many factors influencing Arizona's dramatic growth in manufacturing, one is of particular significance – the variety of competent support services and facilities serving industrial needs. The postwar operations and growth of major divisions of national firms have attracted to Arizona many precision machine shops, tool and die-making

TABLE 6-17
Growth of Arizona Firms Providing Support Service

Industrial Classification	Firms (no.) in 1962	in 1968	Increase (%)
Machinery (except electrical)	80	143	78.8
Fabricated metal products	94	141	50.0
Electrical machinery	36	55	52.8
Rubber and plastic products	13	35	169.2
Primary metal products	17	32	88.2
Instruments and related products	11	18	63.6
Ordnance and accessories	3	4	33.3
Total	254	428	68.5

Source: First National Bank of Arizona (1968).

firms, metallurgists, heat treating and testing facilities, research laboratories, and makers and suppliers of electronic components, optical, and other technical items. More than 400 firms in seven major industrial classifications provide a broad spectrum of services and products. The magnitude of recent growth in the number of support firms is revealed by the 68 percent gain during the period 1962 to 1968, as shown in table 6-17.

This description of growth in Arizona industry, together with the historical "shift analysis," emphasizes the "growth vibrations" being felt throughout the state as a result of the dramatic structural changes already taking place in its economy, of which Arizonans must become increasingly aware. Changes in the public's economic orientation away from agriculture and mining toward manufacturing, and particularly toward the more technologically sophisticated industries, is evident and portends an increasingly favorable "attitude climate" for industrial expansion. This change will contribute directly to the further development of the economy and has important implications for projecting future developments.

Implications for Future Development

Turning to consideration of future development, the question is, will the past trends persist, and, if so, to what extent? Insight into the likelihood of a continuation of Arizona's recent growth experience can be gained from a United States Department of Commerce (1967) study on industrial location and regional economic development. Examination of the locational patterns of American industry over time reveal four significant trends: (1) regional decentralization out of the Northeast to the

South and West, (2) local decentralization out of the large central cities, (3) increasing market orientation of industry, and (4) growth of intellect-oriented industries.

The trend toward regional decentralization in favor of the South and West is expected to continue. This general trend will contribute to future relative growth in Arizona manufacturing. The second trend, the tendency for industry to move from the large central cities to outlying areas, does not seem of great import for Arizona's future industrial picture.

The third trend, toward market orientation as a dominant factor in locational choice, rests on at least two other factors. One is the declining importance of the need to locate near raw materials. Raw materials, for a number of reasons, are no longer as important in most production processes as they once were. This being the case, Arizona stands to gain in the future as its geographical disadvantage relative to raw materials becomes less important. Another aspect of the growing market-orientation of industry is that market-oriented industries grow more rapidly in our contemporary society then do resource-oriented industries. The resource-oriented activities of the economy have been declining in relative importance since 1870.

In the 1950s and 1960s, manufacturing industries, particularly those producing consumer goods, have been proliferating and growing at a rapid rate. Although the major United States markets are still in the Northeastern and North Central states, markets in the Southwest are rapidly expanding. As fast as a regional market passes the threshold of size that permits economical operations, company after company puts branch plants into the market. Even where the economic advantages are small, when one company in an industry branches, competitors tend to follow suit. Herein lies perhaps the strongest impetus to increased economic growth and development of the state. The projections generated in this study rely heavily upon this trend in industrial location. It is assumed that over time an ever-increasing share of the total supply of many consumer goods currently being imported into Arizona will be produced domestically.

The final trend is also important to Arizona's future development. It is difficult to provide a precise definition of "intellect-oriented" industries. Essentially, these industries include such things as research and development activities of both industry and government, much of the aerospace industry, parts of the electronics and precision instruments industries, and a number of other related activities. They are characterized by a high percentage of total employment in scientist, engineer, and other specialized professional categories. Their locational patterns emphasize the desires and needs of the professionals they employ, as well as the external economies they must have in order to flourish.

The recent growth and the potential of this class of industry is explained in part by the fundamental change occurring in the American economy. Exploration of expected industrial patterns of the 1970s has led *Fortune* magazine to conclude that the United States is on the verge of a new era. It found that most working technologists believe the next stage of advance is likely to be the most expansive in this century. The propulsive force of this new age will be the chemical-electric-electronic-aerospace complex which contains the country's technological elite, and which is growing and inter-mixing into one giant highly competitive innovative industry (Lessing, 1967).

The intellect-oriented group of industries is of particular importance to Arizona because it is among the fastest growing segments of the economy; it is attractive in terms of the income characteristics of its employees; it has a high propensity for the generation of new business enterprises; and it has a high output value per unit of water input required.

There are two basic criteria by which to judge whether products intended for national distribution can be successfully manufactured in Arizona. Products must either be small and light or be priced high enough that transportation costs account for only a small part of the total selling price. Products of "intellect-oriented" industries tend to be expensive because of the high-valued labor used in their production. The greater the engineering and scientific content of a product, other things being equal, the higher the selling price; and for any given transport cost, the higher the selling price, the lower the relative transport cost. As industry continues its trend toward the development and production of more and more scientifically sophisticated products, Arizona can become increasingly competitive in the production and sale of nationally distributed products. Whether it will, in fact, do so depends ultimately on its ability to draw and hold the personnel needed by these scientifically-oriented firms.

The projections of this chapter focus upon the less-difficult problem of projecting what *can* happen – and on what can be encouraged to happen – rather than what *will* happen. This being the case, the "intellect-oriented" industries, because of their great growth potential in Arizona, figure heavily in the projections generated.

Projections of Economic Growth and External Trade

The preceding analyses have laid the groundwork necessary for the projections of sector-by-sector gross output and external trade. We have presented projections of population growth, per capita real income, and aggregate state real personal income that state and community leaders have deemed desirable and other analysts have agreed are reasonable. Estimates of within-state final consumer demand were made that were consistent with the population and real personal income projections. We have discussed how a given final in-state consumer demand could be met in alternative ways – through alternative combinations of in-state production and external trade. The general nature of several alternative trade patterns was posited. To provide background for empirical specification of these patterns, a "shift" analysis of past economic growth trends in Arizona was presented along with a discussion of possible future growth potential by individual economic sectors.

The next step in the analysis is to empirically specify the exports and imports, by individual economic sector, that would occur under the several alternative trade patterns. In doing so, we must make sure that (1) the dollar's worth of imports balance the dollar's worth of exports in each of the time periods examined and that (2) in-state final consumer demand remains constant for each sector under each of the alternative trade patterns at the level projected for the given time period. Under these conditions, the output level generated within each economic sector will be different under each trade pattern. Total final demand, an approximation of Gross State Product, will be almost identical under the alternative trade patterns for any given time period.

The reasoning underlying each import and export estimate is documented by Finster (1970). The import and export estimates themselves are presented in the tables of Appendix C. Table C-1 shows the import-export picture for the adjusted base year (1958) economy, which one can compare with the alternative posited trade patterns. Trade Pattern I, the naive pattern of external trade, is that pattern which would exist if the adjusted base-year economy were to grow proportionately at the expected rate of growth of the total economy.

Aggregate and sectoral exports and imports under each alternative trade pattern for each projection year are shown in appendix tables C-2 through C-4. The sectors are arranged according to the water-trade price of water embodied in the products of each. This arrangement was made to highlight the extent to which exports embodying high-priced water are substituted for those embodying low-priced water, and imports embodying low-priced water substituted for those embodying high-priced water in each posited external trade pattern. In moving from the Trade Pattern I through increasingly more water conservation-oriented trade patterns, these substitutions become more extensive.

The gross output levels necessary to support projected consumer demand of Arizonans in combination with the import-export levels shown in appendix tables C-2 through C-4 are shown in table 6-18. These output estimates were made by injecting the import and export estimates into the Input-Output model so as to achieve consistent estimates for all sectors of the Arizona economy. It is these output estimates to which water requirements (column 1 of table 6-3) are attached. Total estimated water requirements for each projected year under each trade pattern are shown in the following section where the total requirement under each pattern is compared to several alternative water supply situations. However, let us first examine the alternative projections of gross output in detail, so that we may see where the trade-offs in economic activity may be made.

Table 6-18 lists the 27 producing sectors of the Arizona economy, along with the value of each sector's gross output in the base year, 1958. The projections under each trade pattern are all in terms of 1958 dollars so that comparisons of real output may be made between all patterns and all years. Note that total gross state output is held approximately constant between alternative Trade Patterns II, III, and IV for each given year.

In Trade Pattern II, gross output of every sector except number 5, cotton, is allowed to increase over the entire period of the projection. Thus, the major adjustment in water use arises by phasing cotton out of irrigated agriculture and leaving that water that would have been used for cotton for expansion of other sectors. This is not an unrealistic projection. Although cotton has been a major economic sector in Arizona in the past, current trends in the demand for cotton, as well as the recent changes in federal agricultural price support programs, indicate drastic adjustments in cotton production. Such adjustments will need to occur regardless of the water situation. That the water may be used elsewhere is merely fortuitous.

The two other heavy water-using sectors, "food and feed grains" (number 4) and "forage crops" (number 9) are shown as steadily increasing from their 1958 base. However, current gross output of the food and feed grains sector is, in fact, already near the high projection shown for 2020. This occurs not because of radically increased acreage or water use, however, but because of greatly increased yields per acre, especially of grain sorghum. Thus, water use estimates which will be derived will be conservative relative to water use per dollar of gross output for the grain sorghum sector and projected values for sector 4 should have been somewhat higher.

TABLE 6-18 — Projections of Gross State Output U

	Producing Sectors	Base Year* 1958	1980	Trade Pattern II 2000	2
1	Meat animals and products	143,384	234,713	314,211	42
2	Poultry and eggs	8,117	40,685	97,208	18
3	Farm dairy products	26,055	53,157	88,073	13
4	Food and feed grains	28,162	32,502	44,466	5
5	Cotton	150,795	53,945	11,229	
6	Vegetables	73,841	165,230	256,175	36
7	Fruits and tree nuts	1,700	3,669	4,793	
8	Citrus fruits	9,899	28,055	51,982	8
9	Forage crops	34,260	43,262	53,278	6
10	Misc. agriculture	26,889	43,639	83,240	15
11	Grain mill products	23,273	49,080	60,328	6
12	Meat and poultry processing	63,135	169,421	324,834	5
13	Dairy products	46,142	99,349	166,545	2
14	Canning, preserving, and freezing	4,161	12,907	23,757	3
15	Misc. agricultural processing	50,453	171,877	362,459	6
16	Chemicals and fertilizers	38,953	181,453	450,943	1,0
17	Petroleum	5,150	47,441	134,721	3
18	Fabricated metals and machinery	98,948	795,620	2,220,960	4,84
19	Aircraft and parts	98,589	620,294	1,478,634	3,07
20	Primary metals	164,418	635,406	1,229,166	1,95
21	Other manufacturing	175,791	837,095	2,152,755	4,6
22	Mining	314,520	838,862	1,099,067	1,4
23	Utilities	187,502	693,660	1,739,225	3,7
24	Selected services	209,831	785,607	1,837,461	3,6
25	Trade and transportation	632,498	1,901,618	4,128,866	7,9
26	Unallocated services	994,541	3,026,464	6,768,136	13,4
27	Construction	500,000	1,463,447	3,159,060	6,1
	Total	4,111,007	13,028,458	28,341,572	55,3

*Trade Pattern I, the naive trade pattern, is that pattern which would exist if the base year (1958) ec were to grow in direct proportion to the expected rate of growth for the total Arizona economy. See tat for expected growth rate.

rnative Trade Patterns (thousands of 1958 dollars)

Trade Pattern III			Trade Pattern IV		
980	2000	2020	1980	2000	2020
2,786	169,742	143,384	202,786	169,742	69,597
7,997	14,153	11,906	27,997	14,153	11,906
9,954	72,174	105,042	49,954	72,174	105,042
2,360	35,000	32,000	18,930	375	199
,760	114,900	113,000	46,206	332	654
,158	192,444	192,444	142,158	192,444	74,410
,735	1,677	1,677	2,735	1,677	678
,230	35,214	31,713	26,230	35,214	31,713
,240	18,670	15,500	26,240	876	328
,501	49,946	30,273	39,501	49,946	30,273
,885	23,273	23,273	36,885	6,347	6,080
,601	199,428	138,191	151,601	199,428	138,191
,197	138,454	206,038	93,197	138,454	206,038
,894	7,209	6,150	8,894	7,209	6,150
,689	226,546	379,293	152,689	226,546	379,293
,380	451,366	1,018,264	185,380	451,366	1,018,264
,053	123,919	308,200	46,053	123,919	308,200
,887	2,234,417	4,956,736	798,887	2,234,417	4,956,736
,568	1,746,697	3,640,847	689,568	1,746,697	3,640,847
,725	1,166,807	1,861,643	626,725	1,166,807	1,861,643
,032	2,187,181	4,847,074	860,032	2,187,181	4,847,074
510	1,022,960	1,361,113	818,510	1,022,960	1,361,113
,750	1,703,980	3,640,547	689,750	1,703,980	3,640,547
,129	2,148,826	4,408,666	851,129	2,148,826	4,408,666
,755	4,201,708	8,175,678	1,914,755	4,201,708	8,175,678
,111	6,860,071	13,637,985	3,039,111	6,860,071	13,637,985
,117	3,150,872	6,084,875	1,461,117	3,150,872	6,084,875
,984	28,297,634	55,371,512	13,007,020	28,113,721	55,002,180

Trade Pattern III was designed to show agricultural adjustment corresponding approximately to the projections generated by the representative-farm linear-programming models. Under this trade pattern, the value of output estimates for sectors 4, 5, and 9 (grains, cotton, and forages) were set at the levels projected as naturally occurring as farmers adjust to rising water costs. Grains remain in the projections in all years at levels above the base year. Forages decline to about one-half of the base year value by 2020. Cotton would remain at about 75 percent of the 1958 value throughout the period of projection. This 25 percent reduction in cotton had in fact already taken place as of the late 1960s. Therefore, cotton is projected as continuing at about the 1966-70 levels. Such a situation would require continued government support. However, such projections illustrate what level of agriculture could remain if such support were forthcoming.

Sector 10, miscellaneous agriculture, is shown as higher than the linear-programming estimates, since the linear-programming estimates did not include all the crops included in this chapter's definition of miscellaneous agriculture.

Sector 11, grain mill products, is posited at no lower than the base year, in order to support the feed grains industry. Also livestock production (sector 1) does not fall as low as the base year until 2020. Finally, sectors 6 and 7, vegetables and fruits, do not decline after reaching their maximum values in 2000. Thus, the agricultural portion of the economy is posited at its maximum reasonable size, given natural adjustment due only to water cost in agriculture and demand for agricultural products. The nonagricultural portion of the economy is posited to have rapid economic growth.

Trade Pattern IV is considerably more water saving than is Pattern II, yet produces only slightly less total value of gross state output. As we will see in a following section, it posits even greater changes than are necessary to stay within Arizona's existing water supplies through the year 2020. The gross value of output of most agricultural sectors is projected as declining over time after 1980. However, many agricultural sectors have higher value of output than in the base year (1958) through 1980 and some are still higher than in the base year in 2020. Farm dairy products grow continuously from 1958. Vegetables grow rapidly through 2000 before declining to 1958 levels in 2020. Meat animals and products (including feedlots) are shown as declining after 1980 but are still larger than the base year in 2000. Major water saving above that saved under Trade Pattern III comes about through drastic decline in the feed grain, forage, and cotton sectors.

Most, but not all, nonagricultural sectors increase more rapidly than under Trade Pattern II, but no faster than shown in Trade Pattern III. The major differences in the nonagricultural sectors of the economy as between pattern II and patterns III and IV are faster posited rates of growth in sectors 19, 21, and 24 – the aircraft, other manufacturing, and services sectors, respectively.

Projections of Water Demand Compared to Possible Supply

Alternative Water Supply Conditions

The approximate annual sources and disposition of water in Arizona are discussed in detail in chapter 1. Briefly they are as follows:

Of the total surface waters annually available to Arizona (about 83 million acre-feet), an estimated 72.5 million acre-feet are lost through evaporation and evapotranspiration by "noneconomic" natural vegetation. An additional 4.2 million acre-feet are used by "economic" natural vegetation – that is, by timber and range forage which has an economic use other than merely "covering the earth." About 1.6 million acre-feet are recharged into the groundwater table. This is a beneficial use since water stored in the ground may be pumped as from a reservoir. Of the remainder, about 2.9 million acre-feet are captured for use or storage. About 1.8 million acre-feet of Arizona's legal allocation from the Colorado River are as yet undeveloped and would be the water source for the proposed Central Arizona Project, although how much of this 1.8 million acre-feet is actually available in the river is still a matter for argument. A 1972 report of the Arizona Water Commission estimates that 1.7 million acre-feet will actually be available for development in 1980. Because of system losses, 1.6 million acre-feet could be delivered by the Project in that same year. In future years, less water would be available for use in Arizona as the upper Colorado River Basin develops and uses its allotted proportion of the available water. Estimates of water available for use by Arizona in the Central Arizona Project (or some alternative development) in the years 2000 and 2020 are 1.3 and 1.2 million acre-feet, respectively. Corresponding estimates of possible Project deliveries are about 1.2 and 1.1 million acre-feet.

Underground reservoirs, the other basic source of Arizona's water supply, differ significantly from precipitation and river inflow as a water supply source in that water can be withdrawn at a rate in excess of the replenishment rate resulting in depletion or "mining" of these reserves. This has been happening in Arizona for quite some time. In recent years, for example, the withdrawal of groundwater for all purposes has averaged

TABLE 6-19

Source of Arizona's Average (1965-1970) Water Use

Source	Million Acre-feet	
Runoff and river flow captured for use	2.9	
Annual groundwater recharge	1.6	
Total annually renewable supply		4.5
Annual groundwater overdraft	3.0	
Total water used		7.5

about 4.6 million acre-feet (Arizona State Land Department, Annual). Since annual recharge of the groundwater reserves is estimated at 1.6 million acre-feet, Arizona's groundwater reservoirs are being depleted at the rate of about 3.0 million acre-feet per year. The length of time this rate of depletion can continue depends upon the rate of pumpage and total amount of economically recoverable water stored underground, estimated at some 600 million acre-feet (Harshbarger et al., 1966), and its distribution.

A summary of sources of Arizona's current water use is shown in table 6-19. The sum of surface waters captured annually and annual groundwater recharge equals 4.5 million acre-feet. The deficit in current requirements is made up by a 3.0 million acre-feet overdraft on the groundwater reservoir.

This information reveals the contingent nature of Arizona's water supply. For example, the water supply is greater if the unallocated portion of Colorado River water is included, and less if supply were to be restricted to annually renewable sources.

For purposes of our subsequent analysis, four alternative water supply conditions for Arizona have been posited (table 6-20). These alternative posited supply conditions will be compared with the requirements generated by the alternative patterns of economic growth and external trade.

The four water supply conditions are as follows:

1. "Existing water use" (7.5 million acre-feet) is Arizona's annually renewable supply, not including Arizona's undeveloped entitlement from the Colorado River, plus the annual overdraft at the average annual rate occurring in the 1960s of 3.0 million acre-feet.

2. "Existing annually renewable water supply" (4.5 million acre-feet) does not include Arizona's undeveloped entitlement from the Colorado River nor the average annual overdraft of 3 million acre-feet.

3. "Potential annually renewable water supply" is the existing renew-

able supply plus the currently undeveloped supply that could be delivered by the Central Arizona Project from the Colorado River. This available undeveloped supply will decline over time as competition for Colorado River water increases. Total "potential annually renewable supply" will equal 6.1, 5.7, and 5.6 million acre-feet in 1980, 2000, and 2020, respectively.

4. "Potential water use" is the potential annually renewable supply plus the average annual level of groundwater overdraft. "Potential water use" will equal 9.1, 8.7, and 8.6 million acre-feet in 1980, 2000, and 2020, respectively.

Components of Water Demand

The results of our alternative projections of the demand for water when compared with the alternative possibilities for future water supplies, are summarized in table 6-21. Water-use categories shown in this table are defined as follows. "Water consumed" is total raw water intake that is consumed within the state of Arizona directly as raw water itself and indirectly as water embodied in goods and services produced either in Arizona or imported into Arizona from outside the state. "Water exported" is raw water embodied in goods and services produced in Arizona and exported out of the state. "Water imported" is the quantity of water embodied in goods and services imported into the state that would have been consumed as raw water in their production if they had been

TABLE 6-20

Alternative Water Supply Conditions in Arizona

Alternative Possibilities	1970	1980	2000	2020
Existing water use	7.5	7.5	7.5	7.5
Less:				
Groundwater overdraft at 1970 rate	3.0	3.0	3.0	3.0
Existing annually renewable water supply	4.5	4.5	4.5	4.5
Plus:				
Additional water available from the Colorado River	1.7	1.6	1.2	1.1
Potential annually renewable water supply	6.2	6.1	5.7	5.6
Plus:				
Groundwater overdraft at 1970 rate	3.0	3.0	3.0	3.0
Potential water use	9.2	9.1	8.7	8.6

TABLE 6-21

Arizona's Projected Water Status and Demand for and Supply of Water (in acre-feet), Under Alternative Trade Patterns, in 1980, 2000, and 2020

	Trade Pattern I	Trade Pattern II	Trade Pattern III	Trade Pattern I[illegible]
1980 projection				
Water use categories				
Water consumed	7,031,565	5,362,242	5,362,242	5,362,24[illegible]
Water exported	13,221,244	3,945,882	5,331,855	3,406,44[illegible]
Water imported	2,729,702	2,521,911	3,672,827	3,672,82[illegible]
Total quantity of raw water demanded	17,523,107	6,786,213	7,021,270	5,095,85[illegible]
Water status under conditions of alternative raw water supplies				
Existing annually renewable supply (4,500,000 a-f)	−13,023,107†	−2,286,213*	−2,521,270*	−595,8[illegible]
Potential annually renewable supply (6,100,000 a-f)	−11,423,107†	−686,213*	−921,270*	1,004,1[illegible]
Existing water use (7,500,000 a-f)	−10,023,107†	713,787*	478,730*	2,404,1[illegible]
Potential water use (9,100,000 a-f)	− 8,423,107†	2,313,787*	2,078,730*	4,004,1[illegible]
2000 projection				
Water use categories				
Water consumed	15,461,338	9,700,691	9,700,691	9,700,6[illegible]
Water exported	29,071,497	4,549,184	7,001,214	3,240,6[illegible]
Water imported	6,002,197	5,123,960	9,201,646	9,201,6[illegible]
Total quantity of raw water demanded	38,530,638	9,125,915	7,500,529	3,739,6[illegible]
Water status under conditions of alternative raw water supplies				
Existing annually renewable supply (4,500,000 a-f)	−34,030,638†	−4,625,915†	−3,000,529*†	760,3[illegible]
Potential annually renewable supply (5,700,000 a-f)	−32,830,638†	−3,425,915†	−1,800,529*	1,960,3[illegible]
Existing water use (7,500,000 a-f)	−31,030,638†	−1,625,915†	529*†	3,760,3[illegible]
Potential water use (8,700,000 a-f)	−29,830,638†	−425,915†	1,199,471*	4,960,3[illegible]

	Trade Pattern I	Trade Pattern II	Trade Pattern III	Trade Pattern IV
projection				
ter use categories				
Water consumed	30,427,336	16,630,343	16,630,343	16,630,343
Water exported	57,211,620	5,961,100	6,316,173	2,022,523
Water imported	11,812,099	9,776,712	14,725,271	14,725,271
tal quantity of raw water demanded	75,826,857	12,814,731	8,221,245	3,927,595
ter status under conditions of alternative raw water supplies				
Existing annually renewable supply (4,500,000 a-f)	−71,326,857†	−8,314,731†	−3,721,245†	572,405‡
Potential annually renewable supply (5,600,000 a-f)	−70,226,857†	−7,214,731†	−2,621,245*	1,672,405‡
Existing water use (7,500,000 a-f)	−68,326,857†	−5,314,731†	−721,245†	3,572,405‡
Potential water use (8,600,000 a-f)	−67,226,857†	−4,214,731†	378,755*	4,672,405‡

issible possibility; more than zero and less than three million acre-feet of groundwater overdraft.
water usage is too high; more than three million acre-feet of groundwater overdraft.
water usage is too low; annually renewable water is wasted.

produced in Arizona. Therefore, the "total quantity of raw water demanded" (raw water needed within the state) is raw and embodied "water consumed" plus embodied "water exported" minus embodied "water imported." The "total quantity of raw water demanded" is that amount of raw water Arizona must provide under each alternative trade pattern for in-state agricultural, industrial, municipal, and domestic use.

"Total quantity of raw water demanded" under each trade pattern may be compared to the posited alternative "raw water supply" conditions for each year of the projection. The difference between total quantity of raw water demanded and the chosen raw water supply condition is termed "water status." A negative water status indicates that more raw water would be needed within the state to meet the projected raw water demand. A positive water status indicates a surplus of raw water within the state over the quantity of raw water demanded.

In summary: [Total raw water demanded in state] equals [raw and embodied water consumed in state] plus [embodied water exported out of state] minus [embodied water imported into the state].

Further: [Water status] equals [posited water supply in state] minus [total raw water demanded in state].

Raw Water Status Under Trade Pattern I

The assumption of Trade Pattern I is that all sectors of the Arizona economy will grow proportionately at the projected overall growth rate for the whole state economy. A glance at table 6-21 reveals the true naiveté of such an assumption as well as the inadequacy of an increase in raw water supply as the sole solution to the water problem in Arizona. Even with the maximum potential raw water supply condition, the raw water deficit would already be 8.4 million acre-feet by 1980 and would be an enormous 67.2 million acre-feet in 2020. It is clear that the structure of the economy *must* change in a way that will cause the total quantity of raw water demanded to fall. Remaining controversy must center around the *degree* and pattern of this necessary structural change in the Arizona economy.

Raw Water Status Under Trade Patterns II to IV

What is the proper quantity of raw water to use and thus the exactly proper trade pattern to choose? The answer is not simple, and we do not attempt a full answer here. It is clear, however, that Arizonans would wish to use at least the existing annually renewable supply; otherwise a valuable resource would simply go to waste. They would want to use at least *some* of their groundwater supply, because if they did not, a valuable resource would go unused. How much of a groundwater deficit is the only question. Probably it should not be a larger annual deficit than currently exists. Probably it should be somewhat smaller. Even if additional water supplies are developed, some groundwater overdraft should exist. Thus, the proper raw water use should be somewhere between the annually renewable supply and the annually renewable supply plus 3.0 million acre-feet of overdraft.

These conclusions may be applied to table 6-21 as follows. The water status under "existing annual renewable supply" and "potential annual renewable supply" should be negative but less than minus 3.0 million acre-feet. The water status under "existing water use" and "potential water use" should be positive but less than plus 3.0 million acre-feet. Using these criteria, the entries in tables 6-21 are coded in three categories: (1) relevant possibility; more than zero and less than three million acre-feet of groundwater overdraft; (2) raw water usage is too high; more than three million acre-feet of groundwater overdraft; and (3) raw water usage is too low; annually renewable water is wasted.

From table 6-21, we see that in 1980 Trade Pattern II (resulting from projected current trends in the Arizona economy and excluding problems of water scarcity or cost) would result in a raw water surplus of about 700,000 acre-feet when compared to a raw water supply equal to the level of existing (1970) raw water use; that is, by 1980, some 700,000 acre-feet less pumpage than in 1970 from the groundwater reservoir would be necessary. If the Central Arizona Project was fully operational by that time, there would be only 686,213 acre-feet of overdraft on the groundwater reservoir rather than the average annual overdraft of the 1960s of about 3.0 million acre-feet.

Trade Pattern III is a synthesis of the representative-farm linear-programming models and the "economic shift" analysis. Under this posited trade pattern, most sectors were projected as changing exactly as in Trade Pattern IV where water-saving activities are actively encouraged. However, those agricultural sectors which were earlier examined in detail, relative to their responsiveness to water cost, were projected by the representative-farm linear-programming models as declining less rapidly than posited under Trade Pattern IV. Under this modification, raw and embodied water consumed within the state remains constant as in all the other patterns, embodied water imported is the same as in Pattern IV, but embodied water exported is greater than in Pattern IV because of the increase in agricultural output. To the extent that the state is posited as running a positive value of net exports under this pattern, rather than having net exports equal zero, the necessary total quantity of raw water demand is somewhat overestimated. Nevertheless, Trade Pattern III is a quite reasonable possibility for 1980. Under this pattern, Arizona would be using about one-half million acre-feet less water by 1980 than during the 1960s.

In 1980, Trade Pattern IV would require about 2.0 million acre-feet less raw water than would Trade Pattern III. Under Pattern IV, only 0.6 million acre-feet of groundwater overdraft would occur. Such a small rate of overdraft is unwise and implies a greater decline than necessary in irrigated agricultural output. Thus, while Trade Pattern IV would generate ample gross state product to maintain Arizona's economic growth, for 1980 it implies more rapid adjustment of the economy than necessary.

Table 6-21 shows for the year 2000 corresponding estimates of "water status." We see that by 2000 water scarcity becomes enough of a factor that it may no longer simply be ignored. To maintain Trade Pattern II would imply a groundwater overdraft of about 4.6 million acre-feet if no additional supplies were developed. Even if potential additional supplies were developed so that the annually renewable supply were equal to 5.7 million acre-feet, a 3.4 million acre-foot overdraft is implied.

However, we see that natural projected adjustment by agriculture to rising groundwater cost (Trade Pattern III) would be adequate for maintaining through the year 2000 a groundwater overdraft of no more than the 3.0 million acre-feet of average annual groundwater overdraft characteristic of the 1960s, even without development of potential supplies. With development of potential supplies, only 1.2 million acre-feet of overdraft would be required.

Adjustment to Trade Pattern IV before the year 2000 would be quite unnecessary. Such adjustment would imply a waste of the state's annually renewable supply.

Finally, table 6-21 looks 50 years into the future to the year 2020. Significant adjustment in the economy *must* occur by this time. Even if potential surface water supplies are developed, Trade Pattern II would still require a 7.2 million acre-foot annual groundwater overdraft.

If adjustment were made only as projected by the representative-farm linear-programming models, as illustrated by Trade Pattern III, either additional surface water supplies would be necessary or the annual groundwater overdraft would need be increased by 0.7 million acre-feet above the annual average of 3.0 million acre-feet of the 1960s. If the additional potential surface supplies were developed, 2.6 million acre-feet of overdraft would still be required.

However, if the Arizona economy adjusted water use in 2020 by as much as implied by Trade Pattern IV, annually renewable water would be wasted under any of the four posited raw water supply conditions. Obviously, what is needed is slightly more decline by 2020 in output of the low-valued crops of irrigated agriculture from that posited by Trade Pattern III, but much less decline in agricultural output than posited by Trade Pattern IV. Thus, by 20 years after the turn of the coming century, only slightly more encouragement of water-saving activities and only slightly more discouragement of water-spending activities will be required in Arizona than implied by mere laissez-faire adjustment to rising water prices. Such slight encouragement and discouragement, wholly without development of the rather small quantity of potential surface water supplies, would enable the Arizona economy to grow at the rapid rates of population, gross state product, and per capita income that were posited in the early part of this chapter.

Summary

The analysis of this chapter has demonstrated that the economy of Arizona can continue its rapid rate of population, output, and income growth over the next 50-year period, through 2020, without obtaining additional raw water supplies. Slightly less change in the economic structure of the state would be necessary if additional supplies, such as from the CAP (Central Arizona Project), were available. But, change is necessary and inevitable, as the projected water requirements for the "naive" Trade Pattern I show. The relevant question is, *how much change of what kind* is necessary?

Results of our alternative projections show that by 2020 change equal to that projected in Trade Pattern III will be necessary even if the CAP is built and some overdraft on the groundwater table continues. However, less change than Trade Pattern IV would create water surpluses even over the existing annually renewable supply and would result in wasted water resources.

It remains to be determined whether the costs or dislike for modifying the economic structure of the state, and hence the raw water demand, is greater or less than the cost or distaste for investing in raw water development schemes. Choice is not costless. However, it has been demonstrated that an economic structure and trade policy is as truly and as efficacious a water policy as is a raw water development policy – and, that some new structure and trade policy must be adopted (some new policy will, in fact, occur naturally) no matter what raw water development policy occurs.

7. Conclusions and Implications

IS WATER SCARCITY a restraint on economic growth even in a desert environment such as Arizona? The answer, plainly evident from the research reported here, can only be – not necessarily. It depends on how Arizonans view the problem, how they approach its analysis, and what solutions they are willing to consider.

If Arizonans, as instinctively behaving animals like the beaver, apply only their habitual responses to the water problem, the answer to that question is: Yes, water scarcity *will be* a restraint on growth. In this approach to problem solving, *supply* of water is the determining factor; supply is indubitably short and will be more so as growth proceeds, ultimately and not very far in the future becoming a restraint on further growth.

But if Arizonans are willing to reprogram their habitual pattern of response to the water problem, to behave like the cognitive analytical beings they are, if they are willing to take advantage of the gains from learning and experience in exploring hypothetical problem solutions, and if they are willing to consider adaptations in the socioeconomic and institutional structure of their society, the answer to the above question is: No. Under these approaches to solution of the water problem, *demand* for water may be the determining factor (given a fixed supply), and the structure of demand is as alterable as is the structure of supply.

However, in a nondoctrinaire search for solutions to the water problem, neither demand nor supply should be taken as fixed, and the search for solution should consider both demand change and supply enhancement in appropriate combinations and with appropriate timing – demand *and* supply are both determining factors in an array of appropriate and relevant mixtures over time. In searching for a solution, supply enhancement must be "costed" into the mix at its *opportunity* costs (other satisfactions foregone by committing resources other than water to water supply enhancing purposes rather than to other purposes for which they could be used). Only those supply enhancement alternatives should be considered further *for which their opportunity costs are less than the demand satisfactions gained from the increased supply of water.* Cost of supply enhancement thus turns out to consist, indirectly, of reductions in demand satisfactions attainable from the required resource inputs other than water or the value of demand satisfactions gained from the increased supply of water in exchange for the values of other demand satisfactions that must be given up.

Scarcity is not peculiar to water alone; *all* economic resources are scarce. Decisions as to development and use of all scarce resources are guided or regulated by sets of man-made institutions designed, it is hoped, to insure that each unit of the scarce resource used up in production or consumption will make its maximum contribution to social satisfaction (welfare). Whether or not the existing institutional sets actually do this for any particular scarce resource, permitting reasonable approximation of such a maximum in its development and use, is a matter determinable through experience and analysis. The allocative efficiency of the institutional sets surrounding the development and use of labor, capital, and land might be analyzed to determine their effect on efficient use of those scare resources.

However, this study is concerned with the allocative efficiency of water-resource institutions in Arizona. Our studies reveal that these institutions perform with considerable inefficiency, probably with less efficiency than do the institutional sets that surround the use of scarce labor, capital, and land resources. We find that the relative inefficiency in water development and use is due to an inadequately developed institutional set surrounding water.

Our analysis determines the degree to which development and use of water in Arizona falls short of a reasonable goal of allocative efficiency; it clearly points up the gains that Arizonans could realize if they reformed their water-related institutional sets to come closer to maximizing the efficiency with which their scarce water is used. Otherwise, water – the state's scarcest natural resource as compared to labor, capital, and land – can in fact become the limiting factor in the state's economic growth.

Our research is designed to determine just how inefficient that institutional set is, the magnitude of gains that are attainable through reforming it, and the comparative cost to the state's economy of various institutional means for resolving – or at least ameliorating – the state's "water shortage."

The solution toward which our research points is to evolve a set of water-related institutions that will facilitate change in water development and use so that each unit of scarce water used up will make its maximum (or at least a greater) contribution to economic well-being directly through its consumption and indirectly through its use in production.

We report herein *only* the gains in economic well-being that are *possible* in Arizona from development and use of its scarce water if the institutional set were reformed in such a way as to remove the restraints now placed on the efficient use of scarce water. We leave to another report our analysis of why the existing institutional set restrains efficient use of scarce water, and our suggestions as to changes that could remove or ameliorate those restraints.

Assuming a Do-nothing Water Policy

We began our analytical discussion by asking: What if Arizona were to do nothing to increase its present water supplies and nothing to change its water institutions, leaving decisions as to how water supplies should be developed and used solely to the holders of water rights responding *only* to the existing capitalistic money-market and government regulated system; during the fifty years after 1966, what would happen, and how drastically, to water use, economic output, and income in Arizona?

For our first answer to this question, we purposely put the situation in the worst possible light by posing a set of *highly restrictive assumptions:*

1. Nonagricultural economic growth in Arizona will occur only in the Salt River Project area and in immediately surrounding areas of Maricopa County at a rate derived from plausible projections of trends made by analysts working in that area; it will progressively displace agriculture from these areas and from use of the land and water resources in them; and no displaced agriculture will move elsewhere in the state, except cotton production, the allotments for which will transfer to other areas of Maricopa County outside the area directly affected by urban growth.

2. No changes will occur in the present set of water related institutions.

3. No changes will occur for better or worse in (a) relative prices of Arizona outputs compared to prices of the inputs required to produce them or compared to prices of outputs produced elsewhere that are competitive with those outputs when produced in Arizona, (b) in tastes and preferences on the part of Arizona producers and consumers, (c) in national agricultural policies, or (d) in any relevant technology of production.

4. There will be a stable (average annual) supply of surface flowing water, hence no change in surface water costs, but there will be no additional supply to substitute for depleting groundwater; thus there will be a continuation of groundwater overdraft, hence continuing decline in groundwater levels, hence a continuous increase in groundwater costs.

5. The state's nonagricultural economy requires such small quantities of water relative to total water use in the state that the price it can afford to pay for water is quite high relative to present and prospective water costs. The groundwater aquifers are so deep that agriculture alone will be affected by increasing groundwater costs, and only that part of the nonagricultural economy affected indirectly by adverse changes in agriculture due to rising groundwater costs will be affected by the declining groundwater stock, the rest of the nonagricultural economy remaining unaffected by rising water costs.

Projected Declines Within Agriculture

We began by focusing our analysis on agriculture because, under the preceding assumptions, only agriculture will be adversely affected by declining groundwater levels. (We relaxed these assumptions at a later stage in the analysis.) Rising groundwater costs, under these assumptions, will generate decline in those agricultural areas that are dependent on groundwater supplies in whole or in part. But, we asked, will that decline over the next half century be so great as to destroy the viability of the Arizona economy? The answer clearly is No.

1. There will be no change whatever in agriculture for better or worse in the lower Colorado-Gila (Yuma) area, in the upper Gila (Safford Valley-Greenlee County) area, or in the Salt River Project area (due to rising groundwater cost).

2. Economic decline due only to rising groundwater costs will occur in irrigated agriculture in the Santa Cruz Valley area (Pinal and Pima Counties), outside the Salt River Project area in Maricopa County, and in the Cochise County area. Hence, all projected declines in agriculture reported below and in table 7-1, will be concentrated in these three areas. The percentage declines reported in table 7-1 take the state's agriculture as a whole for their base; if based on the agriculture in the three adversely affected areas only, the rates of decline would be significantly larger.

Acres in crops in these three areas will decline about 196,000 acres between 1966 and 2015 or, in relation to total acres of crops in the state in 1966, by 18.4 percent (relative to crop acres in the affected areas only, by 28.6 percent). The decline will average about 4.4 percent per decade, or about 0.5 percent per year until 2005; it will slow down markedly

TABLE 7-1

Projected Declines in Irrigated Arizona Agriculture Resulting From Rising Groundwater Costs With and Without Urbanization in the Salt River Project, 1966-2015*

	Projected Declines			
	With Urbanization in SRP		Without Urbanization in SRP	
Cropped acres (1,000 acres)	294.2	27.6%	196.1	18.4%
Water use (1,000 acre-feet)	1,369	28.6%	906	18.9%
Gross farm output (million dollars)	37.1	13.6%	20.3	7.4%
Net farm income (million dollars)	16.9	15.5%	9.9	9.1%

*From Tables 4-6 through 4-11.

thereafter, being only about 0.8 percent between 2005 and 2015, or less than 0.1 percent per year. About 79 percent of the total reduction in acres in crops between 1966 and 2015 due only to rising groundwater costs will occur about equally in alfalfa, barley, and sorghum, the crops of lowest value per acre; the balance of the decline, about 21 percent, will be in acres of wheat, sugar beets, and safflower, the crops of next lowest value per acre. No reduction whatever will occur in acres of the highest value crops – cotton, field fruits and vegetables, seed crops, and citrus.

Water used in agriculture (at farm headgate or well-head) will decline at a fairly constant rate (about 4.4 percent per decade or about 0.4 percent per year) from 1966 to 2005 due to rising groundwater cost; the decline in use will slow down sharply after 2005, to only another 1.9 percent between 2005 and 2015. The overall decline in water use in agriculture due only to rising water cost between 1966 and 2015 will be 906,000 acre-feet (entirely in groundwater), or 18.9 percent of the total of all water used in agriculture in the state in 1966 (29.5 percent of the water used in the three affected areas only). Because decline in water use caused by rising water cost occurs only in the use of groundwater, only a small additional amount of "carriage" water will be saved in those few places where groundwater is pumped and delivered by irrigation districts.

All of the decline in water use due to increasing groundwater cost will take place in the use of groundwater only. Hence, the 906,000 acre-feet of water not used in agriculture in 2015 will be groundwater. Thus, gradually over 50 years, overdraft on groundwater, now about 3.0 million acre-feet, will be reduced about 30 percent, to about 2.1 million acre-feet.

Gross value of farm output will decline more slowly than either acres in crops or water used because only crops of lowest value will be displaced. Between 1966 and 2015, gross value of agricultural output will decline $26,300,000 or, on a statewide basis, by 9.6 percent (on the three-area base only, by 12.0 percent) due only to increasing cost of groundwater. The decline will be fairly uniform – about 2.2 percent per decade – or 0.25 percent per year, during the first forty years (1966-2005) but will slow down sharply after 2005, declining only about 0.7 percent during the decade 2005-2015.

Net farm income will decline in the areas outside the urbanizing area of Maricopa County by $9,900,000 or, on a statewide basis, by 9.1 percent (on the three-area base only, by 15.4 percent) over the 50 years from 1966 to 2015, or by about 0.2 percent per year. The decline will be somewhat more rapid during the first 30 years to 1995, averaging about 2.6 percent per decade; but will slow down to about 1.2 percent per decade during the last 20 years, from 1995 to 2015.

Gross Direct Cost of Declines in Agriculture

The declines in agricultural income brought about by increasing groundwater cost in agriculture, as shown in table 7-1, are only the declines in net incomes to farmers as managers and capital owners; they do not include losses of income by farm labor, either hired or supplied by the farm operator and his family. These income losses must be added to those in table 7-1 to get the full measure of incomes lost to the agricultural sector as a whole.

Furthermore, the above declines relate to the pattern of income changes that will emerge over a span of 50 years, the pattern of changes differing between decades; but the decline experienced in each future decade will continue to be felt as a loss of income far beyond the 50-year projection period.

But we need to know more than the 50-year time pattern of these income losses; we, and the public policy makers, need to know the present value (1966) of the entire stream of future losses in agricultural incomes that will flow from the predictable future increases in groundwater scarcity. Such a figure will be the basis for judging how much the state's economy can afford to pay, or sacrifice in some other form, in order to forestall this inevitable stream of future income losses.

Such a present value of the lost income stream may be derived in any one of three different forms: (1) the present value of the *total* stream of agricultural incomes lost over time to the economy as a whole, (2) the present value of the stream of total agricultural incomes lost *per acre-foot* of water abandoned from use in agricultural production due to increase in its cost over time, or (3) the *flow* (or amortized annual annuity) *value per acre-foot per year* of "abandoned" water in agriculture. These manipulations require choosing a discount rate by which values arising at different points in time may be converted into equivalent values at the present (1966) point in time. We chose two such discount rates, each resting on a 5 percent interest (time preference) requirement on savings which in this case are deferred incomes. However, one of our chosen discount rates presumes that the principal value of the deferred incomes need never be recouped (a presumption of riskless deferment of income) and yields a 5 percent discount factor; the other discount rate chosen presumes that the principal value of deferred income must be recouped within 20 years (a presumption of risk and uncertainty in future returns) and yields an 8 percent discount factor.

Our estimates, based on these considerations, of the gross *direct* cost to the Arizona economy imposed by increasing groundwater cost confronting agriculture are given in tables 5-5 through 5-7. The principal conclusions are: (1) The *total present (1966) value* of the future incomes that will be lost in agriculture (the present direct cost to the Arizona economy) is $142,900,000 (discounted at 5 percent) or $60,700,000 (discounted at 8 percent). (2) This direct cost *per acre-foot* of water abandoned in agriculture is $158 (at 5 percent) or $67 (at 8 percent). (3) The flow (amortized annual annuity) value of this direct cost *per acre-foot per year* of abandoned water is $7.89 (at 5 percent) or $5.36 (at 8 percent).

Gross Indirect Cost of Declines in Nonagricultural Incomes Stemming From Declines in Agriculture

The above projection of declines in agricultural income caused by rising groundwater costs and the present and amortized values of this loss is a decline and cost felt directly only in agriculture – by the owners of farmland and of farm capital, by farm management, and by all contributors of agricultural labor, both that which is hired and that which is supplied by the operator and his family. However, the income decline in agriculture is only part of the total decline in economic income generated by declining groundwater supplies. The decline in agricultural economic activity will generate declines in income among other state residents. The decline in volume of agricultural output will decrease the business of the handlers and processors of that output; decline in the volume of purchases of farm production inputs will reduce the volume of nonagricultural business. These nonagricultural income losses, induced by declines in agriculture, are *indirect* costs to the Arizona economy stemming from declining groundwater supplies confronting agriculture.

In order to derive estimates of these indirect losses in Arizona income, it must be determined which nonagricultural business sectors are affected by declines in agricultural activity and by how much each is affected. The affected nonagricultural sectors can be grouped into two classes that are affected quite differently by declines in agricultural output. In one class are those sectors that supply production inputs to agriculture. These are referred to as *backward linked* to agriculture. We estimated the income loss in these sectors directly from the I-O model of the Arizona economy. In the other class are those sectors that handle and process agricultural output. These are called the *forward-linked* sectors. These sectors present some greater difficulty than do the backward-linked sectors in determining the effect on them of output declines in agriculture. Because our I-O model does not permit a clearcut determination of the forward-linkage effects of declining agricultural output, we made two sets of estimates of indirect income effects, one of which includes *all possible backward and forward linkages,* and the other of which includes *only the backward linkages.* We feel that a valid estimate of the indirect cost to the Arizona economy of a decline in agricultural output is closer to the estimate based on backward linkages only than to the estimate based on both backward and forward linkages. But we recognize that this is an area of uncertainty that requires further research.

These *gross indirect costs* (nonagricultural incomes lost) to the Arizona economy stemming from the increasing scarcity (cost) of groundwater to agriculture are reported in tables 5-9 through 5-11. They are reported there with respect to all the alternatives implicit in the several issues discussed above: (1) backward linkages only, and backward and forward linkages combined, (2) time discount factors of 5 and of 8 percent, and (3) in terms of present value of the total of indirect incomes lost, in terms of the present value of incomes lost per acre-foot of water abandoned in agriculture, and in terms of the annual flow (amortized annual annuity) value of the incomes lost per acre-foot per year of water abandoned in agriculture. The principal conclusions from those tables are summarized in table 7-2.

TABLE 7-2
Gross Indirect Cost to the Arizona Economy Stemming From Decline in Agriculture Due to Increases in Groundwater Cost

Estimate*	Backward Linkages Only		Backward and Forward Linkages	
	at 5%	at 8%	at 5%	at 8%
A (thousands of dollars)	23,824	10,094	793,637	330,522
B (dollars per acre-foot)	26.30	11.14	875.98	346.81
C (dollars per acre-foot per year)	1.32	0.89	43.80	29.18

*A indicates present (1966) **gross total value** (cost) of future incomes lost (indirectly) to the Arizona economy.

B Indicates present (1966) gross total value (cost) of future incomes lost (indirectly) **per acre-foot** of water abandoned from agricultural use.

C indicates flow (amortized annual) gross value (cost) of future incomes lost (indirectly) **per acre-foot per year** of agriculturally abandoned water.

Gross Direct, Indirect, and Total Present Cost Stemming From Rising Groundwater Costs to Agriculture

The total gross present (1966) cost to the Arizona economy, that is, the present value of gross decline in Arizona incomes brought about by increasing groundwater scarcity confronting agriculture, is the sum of the direct and indirect costs (income declines) summarized in the two immediately preceding sections. These total costs are summarized in table 7-3.

Our discussion of these estimates of the total present gross cost to the Arizona economy brought about by agricultural declines induced by the growing groundwater scarcity called attention to the striking spread between the lowest and the highest estimates – from $6.25 per acre-foot per year of water abandoned in agriculture (direct plus indirect backward linkages only evaluated at 8 percent) to $51.67 per acre-foot per year (for direct plus indirect backward and forward linkages evaluated at 5 percent). We pointed out that each of these estimates tends to be an over-estimation due to inherent limitations of the I-O model as an estimator – the backward-linkages-only estimate being only slightly over-estimated, but the backward-and-forward-linkages estimate being grossly over-estimated. Though the data necessary to narrow or eliminate mathematically the spread between these estimates are not available (we are proceeding with research designed to contribute to this end), our knowledge of the structural and functional characteristics that lead to over-estimating bias in the I-O model makes it possible for us to judge the *ordinal* magnitude of that bias. A valid estimate of the total gross cost to the Arizona economy of water-related decline in agriculture will be much closer to the backward linkages only than to the backward-and-forward-linkages estimate under each of the two evaluation factor assumptions.

Furthermore, on grounds not related to the nature of the I-O model as an estimator, the 5 percent evaluation factor is much too low, the 8 percent factor (5 percent discount over a 20-year planning horizon) is significantly more realistic – in fact, a cogent argument can be made based on behavior exhibited in the private investment market that an even higher evaluation factor of 10 percent (a 14-year planning horizon at 5 percent) or even of 13 percent (a 10-year planning horizon at 5 percent) would be more valid. Thus, we believe even our 8 percent evaluation factor to be too low, but, again because an empirical basis for selecting a higher rate is not available, and because of the strong bias in public planning circles for selecting low evaluation factors, we did not select a factor higher than 8 percent. But, clearly, 8 percent is a more valid evaluation factor than is 5 percent.

Were one to take as a plausible estimate (though admittedly an ordinal judgment) that the "true" gross cost to the Arizona economy of the future incomes lost would fall between the backward linkages only and the backward-and-forward-linkages estimates such that about 30 percent of the spread between these two values would be below and 70 percent of it above the "true" value, then our plausible "most likely" estimate of the gross cost to the Arizona economy per acre-foot per year of water abandoned in agriculture (evaluated at 8 percent) would be [($34.54 – $6.25) 0.30] + $6.25 = *$14.74 per acre-foot per year* (amortized annual value evaluated at 8 percent) gross cost to the economy (relevant backward and forward linkages included), or total present 1966 cost per acre-foot of abandoned water would be [($431.83 – $78.16) 0.30] + $78.16 = $184.26, and total present (1966) cost of all water abandoned would be [($391,241,000 – $70,813,000) 0.30] + $70,813,000 = $166,900,000.

It will be noted that throughout the summary in the above three sections, our estimates were continually referred to as being estimates of the *gross* cost to or *gross* decline of incomes in the Arizona economy. Doing so clearly implies that we had not yet gotten the estimates down to their *net* magnitudes, that there were still offsetting values that must be removed from the estimates. When our analysis took this next step, we found that much of the wide disparity in our estimates of *gross* costs to the Arizona economy washed out and that our *net estimates* were much closer together.

TABLE 7-3

Gross Total Cost to the Arizona Economy Stemming From Decline in Agriculture Due to Increases in Groundwater Cost

Estimate*	at 5% Direct	at 5% Indirect	at 5% Total	at 8% Direct	at 8% Indirect	at 8% Total
			Backward Linkages Only			
A (thousands of dollars)	142,902	23,824	166,726	60,719	10,094	70,813
B (dollars per acre-foot)	157.73	26.30	184.03	67.02	11.14	78.16
C (dollars per acre-foot per year)	7.89	1.32	9.21	5.36	.89	6.25
			Backward and Forward Linkages			
A (thousands of dollars)	142,902	793,637	936,539	60,719	330,522	391,241
B (dollars per acre-foot)	157.73	875.98	1,033.71	67.02	364.81	431.83
C (dollars per acre-foot per year)	7.89	43.80	51.69	5.36	29.18	34.54

*A indicates present (1966) **gross total value** (cost) of future incomes lost (present gross cost) to the Arizona economy.
B indicates present (1966) gross total value (cost) of future incomes lost **per acre-foot** of water abandoned from agriculture use.
C indicates flow (amortized annual) gross value (cost) of future incomes lost **per acre-foot per year** of agriculturally abandoned water.

Net Direct, Indirect, and Total Decline in Incomes, Stemming from Rising Groundwater Costs to Agriculture

The difference between *gross* present cost and *net* present cost to the Arizona economy due to declining groundwater supplies confronting agriculture is explained in chapter 5 (although there the concept is referred to not as a *cost* to the economy but as the economically rational amount that can be paid by the economy to forestall the income loss or to "reduce or eliminate the cost"). The crux of the difference between gross and net present cost in this connection lies in the degree to which those whose incomes will be smaller or reduced to zero, all of which income decline goes into the calculation of gross cost, are able to recoup some or all of their lost incomes by transferring to other pursuits whether in or outside of Arizona. Net present cost to the economy thus is that part of the present value of the stream of income loss stemming from growing groundwater scarcity that the adversely affected residents of the state cannot recoup in accessible alternative employments for their personal attributes, or that portion of the income from their capital assets that they cannot recoup by depreciating out the capital in use or by selling it to others.

Gross present cost to the state's economy is the amount by which the present value of the aggregate of incomes credited to that somewhat mystical economic entity – the state – will be smaller than it might otherwise have been. On the other hand, net present cost to the state's economy is the present value of the amount of income which the aggregate of residents who constitute the state's economy will actually lose. Obviously the latter cost is the "true" cost to the state's economy that declining groundwater supplies will generate.*

Our estimates of the net present (1966) cost to the Arizona economy of increasing groundwater scarcity in agriculture are summarized in table 5-16. The salient conclusions derived from that table are that net present cost to the Arizona economy due to increasing groundwater

---

*To be truly the "true" cost to the economy, the aggregate of the net income sacrifices impinging on state residents must be adjusted to reflect adverse effects of such lost incomes on taxing structures and on public revenues for the maintenance and efficient use of public facilities and for nonrecoverable sunk investments in consumer capital assets (homes, for example). Because our analysis of the economic impact of declining groundwater supplies confronting agriculture in Arizona included a built-in recognition of continuing economic and population growth in the Phoenix Metropolitan Area, the problem of declining tax revenues and inefficient use of public facilities and losses in consumer sunk assets that would result if population were actually to *decline* tends to wash out, hence could be ignored in our analysis.

costs confronting agriculture over the course of the 50 years (1966-2015) lies between \$2.43 per acre-foot per year and \$5.94 per acre-foot per year (both estimates being flow or amortized annual values evaluated at 8 percent, the former being direct plus indirect backward linkages only, and the latter being direct plus indirect backward and forward linkages).

If the same plausible estimate as to the "most likely" value between these extremes is made as previously described, our estimate of the "most likely" flow (amortized annual) net present cost to the Arizona economy of increasing groundwater scarcity confronting agriculture is [(\$5.94 − \$2.43) 0.30] +\$2.43 = \$3.50 per year per acre-foot of water abandoned in agriculture if a maximum of 906,000 acre-feet are abandoned by 2015.

Present 1966 net total cost to the Arizona economy and present 1966 net total cost per acre-foot of abandoned water are not given in table 5-16 in order not to clutter the table unduly. The "most likely" estimates for these ways of stating the net present 1966 cost to the economy are (\$3.50/\$0.08) = \$43.75 net present 1966 total cost per acre-foot of abandoned water in agriculture and \$43.75 x 906,000 acre-feet = \$39,600,000 net present 1966 total cost to the Arizona economy.

The "maximum possible" net present (1966) cost to the Arizona economy (if one assumes that 100 percent of the computed decline in incomes attributable to backward and forward linkages between the agricultural and affected nonagricultural sectors is relevant – an assumption we consider to be grossly invalid), is \$5.94 net present (1966) cost per year per acre-foot of water abandoned in agriculture (from table 5-16), \$74.25 total net present (1966) cost per acre-foot (\$5.94/0.08), or \$67,300,000 total net present (1966) cost (\$74.25 times 906,000 acre-feet).

Impact of a Do-Nothing Water Policy on the Arizona Economy

We now can answer the first question asked about the economic impact of a do-nothing policy for dealing with the declining groundwater supply confronting agriculture, assuming, at this stage of the analysis, that the nonagricultural sectors of the economy do not grow beyond their 1966 levels or that their projected growth is not constrained by rising groundwater costs.

Such a policy would have some, but negligible, effects on the Arizona economy over the course of the 50 years between 1966 and 2015. It would have even less adverse effect after 2015 for a long but unmeasured period because declines in agricultural production and income will slow down significantly after 2005 and will not increase significantly until cotton acreage begins to go out of production *due to rising groundwater costs*. Even in 2015, 50 years hence (from 1966), net income in agriculture will still be 91 percent of the level of net income produced in agriculture in 1966, or income in agriculture will have experienced a gross decline of but 9 percent.

Even that decline will be gradual, spread over 50 years, or about 0.2 percent per year, which permits orderly and gradual liquidation of unneeded capital equipment and improvements in agriculture (but not of land) and orderly and gradual out-movement of persons to other employments. Thus, not only will the adjustments not be cataclysmic, but a major portion of the gross decline in the incomes of affected persons will be recouped in other employments.

If we express the gradually declining stream of incomes lost over the course of the 50 years, 1966-2015, due to rising groundwater costs confronting agriculture as a percentage of the present value of incomes in agriculture alone and in the whole Arizona economy if each were to continue undiminished from its 1966 level, we derive even a better picture of the economic impact of a do-nothing policy. These present values and their percentage relations are summarized in table 7-4.

Agriculture will remain an important segment of the state's economy, producing, even in 2015, 91 percent as much income as in 1966. It will, however, have reduced its physical level of activity (in terms of acres of crops) by about 18 percent, but in so doing it will be releasing about 906,000 acre-feet of groundwater per year, either to remain in the groundwater stock or for nonagricultural uses. If we include among the declines in agriculture those attributable to projected nonagricultural growth in the Phoenix urbanizing area, the gross decline in agricultural income will have reached 15.5 percent by 2015; the decline in physical activity in agriculture will have reached 27.6 percent by 2015, with about 1.4 million acre-feet of water then being released (some of which will be surface water) either to remain in the groundwater stock or to supply the rising nonagricultural demands. To the degree, of course, that the groundwater stock is used for nonagricultural demands, the present (1966) rate of decline will not be reduced by agricultural curtailment.

Furthermore, it is necessary to recall that these declines in agricultural and related nonagricultural activities and income due to rising groundwater costs will be heavily concentrated in particular areas of the state rather than spread uniformly over it. They will concentrate in the Santa Cruz Valley (Pinal and Pima Counties) area, in the nonurbanizing parts of Maricopa County, and in Cochise County (and if projected

TABLE 7-4

Present Values and Percentages of Income Decline, 1966-2015, Due to Rising Groundwater Costs Confronting Agriculture

Net decline in value of all incomes in Arizona as percentage of 1966 total income in Arizona	0.07 percent
Present value (evaluation factor of 8 percent) of the stream of annual agricultural incomes if undiminished from its 1966 level of $108,700,000	$ 1,358,750,000
Present value (at 8 percent) of the stream of **gross** decline in agricultural income (to 2015) due to rising groundwater costs	$ 60,700,000
Gross decline in value of income produced in agriculture as percentage of 1966 agricultural income	4.47 percent
Present value (at 8 percent) of the stream of **net** decline in agricultural income (to 2015) due to rising groundwater costs	$ 26,300,000
Net decline in value of income produced in agriculture as percentage of 1966 agricultural income	1.9 percent
Present value (at 8 percent) of the stream of annual total incomes produced in Arizona from all sources if unchanged from its 1966 level of $4,090,000,000*	$51,125,000,000
Present "most likely" value (at 8 percent) of the stream of **net** decline, direct and indirect, in the total of all incomes	$ 39,600,000

*USDC (1967b) table 1: Total Personal Income by States and Regions.

urbanization effects in the Phoenix area are included, declines in agriculture, not due to rising water costs, however, and release of land and water from agriculture, will occur in that urbanizing part of Maricopa County).

Assuming Development of a Supplementary Surface Water Supply to Substitute for Groundwater

Still operating under the restricting assumption that nonagricultural economic growth will not be restrained by growing groundwater scarcity and cost (we relax this assumption later), an increased supply of supplementary surface water will, depending on its quantity, have the effect only of (1) reducing the magnitude and rate of agricultural decline, (2) eliminating that decline altogether, or (3) permitting expansion of agriculture beyond even its present (1966) level. We confine our summary to the second of these, namely, an increased supply of surface water that will make unnecessary any decline in agricultural activity and income whatever. Analyses of the first and third effects can be, if desired, derived from data included in our analyses described in earlier chapters.

Increasing the supply of surface water in the Arizona system is a costly undertaking. If it were not, there would be no problem. Obviously, if new surface water were free, it would be desirable to increase that supply so long as doing so added anything at all to the level of satisfactions Arizonans could derive from its use.

But new surface water is not free. Therefore, the relevant question here becomes: How much can the Arizona economy afford in money cost or any other sacrifice to obtain an increased supply of surface water?

Let us begin with an obvious truism – those individuals, groups, or the Arizona economy as a whole adversely affected by growing groundwater scarcity cannot improve their economic strength or well-being by incurring cost (however one measures it) for supplementary water greater than the loss (cost) prevented by obtaining that water. Thus the loss imposed by increasing groundwater scarcity is a ceiling on the amounts the affected parties or the economy as a whole can pay for water to prevent that growing scarcity.

What one can afford for supplementary water is simply the other side of the coin of what he will lose if he doesn't get it, the latter being the cost of decline in groundwater availability. That cost is the decline in agricultural and related nonagricultural incomes stemming from increasing groundwater costs over the next 50 years (to 2015) if no additional supplies of water are developed.

Increasing the Water Supply in 1966

The steady but gradual decline in groundwater use in agriculture stemming from increase in its cost was projected to reach 906,000 acre-feet per year in 2015. If the decline in agricultural and related nonagricultural output and income that accompanies this decline in water use is to be prevented by increasing the water supply, then an increasing supply reaching 906,000 acre-feet by 2015 will be required. Let us begin by supposing that the requisite additional supply of 906,000 acre-feet were to be made available in 1966, thus preventing any subsequent decline in incomes. We found earlier that the present 1966 net "most likely" cost to the economy of the decline in agricultural and related output and income (evaluated at 8 percent) would be $3.50 per acre-foot per year (amortized annual cost), or $43.75 per acre-foot of water abandoned in agriculture, or a present 1966 total cost (for abandonment reaching 906,000 acre-feet by 2015) of $39,600,000.

If the economy obligates itself in 1966 to pay more than one of these amounts for that supplementary supply of water of 906,000 acre-feet per year to forestall these declines, it will be worse off with the water than without it; if it pays less, it will gain from the transaction; if it pays just these amounts, it will break even, hence, these amounts are the *rational payments in 1966 for an increased supply of 906,000 acre-feet per year of surface water.* [The absolute maximum in 1966 of such rational payments (evaluated at 8 percent) would be those that are possible if the indirect net cost attributable to 100 percent of the possible backward and forward linkages between agricultural and nonagricultural sectors are taken to be the relevant cost – an assumption we consider to be grossly invalid – or $5.95 per acre-foot per year (see table 5-16), $74.25 total present 1966 cost per acre-foot of increased supply (5.94/0.08), or $67,300,000 ($74.25 x 906,000) total present 1966 cost for a total supply reaching 906,000 acre-feet by 2015.]

These estimates have nothing to do with what such an increase in supply might or ought to cost to produce and deliver; they have to do only with what the users – individuals, groups, or the economy as a whole – would find it rational to pay for such a 906,000 acre-foot-per-year increase in supply. In economic parlance, these are various ways of expressing the demand price ceiling for supplementary water and say nothing as to the supply price for such water. The latter is an entirely different question to which we devote no attention in this study.

In the determination of such rational payments for supplementary water neither does the magnitude of the evaluation factor (the discount rate) chosen have any direct economic relation to the magnitude of the interest rate used in the calculation of the cost of developing and distributing that supply. The latter relates to the cost of funds to the developer and supplier of the water, the former to the risks and uncertainties and time preference experienced by the potential buyers of such water relative to the anticipated declines in incomes they will experience that the purchase of such water may forestall. If the developer and supplier of the water is the federal government, for example, it may as a matter of policy offer the water at a cost that includes an interest charge on deferred return of capital invested of, say, 3.5 percent. But that rate is related to government borrowing costs, government risks and uncertainties, and to public policy in determining charges for water it delivers. The evaluation factor (discount rate) used in determining the cost of declining incomes and the gains from preventing them on the part of water buyers is a cost to private parties and is related to private investment costs, private risks and uncertainties, and private time preference for income. The magnitude of these supply and demand rates may be markedly different – one arises in the public sector, one in the private, one is a component in the minimum supply price for supplementary water, the other is a component in the maximum or ceiling demand price for the same water. Hence, a federal interest charge of 3.5 percent, for example, in figuring cost of federally delivered water has no bearing whatever on the relevant discount factor applied to determining the rational ceiling value of such water to its potential buyers.

The above estimates of rational payments for supplementary surface water supplies are the amounts that would be rational for potential buyers to incur now (1966) for increasing amounts of water during each future year just sufficient to prevent declines in income in each of those future years due to groundwater abandonment up to a total of 906,000 acre-feet per year by 2015. They also approximate the rational amounts that could be paid for any annual increases in supply greater than those just needed to offset the declines due to increasing cost of groundwater.

Increasing the Water Supply at Alternative Points in Time From 1975 to 2015

The amounts that can rationally be paid by individuals, groups, or the Arizona economy as a whole for an increased supply of surface water of 906,000 acre-feet will increase, the longer the development of that supply is delayed beyond 1966, at least until 2015. If we summarize the "most likely" estimate of the net cost to the Arizona economy (evaluated at 8 percent) that will be prevented by an increased supply of surface water received at alternative future dates, the rational payments in each of the alternative future years for that increased supply of water will be as shown in the top section of table 7-5.

If we assume that 100 percent of the net cost to the economy of the backward and forward linkages between agriculture and the nonagricultural sectors are chargeable to groundwater decline – an assumption we believe to be grossly invalid – the "maximum possible" rational payments in each alternative future year for an increased supply of 906,000 acre-feet of surface water available in that year would be as shown in the bottom section of table 7-5.

Beneficiaries From Supplementary Water

Who are the potential beneficiaries from increased supplies of supplementary water? This question has been discussed in an earlier chapter. The more cogent points are the following:

1. The owners of farm real estate (or the holders of farm indebted-

TABLE 7-5

Most Likely and Maximum Possible Rational Payments, Evaluated at 8 Percent, That Could Be Paid for an Additional 906,000 Acre-feet of Surface Water in Alternative Years

Year of Development	Dollars Per Acre-foot per Year*	Total Payment per Acre-foot†	Total Payment†‡ (millions of dollars)
		Most Likely Rational Payment	
1975	$ 6.92	$ 86.50	$ 78.4
1985	8.72	90.00	81.5
1995	11.43	142.88	129.4
2005	12.90	161.25	146.1
2015	13.13	164.12	148.7
		Maximum Possible Rational Payment	
1975	$10.10	$126.25	$114.4
1985	14.91	186.38	168.9
1995	19.84	248.00	224.7
2005	22.62	282.75	256.2
2015	22.83	285.38	258.6

*"Most likely" values are calculated from columns 3 and 5 of table 5 - 17; "maximum possible" values are taken directly from column 5.
†Derived from data in column 2 of this table.
‡Total payment in year listed for an increased supply of 906,000 acre-feet.

ness for which farm real estate is pledged as collateral) are the largest potential direct beneficiaries.

2. Owners of farm capital equipment or improvements that can be depreciated through use or liquidated by sale and transfer would benefit to a small degree and only to the extent that supplementary water supplies could be made available to them.

3. Farm labor would benefit hardly at all.

4. Owners of nonfarm real estate would benefit little, if any.

5. Owners of nonfarm depreciable capital equipment or improvements would benefit in proportion to the degree that their business volumes and incomes are actually linked to the volume of agricultural output and only to the extent that supplementary water supplies available to agriculture would forestall decline in that output.

6. Nonfarm labor would benefit but little and then also only in proportion to its linkage to agricultural output and to forestall decline in that output.

7. Among all owners of farm real estate (or its creditors), the greatest potential beneficiaries would be those whose real estate lies in certain areas of Pinal and Pima Counties, in Cochise County, and in the non-urbanizing areas of Maricopa County.

8. Those individuals or groups in any of the above categories would receive the greatest potential benefits the more closely they are associated with the grain and forage industries and with safflower production; insofar as they are associated with the cotton, field fruits and vegetables, sugar beets, and citrus sectors of agriculture, they would receive no or little benefit.

9. Devising a system of payments for supplementary water neatly attuned to the potential benefits of each affected individual or even of any affected group of individuals is difficult, even impossible. The estimates of potential benefits we have presented serve only the nevertheless useful purpose of gauging the aggregate ceiling benefits to the Arizona economy or to major groups within it as a guide to rational decisions on the part of individuals, groups, or public policy makers concerning a rational policy for resolving the water problem insofar, only, as increasing the supply of water is a relevant alternative solution.

The Conventional Wisdom and Rational Payments for Supplementary Water

Why are rational payments for supplementary water so low compared to the values conventional wisdom attaches to them?

The "most likely" and "maximum possible" rational payments for supplementary water supplies, and the estimates of net present cost to the Arizona economy of declining groundwater supplies available to agriculture, provide the final answers to the question posed early in this chapter: Is water scarcity a restraint on economic growth even in a desert environment such as Arizona? To many laymen, our estimates of rational payments will come as a shock, because the payments are so low compared to the values – sometimes cardinal but more often ordinal – expressed so generously as to the ruinous impacts of water scarcity on the viability of the Arizona economy, and the absolute imperative that additional supplies of water be secured if the economy is to survive, let alone prosper and grow.

We began this research with the popular image of the water problem in Arizona derived from the conventional wisdom about it. As our research unfolded, the hard facts of the case, those that cannot be willed into or out of existence if one remains committed to reality, did not support the conclusions of the conventional wisdom. Water scarcity, even growing scarcity, is far less costly to the Arizona economy than is popularly supposed; whatever costliness the scarcity does impose, amelioration is far more a matter of reforming man-made institutional inefficiencies in water administration and management than in reforming its nature-made physical scarcities. At least, this is the case as far into the future as one can project with reasonable comfort.

Thus, it behooves us to explore why the cost of declining groundwater availability (the value of supplementary water supplies) is so low compared to those assumed costs that conventional wisdom has made almost universally accepted.

Conventional wisdom makes several serious errors in analysis, each error in turn building on a preceding one, so that initial errors are compounded by following errors, and final values miss the target altogether. The errors in conventional wisdom analysis are centrifugal, diverging, whereas scientifically valid analysis should strive to be centripetal, converging. Our analysis has made a conscientious attempt to do the latter, and, though we cannot claim to have succeeded completely, our values are at least on target, though they may not hit the bull's-eye.

Conventional Centrifugal Error in Analysis of Water Values

1. The conventional wisdom first figures incomes lost due to declining water availability at the level of average incomes generated per acre-foot of water used in agriculture, even frequently at the level of average income generated in the total economy per acre-foot of water used; the correct figure of incomes lost is at the margin of incomes lost per marginal unit of water abandoned. Within the economy as a whole, agriculture is the marginal user; within agriculture, farmers forego the least valuable uses of water as groundwater becomes more costly; within the limits of our 50-year projections, even in solely groundwater areas, these marginal uses consist only of grain, forage, and safflower production, with some small reduction in cotton yields – not in cotton acreage. Within these fifty years, reductions in agricultural incomes at the margins are not great enough to force complete abandonment of land and water by whole farms, but only some of their least valuable crop acreages, accompanied by some reorganization of farms in which the smallest ones tend to disappear by incorporation into bigger ones. In areas largely or wholly dependent on surface water, not even these adjustments occur. This is the average versus marginal fallacy.

2. The conventional wisdom, secondly, presumes that nonagricultural sectors to which agriculture is both backward and forward linked will decline proportionately to decline in agricultural output and income,

the latter figured at the much too high average rather than marginal level. But the linked effects of agricultural output to nonagricultural sectors also affect the latter only at their margins, the least valuable or more costly part of their activities being foregone when the agricultural output declines; this may, however, force out whole businesses operating solely or largely within adversely affected agricultural areas. The conventional wisdom ignores, especially in relation to nonagricultural sectors forward linked to agriculture, the possibility of their using substitute inputs in their processing activities in partial replacement, at least, for the diminished local supply of inputs from agriculture, again affecting only the margins of profitability. This is another case of the average versus marginal fallacy, though in this case in the nonagricultural sectors; but a linkage fallacy is added, that of the absolute nonsubstitutability of other inputs for locally produced processing inputs.

3. The conventional wisdom, thirdly, figures that all incomes lost when water availability declines is attributable to the lost water alone, thus figuring the value of the lost water to be 100 percent of all incomes lost. This is manifestly untrue because in production as well as in consumption water must be used in conjunction with other physical, biological, human, and capital inputs. This is a technological fallacy. This technological assumption is economically valid only if all other joint inputs are free or have no other productive use to which they can shift, that is, only if or to the extent to which they will remain wholly and permanently unemployed if they lose their opportunity for joint employment with the abandoned water. Such is largely untrue. Many of these displaced joint inputs can and will shift to other employments and be used productively (particularly is this true for labor, management, and some capital equipment and improvements). True enough, such transferability is not 100 percent possible and not costless, but only that part which is not transferable can be counted as income lost due to decline in water availability. This is the basis for the distinction between gross decline and net decline in incomes in our analyses. Presuming, as does the conventional wisdom, that one can charge for replacement water at the level of gross income lost may force all other associated inputs to "work for nothing." This is the nontransferability no-alternative fallacy (respecting nonwater inputs associated with water use).

4. The conventional wisdom, fourthly, figures that any income lost, no matter when in time, due to declining groundwater availability – even as distant as 2015 or beyond – is worth *now* 100 percent of its *then* value and justifies expenditures *now* equal to 100 percent of that *then* value in order to prevent that *then* value of the lost incomes. Doing so ignores the existence and the costs of time preference and of risks and uncertain-

ties confronted by *present* producers and consumers when confronting the question of incurring known *present* costs to reduce or prevent *future* income declines. This is the "time is costless" fallacy.

5. We summarize how this linked chain of fallacies arrives at values (costs) attributable to declining groundwater supplies that are much too high:

(a) It begins with values that are too high due to the *average versus marginal* fallacy (1) within agriculture, and (2) within the affected nonagricultural sectors.

(b) It compounds this error by relating decline in the forward linked agricultural processing sectors directly and proportionately to decline of agricultural output due to the linkage fallacy of absolute nonsubstitutability of other for locally produced processing inputs.

(c) It further compounds the error by the *nontransferability no-alternative* fallacy by failing to debit these already too high values by the alternative productive earning power of the displaced nonwater inputs (not crediting them with any productive value apart from the displaced water with which they had been used).

(d) It further compounds the error by the "time is costless" fallacy, failing to debit for time preference and risk and uncertainty the future values of future incomes lost in determining present (now or close-up) values of the stream of incomes lost to determine the present net cost to the economy of the expected future decline in incomes.

Thus it is that conventional wisdom analysis begins with a value that is too high for water that is abandoned in production due to increase in its cost followed by failure to debit that already too high value by a series of costs the economy will confront in preventing any decline in the stream of income stemming from that abandonment – a series of costs the economy will face whether or not analysts (or decision-makers who must act) ignore them.

Conventional Constraints on Available Options

Building absolute constraints into the analyses of options increases the economic cost of income decline stemming from growing groundwater scarcity when these constraints rule out lower cost or more efficient alternatives. Four absolute constraints usually incorporated into the conventional wisdom, usually implicitly rather than explicitly, do just that.

1. Conventional wisdom frequently asserts that any decline in agriculture and agricultural incomes is bad (without defining what "bad" is or how much the "badness" costs) and imposes a multiplied and proportional income loss on the nonagricultural economy (without specifying

the linkages through which this occurs or the magnitude of their adverse effects). This is the agricultural fundamentalist fallacy.

2. It also frequently incorporates the implicit assumption that productive resources used to prevent decline in water availability and consequent decline in related incomes have no alternative value-producing uses in the Arizona economy; hence, their opportunity costs on the well-being of Arizonans can be ignored when determining the value of income losses prevented by investments that offset declining groundwater availability; the gross gains from preventing the losses are not debited by the opportunity costs of the resources committed to such prevention.

3. Conventional wisdom also tends to argue, again implicitly, that present water supplies are or ought to be "locked into" present structures and patterns of use, that existing agricultural water users ought to be insulated against pressures for change due to declining groundwater availability and rising nonagricultural demands for water, from which it follows that the nonagricultural economy and population growth in the state will be rigidly restrained unless increased supplies of water from other sources are obtained.

4. It further incorporates the implicit constraint upon its analyses that the structure of the state's economy is rigid and invariant in fact, or that flexibility and change in that structure is undesirable in policy insofar as water use is concerned, assigning to decline in water availability the entire cost of any consequent restraint on economic and population growth in the absence of increased supplies of water.

Water as a Constraint on Projected Economic Growth

Thus far we have summarized the projected adjustments in agriculture caused by rising water costs and the costs such agricultural changes will impose on the Arizona economy. At that stage of the analysis, we disregarded the growth that will, in fact, be taking place in the nonagricultural sectors of the economy. Our projections of downward adjustments in agriculture and their related adverse impacts on the nonagricultural economy thus do not imply downward adjustments in the overall economy but only that they will constitute a drag on the amount of overall economic growth that might otherwise take place.

We introduced explicit recognition of the state's prospective economic growth and asked the question: If economic growth of Arizona occurs during the 50-year period 1970-2020 at a rate and magnitude consistent with projections of national growth and regional shifts in the pattern of that growth (favoring the Southwest), will Arizona water

TABLE 7-6

Summary of Projected Growth of the Economy of Arizona*

Year	Total Population	Total Real Personal Income (millions of 1958 dollars)	Per Capita Personal Income (1958 dollars)
Actual Data			
1958	1,193,000	2,222	$1,863
1968	1,663,000	4,234	2,546
Projected Data			
1980	2,143,000	6,246	2,915
2000	3,321,000	13,734	4,136
2020	5,003,000	27,028	5,402

*Compiled from tables 6-1 and 6-2.

supplies be sufficient to meet the total demands for water that such growth will generate?

The projected growth of the state's economy, under the conditions set forth in the first part of that question, we find in table 7-6.

We do not consider whether such growth is itself desirable; many think not. We simply take as given the conventional wisdom that such growth is good and will take place if water does not restrain it in one way or another. We are concerned only to explore whether or not water supplies necessarily will restrain it.

We compare the demands for water generated by this growth to four alternative levels of water supply available in the state. The magnitudes of the three most significant of these supply levels are taken to be as shown in table 7-7.

Our analysis then undertook to determine the volumes of water that would be demanded at future points in time by an economy of the size and growth rate described earlier. We could not proceed as previously, where we projected water demands by agriculture through use of optimizing linear-programming models. Analytical models capable of such a complex task for the whole of the economy were not available to us. So we proceeded in a different manner.

There is no one structural makeup of an economy such as Arizona's that is necessary to generate the levels of real personal income projected. The terms "structure" or "structural makeup" or "structural form" of the Arizona economy used throughout this discussion refer to the *relative economic size* in terms of output and income of *each* of the *27 economic sectors* which together compose the whole of the Arizona economy.

Because the real personal income to be produced by the Arizona economy as a whole at each future point in time to 2020, as projected in this study, remains the same regardless of the structure posited for the economy, each posited structural form must always be appropriately balanced to make "economic sense" relative to external-internal trade patterns, markets, and internal conditions of production. Therefore, the several structures of the economy we posit are not free to take on any form but only a form that makes plausible economic sense. We explain in chapter 6 the way in which structure of the economy was determined in our analysis for each level of income at each point in time in recognition of this restraint upon it.

There may be one "best" structural makeup for the Arizona economy, but in order to determine that one best structure and its water demands we would need the unavailable complex analytical model referred to above. So we proceeded instead by positing several (of which four are reported in chapter 6) plausible alternative structural makeups of the economy, each producing the same amount of projected real personal income, and determined the level of water demand each of these alternative structural forms of the economy would generate. The logic, analytics, and economic rationale of this approach are discussed in chapter 6.

It turns out that the crucial difference for our analysis between the several plausible structural forms of the Arizona economy, each of which will produce the same amount of real personal income and rate of growth, lies in the degree to which the external trade-pattern of the Arizona

TABLE 7-7

Alternative Water Supplies (in millions of acre-feet) Available in Arizona

Supply	Year		
	1980	2000	2020
Existing annually renewable supply (including recurring groundwater recharge)	4.5	4.5	4.5
Potential annually renewable supply (including development of additional undeveloped entitlement to Colorado River surface supplies)	6.1	5.7	5.6
Existing level of water use (including 3.0 million acre-feet of overdraft on the groundwater stock)	7.5	7.5	7.5

*Compiled from table 6-20.

economy involves the sale (embodied in products, of course) of high-priced water and the purchase (again embodied in products) of low-priced water to fill part of its water needs. We find that the different plausible structural forms projected for the Arizona economy vary widely in the degree to which such favorable exchange occurs in each.

The 1972 Arizona economy depends heavily on the external sale of agricultural products that embody large quantities of low-valued water in exchange for the importation of manufactured products that contain small quantities of high-valued water. In any economy where water is as scarce as it is said to be in Arizona, one would expect dependence on the sale (embodied in products) of small quantities of water of high value in exchange for products dependent on large quantities of water of low value, the exact reverse of the way the Arizona economy, as it is structured in the early 1970s, performs. That the economy is now using large quantities of water to produce low-valued products simply shows that water in Arizona (as of the early 1970s) is relatively inexpensive and relatively abundant.

The structure of the Arizona economy in the early 1970s, and the relative inexpensiveness and abundance of the water supplies that support it, are not necessarily inappropriate, considering the conditions out of which the economy developed, conditions that still exist to a considerable degree. Among these conditions, two deserve particular mention.

(1) Arizona is a young economy in terms of its economic development. Typical of all young economies, the production of primary products, derived directly from its natural resources, chiefly agricultural products dependent on large quantities of low priced irrigation water, has been emphasized in its growth as described in chapter 1. Though there are now strong signs of transition to an economy emphasizing secondary and tertiary economic sectors using less water per dollar of output, transition has only recently gotten strongly underway.

(2) The institutional conditions surrounding water use in Arizona have fostered "cheap" water necessary for irrigation use in spite of its apparent scarcity. Publically assisted development, subsidization of water prices to agriculture by other products of water use (chiefly electricity), groundwater policies fostering short run rather than long run maximization of income – all taken together have fostered cheap water prices and plentiful available supplies, thus furthering the agricultural development so desirable for initial economic growth.

For these reasons, the present structure of the Arizona economy and the water use that it generates may be economically rational. But it is the rationality of that use in the future, not that of the past and present with which our research is concerned. Future rationality may well call for shifting the structure of the Arizona economy away from what it is now, based on past conditions, toward what it must be in the future, based on future conditions. It is toward these future demands for water that our research reported in chapter 6 and summarized here is directed.

The four alternative structural forms of the Arizona economy that we developed for our analytical purposes, each structural form except Number I being attainable given appropriate public policy and action, were:

Trade Pattern I. The existing (1958) structural form of the economy simply expanded in scale to attain the projected growth and amount of real personal income projected for the state's economy as a whole – a "naive" structure.

Trade Pattern II. That structural form of the economy that one might expect would evolve, "naturally" and "automatically" under free-market forces, if water were so plentiful and low priced and so unrestrained in its allocation among uses and locations of use that it would be no restraint whatever on the structural makeup of the economy.

Trade Pattern III. That structural form of the economy that would evolve if water-transfer policies were modified to facilitate transfers among uses and locations of use and if programs were pursued to encourage growth of those nonagricultural sectors in which water generates high values per unit of water used, while at the same time allowing those parts of agriculture that are water-cost sensitive to decline due only to increasing water costs as projected in chapter 4. We believe Trade Pattern III to be closest to a prediction of the structural form the Arizona economy will assume if a "do-nothing" policy toward agricultural adjustments is pursued.

Trade Pattern IV. That structural form of the economy that would evolve if water transfer policies were modified to facilitate transfers among uses and locations of use and if programs were pursued to encourage growth of those nonagricultural sectors in which water generates high values per unit of water used (as in Trade Pattern III) but if in addition steps were taken to bring about further declines in agriculture (compared to Trade Pattern III) specifically to realize further releases of water within agriculture.

For each of these posited structural forms of the Arizona economy, each producing the same total amount of real personal income at each future point in time to 2020, we determined its aggregate gross in-state demand for raw water, including delivery and distribution losses. The volume of this demand is only for water to be used in production. Therefore, we estimated and added the volume of water to be demanded for

TABLE 7-8 — Projected In-state Raw Water Demands, Raw Water Supplies, and Deficit or Surplus in Supplies Relative to Alternative Structures of the Economy, Each of Which Will Generate the Same Rate of Growth and Magnitude of the Economy, Arizona, 1980-2020

	1980		
	Trade Patterns*		
	I	II	III
Total in-state raw-water demand (thousand acre-feet)	17,523	6,786	7,021
In-state raw-water supply (thousand acre-feet)			
1. Existing annually renewable supply†	4,500	4,500	4,500
Deficit (—), surplus (+) of supply	—13,023‡	—2,286§	—2,521§
2. Potential annually renewable supply†	6,100	6,100	6,100
Deficit (—), surplus (+) of supply	—11,423‡	—686§	—921§
3. Existing level of water use†	7,500	7,500	7,500
Deficit (—), surplus (+) of supply	—10,023‡	+714§	+479§

*See text of Chapters 6 and 7 for definition of trade patterns.
†See text of Chapters 6 and 7 for definition of water-supply conditions.
‡Raw water usage is too high; more than three million acre-feet of groundwater overdraft.

consumption (nonproduction) purposes, including general municipal uses, by a population of projected numbers.

Thus we derived an estimate of projected total in-state demands for "raw water" to 2020 for production and consumption purposes for each of the posited alternative structural forms of the Arizona economy if the economy were to grow in income and population as projected.

By comparing these derived demands for raw water in the state with the levels of available water supplies, we reveal whether and to what degree in-state water supplies will be adequate to meet the future demands of the growing economy. The results of this comparison are summarized in table 7-8.

Among the more important implications one can draw from these results are the following:

Trade Pattern I is an extreme posited economic structure designed to demonstrate that structure of the Arizona economy *must* change if

2000				2020			
Trade Patterns*				Trade Patterns*			
I	II	III	IV	I	II	III	IV
38,531	9,126	7,500	3,740	75,827	12,815	8,221	3,928
4,500	4,500	4,500	4,500	4,500	4,500	4,500	4,500
-34,031‡	−4,626‡	−3,000§	+760#	−71,327‡	−8,315‡	−3,721‡	+572#
5,700	5,700	5,700	5,700	5,600	5,600	5,600	5,600
-32,831‡	−3,426‡	−1,800§	+1,960#	−70,227‡	−7,215‡	−2,621§	+1,672#
7,500	7,500	7,500	7,500	7,500	7,500	7,500	7,500
-31,031‡	−1,626‡	+1§	+3,760#	−68,327‡	−5,315‡	−721‡	+3,572#

issible possibility; more than zero but less than three million acre-feet of groundwater overdraft.
water usage is too low; annually renewable water is wasted.

it is to realize the growth projected for it within the limitations imposed by its water supplies. If the Arizona economy, structured as it was in 1958, were merely to increase in scale, as in Trade Pattern I, to produce the projected levels of output and income, water shortages would be so tremendous even by 1980 that to overcome them simply by increasing water supply would be patently out of the question. If the state's economy were expected or forced to grow within the structural form of Trade Pattern I, water supplies would be a restraint on the magnitude and rate of growth. The question then is: What and how much change in its economy should Arizona anticipate or encourage in order to realize the projected growth within the limitations of its available water supplies?

Trade Patterns II, III, and IV are posited to test the possibility that a viable economy exhibiting the growth projected can be realized in Arizona within the limitations of its existing water supplies.

Trade Pattern II is an economic structure that would evolve if water were so plentiful and cheap that it would be no restraint whatever on growth. Nevertheless, even under this extreme condition as to water supplies, Trade Pattern II is a viable economy in Arizona at least through 1980, at which time it would be using 0.7 million acre-feet of water less than the existing level of water use, including the 3.0 million acre-foot overdraft.

Trade Pattern III yields a viable Arizona economy to somewhere around the year 2000, within the limitations of the state's existing level of water use. Thus, it seems likely, that if the state does nothing different relative to water supplies than it is now doing but modifies water policies to permit more flexible transferability of water among uses and locations of use, it can grow at the projected rate for another 25 to 30 years without restraint from existing water supplies. Expanding within the structure of Trade Pattern III, by the year 2000 aggregate real personal income in the state would be tripled over that of 1968, per capita real income would be larger by two-thirds, and population would be doubled – all at a level of water demand no greater than the present (early 1970s) level of water use (including 3.0 million acre-feet of overdraft). If 1.2 million acre-feet of additional surface supply are by that time available, this growth could be secured with overdraft reduced to 1.8 million acre-feet.

By 2020, Trade Pattern III will be generating a 0.7 million acre-foot deficit over the level of existing water supplies that includes a 3.0 million acre-foot overdraft. But if, beyond 2000, further structural change of the economy is engendered by policy actions involving purposeful curtailment of agriculture to release additional supplies of water for transfer to nonagricultural uses to the extent posited in Trade Pattern IV, the state will not only be using none of its stored stock of groundwater but will be "wasting" water by not using 0.5 million acre-feet of its annually renewable supply. Therefore some effort between 2000 and 2020 to alter the structure of the agricultural economy beyond that which produced Trade Pattern III but nowhere near as vigorously as that which would generate Trade Pattern IV would create an economy that would be economically viable through 2020 on the basis of existing levels of annually renewable water supply.

Trade Pattern III and Trade Pattern IV are identical in the size and rate of growth of their nonagricultural sectors. They differ only in the more rapid and drastic reductions in the size of some of the agricultural sectors in Trade Pattern IV than in Trade Pattern III. Trade Pattern IV in 2020 demands 3.6 million acre-feet less water than does Trade Pattern III in 2000, a reduction in water demand caused solely by reductions of these agricultural sectors during the 20 years. However, to stay within existing water supplies, including a 3.0 million acre-foot overdraft, would require a reduction in water demand of only 0.6 million acre-feet. Thus, change in the structure of the economy between 2000 and 2020 toward Trade Pattern IV (from Trade Pattern III) by curtailing agricultural sectors would need to be only about one-sixth as drastic on agriculture in terms of water use as our posited Trade Pattern IV would require.

As the foregoing summary indicates, water supplies in Arizona will be a restraint on its economy – however, not necessarily a restraint on its *growth* but on its *structure*.

Several general comments on these projected comparisons of water demand, water supply, and structure of the Arizona economy should be made:

A continuing overdraft from the groundwater stock of at least 2.1 million acre-feet appears to be economically rational at least through 2020. Our projections of agricultural declines due to increasing groundwater costs found agriculture remaining fully viable (though at reduced levels of activity and income) through 2015 in spite of increased groundwater costs confronting the industry due to a continuous overdraft on the groundwater stock gradually declining to about 2.1 million acre-feet per year in 2015.

Trade Pattern III in 2020 includes no more agriculture, and Trade Pattern IV includes less agriculture than do these projections of a viable agriculture through 2015. If the agricultural component of these Trade Patterns is economically viable through 2015 in spite of the continuous overdraft on the groundwater stock, the nonagricultural sectors of these Trade Patterns also will be economically viable in relation to groundwater costs because these sectors are all far less sensitive to water costs than are any of the agricultural sectors. It follows that use of the accumulated groundwater stock at least to the extent of a gradual decrease to a 2.1 million acre-foot annual overdraft by 2020 would not jeopardize the economic viability of any economic structure that generates a water demand not greater than this posited level of water use.

The water supplies to which demands are compared include no prospective quantities of treated and recycled sewage effluents which may add 0.2 million acre-feet in 1980 (Tucson and Phoenix Metropolitan Areas) and 0.4 million acre-feet in 2000. No estimate of its probable volume for 2020 is available to us, but it surely will increase 50 percent over its 2000 level, in line at least with population growth, or to 0.6 million acre-feet. These volumes, though seemingly small in relation to total water supplies, seem much larger when viewed as possible offsets to water deficits in future years. Note that Trade Pattern III requires in 2020 only 0.7 million acre-feet additional water supply over the present level of use that includes a 3.0 million acre-foot overdraft. This approximates the amount potentially available from recycled sewage effluent.

We conclude that state policies designed to affect the *demand* for in-state raw water are an equally effective alternative to policies affecting the *supply* of in-state raw water. Such demand-affecting policies will be those that (1) provide a favorable *climate* for industrial (nonagricultural) growth, including outlay of public funds to encourage, even subsidize, non-agricultural, industrial, commercial, and consumer in-migration, and (2) facilitate transfer of productive resources, especially water, from low return uses in agriculture to high return uses, agricultural and non-agricultural.

Finale

Our analyses yield conclusions that policy makers and citizens in Arizona must face, frankly and objectively, when hard choices must be made between alternative sacrifices and alternative benefits that will result from alternative means to resolve or allay the "water problem" in this water-scarce desert environment.

Solutions to the problem are not found only in what to do about water *supplies* but often, even more importantly, in what to do about *demands* for water through state policies encouraging, even aiding, change in the structure of the state's economy and pattern of water uses. The latter policies are logically no less appropriate or possible than state policies encouraging, even aiding, increases in water supplies.

Our analysis raises serious questions about the economic sacrifices and benefits stemming from efforts to increase water supplies in the near future (say the next 40 to 50 years) as a viable, gainful solution to the problem. However, throughout our discussions of structural changes in the economy that will permit growth within existing levels of water use mention continuously has been made regarding the necessity to modify state water policies to facilitate water transferability between uses and locations of use.

Water supplies in the state are adequate for continuous growth of the state's economy. What are needed are policy actions to facilitate changing structure of the state's economy and the transferability of water among uses and locations of use. Currently, the water problem is a management, an institutional, a *policy* problem – a problem of demand for water more than one of supplies – a problem of man-made rather than of nature-made restraints.

Growing water scarcity may, but need not necessarily, constrain economic growth in Arizona. The extent to which it will restrain growth will depend on the willingness of Arizonans and their political and professional leadership to face up to the questions involved, on their willingness to consider all relevant optional means for resolving the water problem, demand-decreasing and demand-shifting as well as supply-increasing actions, on their willingness to contemplate objectively change in long-standing and relatively inflexible laws and institutions surrounding water. Given readiness on the part of Arizonans to operate at these levels of willingness, the water problem can be solved smoothly and at a level of sacrifice on the part of water users and all citizens that is a minimum relative to the costs of water development alternatives and at total costs that are not above the possible net gains.

The problem and its solution are far more man-made problems of ownership, management, and transfer of water than they are nature-made problems of scant and declining supplies.

APPENDIX A

Representative-Farm Firms

The general conditions surrounding irrigated agriculture in the major farming areas of Arizona were described in chapter 4. In this appendix, using the detailed information derived from the 600 personal interviews of farm operators, we define representative farms for each of the study areas described. These representative-farm models are the basis of the fifty-year projections developed with the assistance of our linear-programming models.

Defining Representative-Farm Firms

When defining or specifying representative-farm situations, it is essential that farms be stratified according to the most crucial factors which affect the decision-making process. This done, a typical farm may be selected or synthesized to represent the group. Many criteria might be an appropriate basis upon which to stratify: size, management ability, soil productivity, water availability, age or education of the farm operator, net worth or capital position; all might be listed as crucial variables.

Arizona's major irrigated crop farming areas were first divided into six basic study areas, some of which were further divided into subareas on the basis of the form and cost of their water supplies. Within each subarea, it is believed that economies of size are most important in differentiating methods of production and adjustment decisions. For this reason, and because land area is the least flexible resource reflecting size of operation, the typical farm models developed within each subarea purport to represent groups of farms having similar size characteristics as differentiated by land area. Thus, for each study subarea within the state, typical farm models are specified and identified according to acres of irrigated cropland.

The procedure for differentiating the strata to be represented by each model was established after the survey was completed and after careful study of the arrayed data. All farms within the sample for each area were arrayed according to cropland acres. By inspection, different sets of breaking points were identified as being possible appropriate boundaries for stratifying various representative farms according to size. Five variables were considered as being important in differentiating levels of operation by size: these were cropland acres, number of wheel tractors, number of crawler tractors, number of full-time nonsupervisory employees, and number of hired supervisors. While the strata were identified and divided on the basis of cropland acres, the other variables were important in determining where divisions between strata should be made. The rankings for each of the five variables were reviewed, and the set showing the greatest number of "best" rankings was selected as the basis for the stratification used to develop the typical farm firms for each study subarea.

Within each study subarea and for each size of farm, pumping depths, pumping costs, government allotments, machinery availabilities, and other restrictions were specified.

Subarea Definitions

Farms in the Yuma, Graham, Greenlee, and Cochise County study areas were stratified mostly by size. Since geographical differences and water-supply conditions in those areas were closely correlated with size, we do not make distinctions by geographical area within each of these counties herein. The total county study areas are shown in figure 4-2 of the text.

The analysis of Maricopa, Pinal, and Pima counties was more complicated, because of the various conditions of water supply encountered in these counties, including groundwater depths, water quality, rate of decline, and the conjunctive use of surface and groundwater supplies. Therefore, each of these county study areas was divided into subareas for intensive study. These subareas are delineated in figures A-1 to A-3, with abbreviations used in these figures explained in table A-1a, b, c.

Figure A-1 shows the study areas within Maricopa County, the most complicated situation. Farms in the Salt River Project and Roosevelt Water Conservation District are generally of similar sizes and type but face different proportions of surface and groundwaters as described in the text. Farms outside the Salt River Project Irrigation District, which (including the RWCD) we call the Maricopa County groundwater areas because they obtain *most* of their water from the ground, are classified into two other groups on the basis of water depth, water quality, farm sizes, and basic cropping patterns. We call these two areas Maricopa A and Maricopa B.

Maricopa A consists of farms in the Roosevelt Irrigation District,

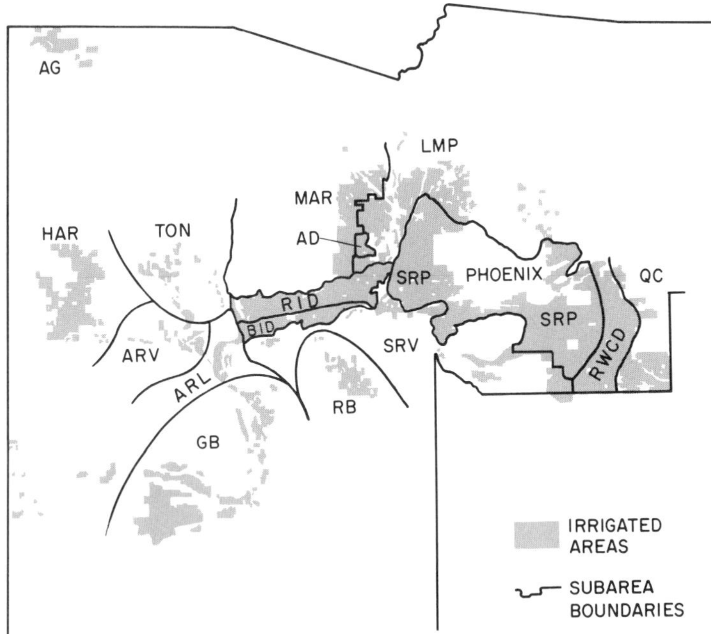

Fig. A-1. *Study areas within Maricopa County.*

Table A – 1a: Explanation of Symbols in Fig. A – 1.

SRP	Salt River Project
RWCD	Roosevelt Water Conservation District
Groundwater Areas	
Maricopa A	Shallow groundwater levels, poor quality water
RID	Roosevelt Irrigation District
BID	Buckeye Irrigation District
ARL	Arlington Canal Company
SRV	Farms not in a district located south and west of the Salt River Project extending west to Buckeye
ARV	Area along Centennial Wash west of Arlington Canal Company service area
GB	Area between Gillespie and Painted Rock Dams
Maricopa B	Deep groundwater levels, good quality of water
MAR	Maricopa County Municipal Water Conservation District No. 1
AD	Adaman Mutual Water Company
LMP	Pump water area located around Litchfield Park, Marinette and Peoria
TON	Tonopah area located west of the Hassayampa River
HAR	Harquahala Valley
AG	Aguila
RB	Rainbow Valley
QC	Queen Creek area in eastern Maricopa County outside of the SRP and RWCD

the Buckeye Irrigation Company, and Arlington Canal Company service areas plus farms relying solely upon private farm wells located in the vicinity of the Gila River from the southern edge of the Salt River Project to the Painted Rock Dam west of Gila Bend. This area is characterized by a cropping pattern consisting chiefly of cotton, alfalfa, and grains. Pumping lifts in this area averaged less than 300 feet in 1966. Rates of decline in water levels were relatively small, generally four feet per year or less. Quality of water is relatively poor, and the quantity of water applied per acre of crop grown was measurably higher than in Area B. Most of the water in this area contains more than 1,500 parts per million (PPM) of total dissolved salts, which puts it in the high to very high salinity hazard range for irrigation water (Smith et al., 1964).

Maricopa B consists of farms in the subareas serviced by Maricopa County Municipal Water Conservation District No. 1 and the Adaman Mutual Water Company, plus farms relying solely upon private farm wells in McMullen Valley near Aguila, Harquahala Valley, the Tonopah area, Rainbow Valley, the Litchfield Park-Marinette-Peoria area, and the Queen Creek area in the southeastern part of Maricopa County. Cropping patterns in this area include substantial acreages of vegetables, grapes, and citrus fruits as well as cotton, grains, and forage. Pumping lifts generally were 300 feet or greater. Rates of decline in the water table were quite high, with the bulk of these subareas declining at a rate of seven feet or more per year. Water quality generally was quite good, with moderate to small amounts of total dissolved salts, and the rate of water application per acre of crop grown was somewhat less than in Maricopa A.

Pinal County, as shown in figure A-2, was divided into six subareas for study. These areas were delineated on the basis of relatively homogeneous groundwater depths so as to be adaptable to analysis using the analog model of the groundwater system as described in Anderson (1968) and Burdak (1970). The Maricopa and Stanfield subareas had the deepest pumping depths in 1966; the Casa Grande and Coolidge subareas had the shallowest. The Casa Grande and Coolidge subareas lie adjacent to the Gila River and include surface waters delivered by the San Carlos Irrigation Project.

Figure A-3 shows three subareas for Pima County. These three divisions were made on the basis of the original (1966) pumping depths and experienced decline rates in pumping levels in the preceding five-year period. First-period (1966) pumping levels and groundwater decline rates were as follows:

Study Area	Pumping Level	Decline Rate
A	152 feet	2.9 feet/year
B	281 feet	4.5 feet/year
C	375 feet	4.2 feet/year

The basic stratifications by farm size within each study area are given in table A-2, along with information on number of farms by size and total acres by size in 1966.

Resource Characteristics

A complete description of all the relevant characteristics of each of the representative-farm firms developed for this analysis is transcribed in the dissertation or thesis and file report developed for each of the study

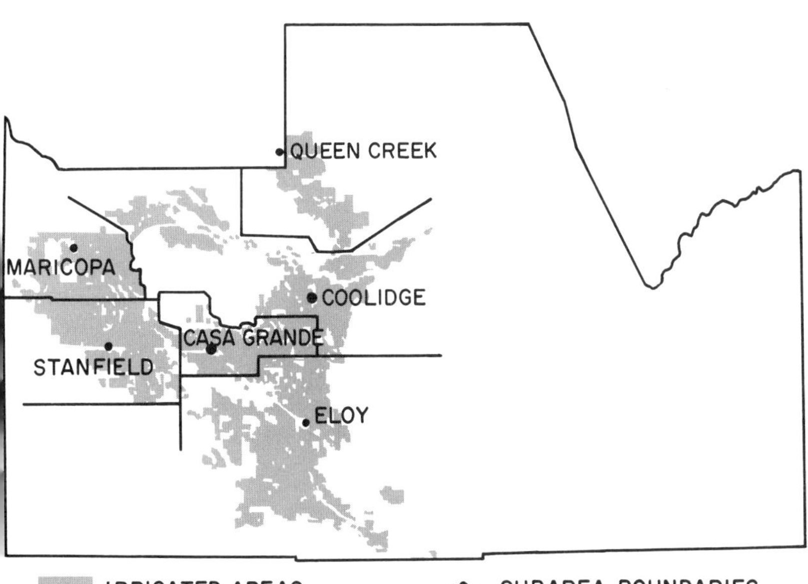

Fig. A-2. *Study areas within Pinal County.*

Table A – 1b: Explanation of Symbols in Fig. A – 2.

Casa Grande Coolidge	Conjunctive use of surface and groundwaters including the area of the San Carlos Irrigation Project
Eloy Maricopa Stanfield Queen Creek	Groundwater only

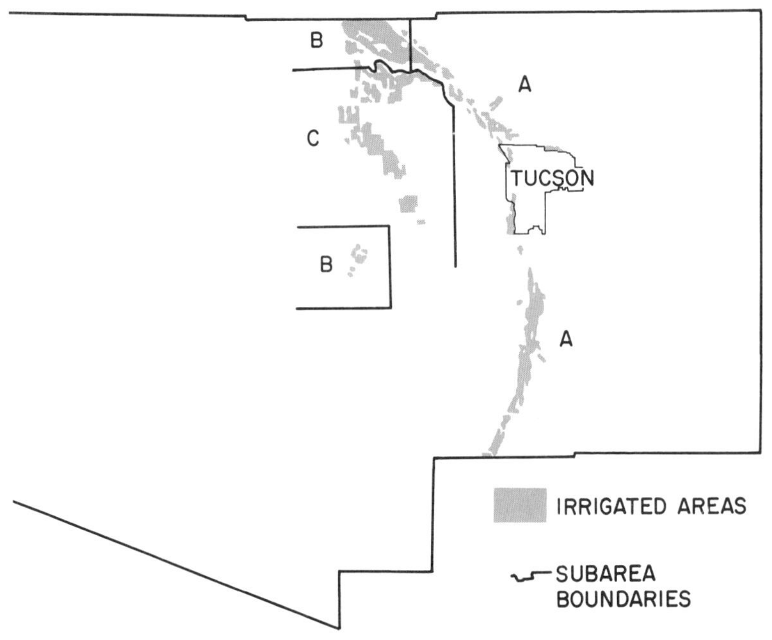

Fig. A-3. *Study areas within Pima County.*

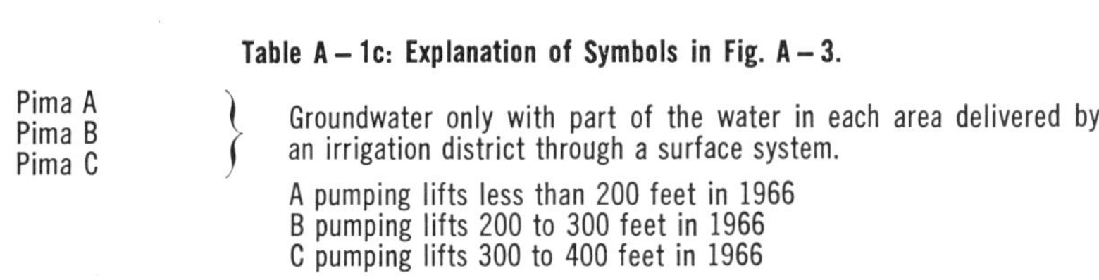

Table A – 1c: Explanation of Symbols in Fig. A – 3.

Pima A Pima B Pima C	Groundwater only with part of the water in each area delivered by an irrigation district through a surface system. A pumping lifts less than 200 feet in 1966 B pumping lifts 200 to 300 feet in 1966 C pumping lifts 300 to 400 feet in 1966

areas (Stults, 1966; Comer, 1967; Lee, 1967; Jones, 1968; Mack, 1969; Burdak, 1970; Hock, n.d.). Only a brief review of some of the basic assumptions concerning these characteristics is given here.

Land. Land in each study area is assumed to be homogeneous in its productivity level. While soil types, fertility, and slope do differ somewhat in each area, there are insufficient data to provide a basis for differentiating productivity levels, either geographically or between farm sizes.

Interviews with informed Agricultural Extension Service personnel support the view that no major geographic patterns of differential soil productivity levels exist, and the data from the farm survey give no evidence indicating different productivity levels between farm-size groups based on soil conditions.

Throughout the study area, soils are generally deep, well suited to the types of crops grown, and require similar inputs of productive factors necessary to produce alternative crops. Accordingly, the assumption of a homogeneous soil productivity level among size groups within a study area is a useful and reasonable simplification.

We take the view that agricultural land will remain in production so long as the value of the crops grown on that land is large enough to cover all other costs except land cost. Agricultural land is completely fixed in location and is undepreciable. As such, it is the final residual beneficiary of agricultural productivity. If the residual is high, the value of land will be high. If the residual is low, the value of land will be low, but it will remain in use as long as the residual is above zero. Therefore, land values do not enter into the projected adjustment decisions, and we do not include estimates of land values in table A-3, where the values of depreciable investments are listed by area and farm size.

Buildings. Farm building inventories were obtained for each farm surveyed. The range and type of buildings on farms in each size category were found to be quite diverse. In many instances, farms had buildings which were not being employed in their present enterprise organization. When synthesizing the typical building inventory for each size group, buildings not currently in use were excluded on the assumption that they had no value in the operation and would not be repaired or replaced.

Most farms surveyed had some type of shop building(s); however, their size, condition, and age varied considerably. Labor and management housing was typically present on farms in the larger size groups. Farms in the largest size group always had some type of office building.

While valuation of farm buildings is important in computing net return on capital invested, it is not crucial, or even necessary for solution of the linear-program models of crops grown and water use. Therefore, while representative-building inventories were specified in order to be able to develop estimates of fixed costs and residual farm profits, the rather large variation in actual values between farms did not cause analytical problems for the projections.

Irrigation Facilities. A complete listing of all irrigation facilities and equipment was obtained in the farm survey, including wells, pumps, ditches, and other minor irrigation equipment such as shovels, ditch checks, and siphons. Representative-farm model costs for irrigation facilities and equipment are presented in table A-3 by size group and study area.

Machinery Inventories. A detailed inventory of farm machinery and equipment for each of the typical farm models was based on data collected in the farm survey. Costs of individual pieces of equipment were determined from interviews with retail machinery dealers in the relevant study areas. It was assumed that these machinery inventories remain constant over time within each of the farm size groups within each area. This assumption, along with the assumptions of constant levels of technology and prices, makes production costs, with the exception of water costs, constant over time. Data on the total value of the machinery investment by farm size and area are shown in table A-3.

Custom Operations. Farm survey data indicated that many small farms did not typically own the more expensive tillage and harvesting equipment. Operations performed by these pieces of machinery were custom hired. A complete listing of custom operations and their associated costs for the various study areas may be found in Young et al. (1968).

Labor. The supply function for all classes of labor is assumed to be perfectly price elastic; that is, any number of laborers of each particular class can be hired at a constant wage rate. Various classes of labor and their associated costs per hour or specific job may be found in Young et al. (1968).

Capital. An infinitely elastic capital supply function is assumed for each of the study areas, as well as for individual farm models. It is assumed that farm operators – if not as individuals, at least in the aggregate – may obtain as much capital as they need at constant interest rates. In reality, there is a large variety of sources of capital, and individual farm operators may encounter capital rationing in the short run. However, it is unlikely that farming as an aggregate sector of the economy would be adversely affected by a lack of capital in the long run of the projection period.

Management. Many levels of management ability are found at any one time in any sector of the economy. In some instances, the range of abilities may be as wide as the number of firms. However, over time, the less efficient management will either improve or be replaced by those who are more efficient. Since we are concerned with projections over the long run, management ability in this study is assumed to be homogeneous within each size group as well as between size groups.

Water Availability by Study Area and Representative Farm. A general outline regarding the sources and availability of water by irrigation districts was presented with the general descriptions of the study areas earlier in this chapter. However, as noted, water availability varies between irrigation districts and among representative-farm models. Water availability by study area and representative model within each area are presented below.

In Yuma County, water availability varies according to the irrigation district in which a farm is located, as well as from year to year. Since the model farms in this area do not represent a particular irrigation district it is necessary to assume that water availability is homogeneous for all farms and the amount of water available represents a weighted average for all the districts.

Average water use per irrigable acre in Yuma County (not including lands located in the major citrus producing areas) is 5.7 acre-feet per year. Accordingly, it is assumed that water and land occur in a constant proportion of 5.7 acre-feet of water to one acre of land on each of the farm size groups. It is further assumed that water is of a homogeneous quality so that any adverse quality problems that exist are uniform across all farms.

In the Salt River Project, five different categories of water are available. These are assessment, normal flow, stored and developed, project pump, and private pump.

Assessment water up to two acre-feet is delivered upon request to all project lands once the basic assessment has been paid. Normal flow water is, likewise, delivered upon demand to land having a normal flow right. Although not all project lands have a normal flow right and not all such rights are fully used, an average of one-half acre-foot per acre of this right for all cropland is assumed. Stored and developed water is allocated depending upon its availability, but has typically amounted to one acre-foot per project acre (Salt River Valley Water Users' Association, Annual). This amount is assumed to be available to all cropland in the model farms.

Pump water available from SRP pumps can vary from zero to two acre-feet. As of 1967, 163,580 acres of project land had project pump water rights of 242,376 acre-feet. The opportunity to purchase this right from the project is still available. On this basis, it is assumed that each acre of land employed in agriculture in the SRP has a project pump water right of two acre-feet per acre. In addition to project water, private wells exist on all farms except those in size group I. It is assumed there is no limit on water obtainable from these wells.

Project water is available to each size group in the SRP in equal quantities per acre. The only variation among size group models is that group I farms have no private pump water.

In the Roosevelt Water Conservation District, project water is available on an equal share basis to each acre. The only limitation on project water is a three acre-foot maximum per acre during the prorate period. During the remaining part of the year there are no quantity restrictions on water available from the project. Group II farms in this project have an average of 0.6 of an irrigation well per farm. Water from this source is assumed to be available to all farms in this size group.

Maricopa County agricultural study areas A and B, outside the major surface-supplied water area, have a considerable mixture of water conditions. These vary by geographical location and farm model size. Many farms which are wholly within an irrigation district must rely entirely upon district supplied water. Other farms within districts have water supplied both from their own wells and from the district. The third situation is one of farms with no irrigation district affiliation supplying all their water needs via their own private irrigation wells.

Maricopa A is broken into four farm sizes with 19 different models. Seven of these models depend entirely upon district water, eight models have both district and private well water available, and the remaining four models depend entirely upon groundwater from privately owned wells.

Groundwater study area B of Maricopa County is divided into five farm sizes with 24 different models representing various water supply situations. Two models rely entirely upon irrigation district supplied water, five models have both district and private water sources, and the remaining 17 models have water supplied from privately owned wells.

Pinal County agriculture is almost totally dependent upon groundwater supplied to users via private farm wells. Only a small quantity of surface water is available. This area, like Maricopa Areas A and B, received special attention in the analysis because groundwater, groundwater level decline, and rising water costs are of such importance to its agriculture. Four different farm sizes are postulated for this study area. The total area is stratified into six subareas, four with only private wells and two with a combination of surface and groundwater supplies. Each of these four models is further subdivided into shallow, medium, and deep pumping lift categories as determined from farm survey data. Each farm size in each lift category has a specified quantity of water available to it. The limiting factor relative to water availability is its production during heavy use periods in January and July.

Pima County irrigation water availability is assumed to be unlimited. Water use is governed only by available land on which to apply it and the water's cost. Three farm sizes are assumed, with all three being applicable to three different groundwater areas in the county. All water used for agricultural purposes in the county is originally obtained from groundwater sources, although the farmer may obtain it as private pump water, irrigation district pump water, or as sewage effluent.

In Graham and Greenlee counties, water for irrigation is obtained from both canal companies and farm wells. In Graham County, canal companies provide an average of 2.78 acre-feet of water per acre at an assessment cost of $7.53 per acre. In Greenlee County, an average of $1.88 per acre-foot per acre is supplied by the canal companies at an assessment cost of $6.00 per acre. In both counties, the remaining water needs for all crops are supplied by farm wells.

In the Cochise County study area, all irrigation water is obtained from farm wells. Water quantity is assumed to be unlimited in all four farm models. The cost of water per acre-foot does vary by farm model, due to differences in types of well equipment and power sources.

Alternative Enterprise Combinations. Cropping patterns differ among farms within the study areas. Some farms specialize in the growing of specific crops, while others are diversified and may grow as many as six crops. The farm survey indicated that specialty crops are grown principally on farms represented by specific size groups. Only those crops considered to be important in terms of acreage or acreage adjustments over time are included in the farm models. The specialty crops occupying small acreage or considered to be insignificant in terms of water use are not included in models as typical cropping alternatives. These specialty crops and their water use were projected as being unaffected by rising water costs and thus the amounts grown will be affected only by market demand. Note (from table 4-1) that citrus and vegetables totaled only 11 percent of total Arizona crop acreage in 1970. In our projections, we have held their acreage constant. In actuality, acreage will increase gradually, but never comprise a major percentage of Arizona crop acreage. Because these crops have a high per acre value, they will not be affected by water allocation decisions made at the margin of irrigated agriculture. The crops indicated as typical in table A-4 summarize these alternative enterprise possibilities for all study areas. The actual projected crops grown are selected from these lists in the solution of the representative-farm linear-programming models.

Costs and Returns for the Representative Farms

The previous material has described the environment and restraints within which Arizona farms are operated and the general organizations of the farms in face of these factors. This section describes the specific assumptions related to yields, prices, and farm operations that lead to the estimates of net income per acre per crop by farm size and study area, necessary as inputs into the representative-farm linear-programming models, and lists the derived information.

Calendars of Operations and Budgets

Complete detailed calendars of operations and per acre budgets for each alternative crop for each farm size model by study area are described in Stults, 1967; Comer, 1967; Lee, 1967; Jones, 1968; Mack, 1969; Burdak, 1970; and Hock, n.d. The inputs and types of operations for each crop were obtained from the farm surveys in each area. There was little variance among farms as to operations performed and physical inputs in the production of identical crops. Consequently, calendars of operations for individual crops are similar (but not identical) for all representative-farm models within each study area. Equipment necessary to perform each operation was costed using the specific machinery inventory of each relevant representative-farm model. Per acre and per hour costs of an operation performed by a particular size and type of machine on any given size farm model are listed in Young et al. (1968).

Yields, Product Prices, and Gross Returns

Most yields, product prices, and gross returns per acre, used in the linear-programming models, are listed in table A-5 by study area. Yield data were obtained from the farm survey and from irrigation district crop reports. Prices are in most cases based on the five-year period 1961 through 1965. Cotton support payments are based on the 1966 federal cotton program.

In contrast to most study areas where only one estimate of yield per acre was used for each crop, in Pinal and Pima counties it was possible to develop additional information on the relationship between yield per acre and the amount of water applied. Therefore, the programming models for these areas were more detailed, allowing the possibility for adjusting per acre water use in response to changing water cost, in addition to the standard possibility of adjusting the number of acres of each crop. These yield-water-use relationships are displayed in table A-6.

Net Returns Over Variable Operating Costs

Variable operating costs are those costs which are directly related to the production of a specific enterprise. They are incurred in a particular amount only if a particular crop is grown, the total amount being related to the level of output per acre. Example of variable costs are hourly labor, machine operating costs, and costs of inputs such as seed and fertilizer.

Fixed costs, in contrast, are incurred at a constant level whether a particular crop is grown or not, or, for that matter, whether or not any crops are grown. Examples are real estate taxes, real estate costs, and most capital depreciation.

Obviously, a crop must return more than its variable operating costs per acre, or it would not be grown at all. Variable operating costs are "out-of-pocket" costs. The difference between total variable operating costs on a farm and total gross return for the farm is the residual available to pay for the fixed costs of the farm. These fixed costs may not have to be paid in the short-run. It is this residual that is the return to owners of real estate, capital, and management. Naturally, farm operators (who are at least partial owners of the real estate, capital, and management) want this residual to be as large as possible. Therefore, the acreage of crops to be grown is selected on the basis of this residual for each crop, the *per acre net return over variable operating cost.* The representative-farm linear-programming models maximize net return over variable operating cost for the entire farm, based on the estimates of per acre net return over variable operating cost for each crop, within the constraints imposed on growing each crop by the institutional, physical, and biological situation of the area.

Variable operating costs per acre for producing each enterprise on each representative-farm model are presented in table A-7. Total variable operating costs per acre subtracted from gross returns per acre yields net returns over variable operating costs (also shown in the same table).

The variable operating costs listed in this table *do not* include the cost of water. Therefore, the residual between gross returns and operating costs, net returns above operating costs, must be large enough to make a payment for water before any return would be left over as payment for the fixed factor of real estate, capital, and management. Irrigation water conditions and costs in each of the study subareas differ both in the initial period (1966) and in each future projection period. These differences are because of current (1966) groundwater levels and surface-water sources and future projected rates of change in available water sources differ by subarea. In addition, estimated water costs not only differ by study area but also by farm model within study areas. This results from differences in location within an area, type of pumping equipment employed, type and cost of power used, and priority of surface water rights attached to land.

TABLE A-2
Cropland Acreage and Number of Farms by Representative-Farm Size, According to Study Area, in 1966

Study Area & Farm Sizes	Farm Size Group					
	I	II	III	IV	V	New Farms
Yuma County						
Range in acres	30-120	121-320	321-640	641-1,500	>1,500	
Average acres per farm	77	207	481	980	3,912	
Number of farms	112	105	84	39	12	
Total acres	8,624	21,714	40,194	38,038	45,430	
Graham County						
Range in acres	30-157	180-402	580,925			
Average acres per farm	82	284	855			
Number of farms	71	93	31			
Total acres	5,804	26,317	26,521			
Greenlee County						
Range in acres	30-160	161-480	>480			
Average acres per farm	67	280	550			
Number of farms	21	13	2			
Total acres	1,411	3,639	1,101			
SRP & RWCD						
Range in acres	30-200	201-600	601-1,200	>1,200		
Average acres per farm	100	400	900	1,800		
Number of farms	313	151	42	23		
Total acres	31,320	60,768	37,728	41,184		
Maricopa Area A						
Range in acres	30-325	326-700	701-2,800	>2,800		
Average acres per farm	160	540	1,200	9,500		
Number of farms	87	55	49	4		
Total acres	13,920	29,700	58,800	38,000		

Study Area & Farm Sizes	Farm Size Group I	II	III	IV	V	New Farms	Totals
opa Area B							
ge in acres	30-250	251-610	611-1,435	1,436-2,800	>2,800		
rage acres er farm	130	430	1,000	2,200	6,000		
ber of farms	69	38	42	18	14		181
l acres	8,970	16,340	42,000	39,600	84,000		190,910
e County							
ge in acres	30-200	200-500	500			400-1,280	
rage acres er farm	86	288	891			696	
ber of farms	112	130	32			72	346
l acres	9,632	37,440	28,512			50,000	124,584
ounty							
e in acres	30-220	221-520	521-961	>960			
age acres r farm	106	341	675	1,705			
ber of farms	103	107	111	79			400
acres	10,918	36,438	74,925	134,695			256,976
ounty							
e in acres	30-520	521-960	>960				
age acres r farm	303	722	2,639				
ber of farms	24	13	13				50
acres	7,262	9,388	34,309				50,959

TABLE A-3

Average Value (in Dollars) of Depreciable Investment by Size of Farm, According to Study Area, in 1966

Study Area & Investment Group	Farm Size Group I	II	III	IV	V	Ne Far
Yuma County	(77 acres)	(207 acres)	(481 acres)	(980 acres)	(3,912 acres)	
Power units	4,420	9,292	19,503	32,922	82,554	
Field equipment	3,982	16,945	33,462	58,620	156,136	
Irrigation equipment	3,600	9,150	20,960	45,750	178,874	
Trucks and misc.	2,700	6,300	10,900	16,650	47,700	
Total	14,702	41,687	84,825	153,942	465,264	
Graham County	(82 acres)	(284 acres)	(855 acres)			
Power units	5,635	13,267	24,003			
Field equipment	15,336	24,822	48,383			
Irrigation equipment	6,700	15,310	39,973			
Trucks and misc.	1,560	3,295	7,333			
Total	29,231	56,694	119,692			
Greenlee County	(67 acres)	(280 acres)	(550 acres)			
Power units	5,356	11,851	15,051			
Field equipment	6,934	27,239	31,423			
Irrigation equipment	10,130	17,128	25,831			
Trucks and misc.	1,560	1,620	4,080			
Total	23,980	57,838	76,385			
SRP & RWCD	(100 acres)	(400 acres)	(900 acres)	(1,800 acres)		
Power units	4,861	21,658	32,587	59,055		
Field equipment	10,018	34,727	64,614	108,669		
Irrigation equipment	2,790	36,910	62,202	113,173		
Trucks and misc.	3,750	8,300	16,300	20,500		
Total	21,419	101,595	175,703	301,397		
Maricopa Area A	(160 acres)	(540 acres)	(1,200 acres)	(9,500 acres)		
Power units	8,203	22,417	29,398	126,261		
Field equipment	15,510	31,818	34,997	176,115		
Irrigation equipment	10,447	16,791	59,725	390,477		
Trucks and misc.	2,224	4,975	8,467	40,593		
Total	36,384	76,001	132,587	733,446		

Study Area & vestment Group	Farm Size Group I	II	III	IV	V	New Farms
pa Area B	(130 acres)	(430 acres)	(1,000 acres)	(2,200 acres)	(6,000 acres)	
er units	9,722	13,636	32,557	36,487	108,674	
equipment	28,133	24,635	29,280	62,889	199,089	
ation equipment	19,799	42,828	86,968	146,651	449,404	
ks and misc.	3,114	4,746	10,929	11,799	39,221	
l	60,768	85,845	159,734	257,826	769,388	
e County	(86 acres)	(288 acres)	(891 acres)			(696 acres)
er units	13,660	18,540	45,800			10,680
equipment	6,070	11,470	23,340			4,290
ation equipment	10,580	38,480	140,200			65,010
ks and misc.	1,950	7,010	10,680			3,420
	32,260	75,500	220,020			83,400
County	(106 acres)	(341 acres)	(675 acres)	(1,705 acres)		
er units	4,861	11,748	19,998	54,096		
equipment	13,601	24,020	37,101	48,799		
ation equipment	23,348	52,021	113,641	224,885		
ks and misc.	3,477	11,239	17,178	21,670		
	45,287	99,028	187,918	349,450		
ounty	(303 acres)	(722 acres)	(2,639 acres)			
r units	10,438	21,393	66,988			
equipment	21,340	39,681	60,422			
ation equipment	46,223	121,548	278,467			
ks and misc.	9,987	18,375	26,833			
	87,988	200,997	432,710			

TABLE A-4

Alternative Crop Enterprises for Representative Farm Models
(X indicates eligible alternative cropping pattern for size group)

Study Area & Crop Enterprise	Farm Size Group I	II	III	IV	V	Ne Far
Yuma County	(77 acres)	(207 acres)	(481 acres)	(980 acres)	(3,912 acres)	
Short-staple cotton (solid planted)	X	X	X	X	X	
Short-staple cotton (skip-row planted)	X	X	X	X	X	
Alfalfa (for hay only)	X	X	X	X	X	
Alfalfa (for hay and seed)		X	X	X		
Alfalfa (for hay and grazing)			X	X	X	
Alfalfa (for green-chop ensilage)					X	
Barley	X	X	X	X	X	
Wheat		X	X	X	X	
Grain sorghum	X	X	X	X	X	
Bermuda grass for seed		X	X	X		
Lettuce			X	X	X	
Cantaloupe			X	X	X	
Sudan grass					X	
Graham County	(82 acres)	(284 acres)	(855 acres)			
Long-staple cotton (solid planted)	X	X	X			
Short-staple cotton (solid planted)	X	X	X			
Grain sorghum	X	X	X			
Barley	X	X	X			
Alfalfa (for hay only)	X	X	X			
Sugar beets			X			
Greenlee County	(67 acres)	(280 acres)	(550 acres)			
Short-staple cotton (solid planted)	X	X	X			
Alfalfa (for hay only)	X	X	X			
Grain sorghum	X	X	X			
Barley		X	X			
SRP & RWCD	(100 acres)	(400 acres)	(900 acres)	(1,800 acres)		
Short-staple cotton (solid planted)	X	X	X	X		
Short-staple cotton (skip-row planted)	X	X	X	X		
Alfalfa (hay and pasture)	X	X	X	X		

Study Area & Crop Enterprise	Farm Size Group I	II	III	IV	V	New Farms
d RWCD (cont'd)	(100 acres)	(400 acres)	(900 acres)	(1,800 acres)		
lfa (for hay only)	X	X	X	X		
ar beets		X	X	X		
ey	X	X	X	X		
n sorghum	X	X	X	X		
ey-grain sorghum ouble cropped)	X	X	X	X		
at	X	X	X	X		
uce		X	X			
toes		X	X			
ots		X	X			
onions		X	X			
pa Area A	(160 acres)	(540 acres)	(1,200 acres)	(9,500 acres)		
-staple cotton	X	X	X	X		
t-staple cotton	X	X	X	X		
r beets		X	X	X		
ower	X	X	X	X		
at	X	X	X	X		
y	X	X	X	X		
sorghum	X	X	X	X		
ey-grain sorghum ouble cropped)	X	X	X	X		
fa (for hay and sture)	X	X	X	X		
a Area B	(130 acres)	(430 acres)	(1,000 acres)	(2,200 acres)	(6,000 acres)	
-staple cotton	X	X	X	X	X	
t-staple cotton	X	X	X	X	X	
r beets			X	X	X	
ower		X	X	X	X	
t			X	X	X	
y	X	X	X	X	X	
sorghum	X	X	X	X	X	
y-grain sorghum uble-cropped)	X	X	X	X	X	
fa (for hay and sture)	X	X	X	X	X	
g lettuce		X	X		X	
ettuce		X	X		X	
oes			X		X	

(cont'd ⟶)

Table A-4 — Alternative Crop Enterprises (cont'd)

Study Area & Crop Enterprise	Farm Size Group					
	I	II	III	IV	V	New Farm
Cochise County	(86 acres)	(288 acres)	(891 acres)			(696 a
Long-staple cotton (solid planted)			X			
Short-staple cotton (solid planted)	X	X	X			
Grain sorghum	X	X	X			X
Barley	X	X	X			
Alfalfa (for hay only)	X	X	X			
Sugar beets		X	X			
Wheat		X	X			X
Spring lettuce		X	X			
Fall lettuce		X	X			
Pinal County	(106 acres)	(341 acres)	(675 acres)	(1,705 acres)		
Long-staple cotton	X	X	X	X		
Short-staple cotton	X	X	X	X		
Barley	X	X	X	X		
Grain sorghum	X	X	X	X		
Alfalfa (for hay only)	X	X	X	X		
Wheat	X	X	X	X		
Pima County	(303 acres)	(722 acres)	(2,639 acres)			
Long-staple cotton	X	X	X			
Short-staple cotton	X	X	X			
Barley	X	X	X			
Grain sorghum	X	X	X			
Alfalfa (for hay only)		X				
Wheat	X					
Spring lettuce			X			
Fall lettuce			X			

TABLE A-5

Summary of Yields, Prices, and Gross Returns per Acre for Selected Crop Enterprises, According to Study Area in 1966

Study Area, rop Enterprise, and vernment Payment	Unit*	Yield	Price per Unit	Gross Return (dollars)	Total Return per Crop (dollars)
a County					
t-staple cotton					
d planted)					580.98
rst pick lint	lb	783	0.25	195.75	
econd pick lint	lb	522	0.20	104.40	
rap lint	lb	145	0.12	17.40	
ed	lb	2,385	0.025	59.63	
pport & diversion pmt				203.80	
t-staple cotton					
planted 4 x 4)					339.52
rst pick lint	lb	493	0.25	123.25	
cond pick lint	lb	329	0.20	65.80	
rap lint	lb	92	0.12	11.04	
ed	lb	1,501	0.025	37.53	
pport & diversion pmt				101.90	
fa					
y only	tons	7	25.00	175.00	175.00
fa					196.25
y	tons	5.25	25.00	131.25	
ed	lb	200	0.265	53.00	
raw	tons	1	12.00	12.00	
fa					164.50
y	tons	5.5	25.00	137.50	
azing	AUD	180	0.15	27.00	
fa					
een Crop	tons	30	6.50	195.00	195.00
y					91.00
ain	tons	1.7	50.00	85.00	
raw	tons	0.5	12.00	6.00	
t					96.00
ain	tons	1.5	60.00	90.00	
raw	tons	0.5	12.00	6.00	
num	tons	2	44.00	88.00	88.00
uda					289.00
ass seed	lb	800	30.00	240.00	
raw	tons	3.5	14.00	49.00	

= Animal unit days; AU = Animal units.

(cont'd ⟶)

Table A-5 — Summary of Yields, Prices, and Gross Returns (cont'd)

Study Area, Crop Enterprise, and Government Payment	Unit*	Yield	Price per Unit	Gross Return (dollars)	To Ret per (dol
Cantaloupes	crates	145	5.60	812.00	812
Lettuce	cartons	390	2.48	967.20	967
Sudan					102
Grass	tons	15	6.50	97.50	
Soil improvement				5.00	
Graham County					
Short-staple cotton					
(group I farms)					32
Lint	lb	770	0.225	173.25	
Seed	tons	0.679	48.00	32.59	
Scrap	lb	50	0.12	6.00	
Pasture	AU	0.250	2.00	0.50	
Support payment				81.95	
Diversion payment				30.45	
Short-staple cotton					
(group II farms)					31
Lint	lb	750	0.225	168.75	
Seed	tons	0.663	48.00	31.82	
Scrap	lb	50	0.12	6.00	
Pasture	AU	0.25	2.00	0.50	
Support payment				80.07	
Diversion payment				29.75	
Short-staple cotton					
(group III farms)					34
Lint	lb	815	0.225	183.38	
Seed	tons	0.714	48.00	34.27	
Scrap	lb	100	0.12	12.00	
Pasture	AU	0.25	2.00	0.50	
Support payment				86.19	
Diversion payment				32.02	
Long-staple cotton					
(group I farms)					37
Lint	lb	735	0.464	341.04	
Seed	tons	0.573	48.00	27.50	
Scrap	lb	50	0.12	6.00	
Pasture	AU	0.25	2.00	0.50	

*AUD = Animal unit days; AU = Animal units.

Study Area, Crop Enterprise, and Government Payment	Unit*	Yield	Price per Unit	Gross Return (dollars)	Total Return per Crop (dollars)
-staple cotton					
p II farms)					357.51
nt	lb	700	0.464	324.80	
ed	tons	0.546	48.00	26.21	
rap	lb	100	0.12	6.00	
sture	AU	0.25	2.00	0.50	
-staple cotton					
p III farms)					396.12
nt	lb	765	0.464	354.96	
ed	tons	0.597	48.00	28.66	
rap	lb	100	0.12	12.00	
sture	AU	0.25	2.00	0.50	
sorghum					
p I farms)					79.62
ain	tons	1.84	43.00	79.12	
sture	AU	0.25	2.00	0.50	
sorghum					
p II farms)					71.88
ain	tons	1.66	43.00	71.38	
sture	AU	0.25	2.00	0.50	
sorghum					
p III farms)					95.10
ain	tons	2.2	43.00	94.60	
sture	AU	0.25	2.00	0.50	
y (group I farms)	tons	1.8	50.00	90.00	90.00
y (group II farms)	tons	1.96	50.00	98.00	98.00
y (group III farms)	tons	1.9	50.00	95.00	95.00
a (group I farms)					150.75
y	tons	5.95	25.00	148.75	
ture	AU	1.0	2.00	2.00	
a (group II farms)					154.50
y	tons	6.1	25.00	152.50	
ture	AU	1.0	2.00	2.00	
a (group III farms)					167.00
y	tons	6.6	25.00	165.00	
ture	AU	1.0	2.00	2.00	
beets for sugar	tons	18	11.87	213.66	249.30
port payment				35.64	

(cont'd ⟶)

Table A-5 — Summary of Yields, Prices, and Gross Returns (cont'd)

Study Area, Crop Enterprise, and Government Payment	Unit*	Yield	Price per Unit	Gross Return (dollars)	T Re per (do
Greenlee County					
Short-staple cotton					
(group I farms)					29
Lint	lb	700	0.225	157.50	
Seed	tons	0.624	48.00	29.95	
Scrap	lb	50	0.12	6.00	
Pasture	AU	0.250	2.00	0.50	
Support payment				75.36	
Diversion payment				28.00	
Short-staple cotton					
(group II farms)					29
Lint	lb	670	0.225	150.75	
Seed	tons	0.601	48.00	28.85	
Scrap	lb	100	0.12	12.00	
Pasture	AU	0.25	2.00	0.50	
Support payment				72.53	
Diversion payment				26.95	
Short-staple cotton					
(group III farms)					3
Lint	lb	700	0.225	157.50	
Seed	tons	0.624	48.00	29.95	
Scrap	lb	100	0.12	12.00	
Pasture	AU	0.25	2.00	0.50	
Support payment				75.36	
Diversion payment				28.00	
Grain sorghum					
(group I farms)					
Grain	tons	1.58	43.00	67.94	
Pasture	AU	0.25	2.00	0.50	
Grain sorghum					
(group II farms)					
Grain	tons	1.5	43.00	64.50	
Pasture	AU	0.25	2.00	0.50	
Grain sorghum					
(group III farms)					
Grain	tons	1.51	43.00	64.93	
Pasture	AU	0.25	2.00	0.50	
Barley (group II farms)	tons	1.64	50.00	82.00	
Barley (group III farms)	tons	1.50	50.00	75.00	

*AUD = Animal unit days; AU = Animal units.

Study Area, rop Enterprise, and overnment Payment	Unit*	Yield	Price per Unit	Gross Return (dollars)	Total Return per Crop (dollars)
lfa (group I farms)					145.75
lay	tons	5.75	25.00	143.75	
'asture	AU	1.00	2.00	2.00	
lfa (group II farms)					155.75
lay	tons	6.15	25.00	153.75	
'asture	AU	1.00	2.00	2.00	
lfa (group III farms)					152.00
lay	tons	6.00	25.00	150.00	
'asture	AU	1.00	2.00	2.00	
icopa County: and RWCD					
rt-staple cotton id planted)					462.76
int	lb	1,150	0.22	253.00	
eed	tons	0.91	50.00	45.70	
upport payment				103.15	
iversion payment				61.91	
rt-staple cotton planted 4 x 4)					552.44
int	lb	1,500	0.22	330.00	
eed	tons	1.15	50.00	57.38	
upport payment				103.15	
iversion payment				61.91	
ar beets					271.60
ugar	tons	20	10.94	218.80	
asture	acres	1	10.00	10.00	
upport payment				42.80	
ey	cwt	32	2.50	80.00	80.00
n sorghum (late planted)	cwt	34	2.50	74.80	74.80
n sorghum (early planted)	cwt	41	2.50	90.20	90.20
at	cwt	33	3.00	99.00	99.00
ey-grain sorghum ble-cropped)					154.80
arley	cwt	32	2.50	80.00	
rain sorghum	cwt	34	2.50	74.80	
fa					175.00
ay	tons	6.5	25.00	162.50	
asture	days	25	0.50	12.50	

(cont'd ⟶)

Table A-5 — Summary of Yields, Prices, and Gross Returns (cont'd)

Study Area, Crop Enterprise, and Government Payment	Unit*	Yield	Price per Unit	Gross Return (dollars)	To Ret per (dol
Maricopa County: SRP and RWCD cont'd					
Spring lettuce	cartons	475	2.00	950.00	950
Fall lettuce	cartons	390	2.30	897.00	897
Potatoes	cwt	275	3.10	825.00	825
Dry onions	cwt	300	4.10	1,230.00	1,230
Carrots	cwt	260	5.20	1,352.00	1,352
Maricopa County: Groundwater Areas A and B					
Long-staple cotton (solid planted)					28
Picked lint	lb	560	0.46	257.60	
Seed	lb	995	0.025	24.88	
Long-staple cotton (skip planted 4 x 4)					35
Picked lint	lb	700	0.46	322.00	
Seed	lb	1,244	0.025	31.10	
Long-staple cotton (skip planted 2 x 1)					40
Picked lint	lb	800	0.46	368.00	
Seed	lb	1,420	0.025	35.50	
Short-staple cotton (solid planted)					45
Picked lint	lb	1,035	0.22	227.70	
Scrapped lint	lb	115	0.12	13.80	
Seed	lb	1,875	0.025	46.88	
Support payment				103.15	
Diversion payment				61.91	
Short-staple cotton (skip planted 4 x 4)					51
Picked lint	lb	1,260	0.22	277.20	
Scrapped lint	lb	140	0.12	16.80	
Seed	lb	2,284	0.025	57.10	
Support payment				103.15	
Diversion payment				61.91	
Short-staple cotton (skip planted 2 x 1)					55
Picked lint	lb	1,350	0.22	297.00	
Scrapped lint	lb	150	0.12	18.00	
Seed	lb	2,450	0.025	61.25	
Support payment				103.15	
Diversion payment				80.49	

*AUD = Animal unit days; AU = Animal units.

Study Area, rop Enterprise, and overnment Payment	Unit*	Yield	Price per Unit	Gross Return (dollars)	Total Return per Crop (dollars)
fa					134.00
ay (area A only)	tons	5	25.00	125.00	
asture (area A only)	days	30	0.30	9.00	
ey (area A only)	cwt	35	2.50	87.50	87.50
at	cwt	33	3.00	99.00	99.00
n sorghum (early planted)	cwt	41	2.15	88.15	88.15
n sorghum (late planted)	cwt	36	2.15	77.40	77.40
ower	cwt	25	4.50	112.50	112.50
r beets (for sugar)	tons	20.5	11.83	242.52	282.90
pport payment				40.38	
fa					175.00
y (area B only)	tons	6.5	25.00	162.50	
sture (area B only)	days	25	0.50	12.50	
y (area B only)	cwt	33	2.50	82.50	82.50
ettuce (area B only)	cartons	390	2.30	897.00	897.00
g lettuce (area B only)	cartons	475	2.00	950.00	950.00
toes (area B only)	cwt	275	3.10	825.50	825.50
ise County					
-staple cotton					
p I farms)					264.01
t	lb	615	0.225	138.38	
ed	tons	0.557	48.00	26.76	
rap	lb	50	0.12	6.00	
sture	AU	0.250	2.00	.50	
pport payment				67.35	
ersion payment				25.02	
-staple cotton					
p II farms)					325.17
t	lb	800	0.225	180.00	
ed	tons	0.702	48.00	33.69	
ap	lb	50	0.12	6.00	
sture	AU	0.250	2.00	0.50	
pport payment				73.48	
ersion payment				31.50	
-staple cotton					
p III farms)					328.97
t	lb	810	0.225	182.25	
ed	tons	0.710	48.00	34.08	
ap	lb	50	0.12	6.00	
ture	AU	0.250	2.00	0.50	
pport payment				74.29	
ersion payment				31.85	

(cont'd ⟶)

Table A-5 — Summary of Yields, Prices, and Gross Returns (cont'd)

Study Area, Crop Enterprise, and Government Payment	Unit*	Yield	Price per Unit	Gross Return (dollars)	T Re per (do
Cochise County cont'd					
Grain sorghum (group I farms)					10
Grain	tons	2.37	43.00	101.91	
Pasture	AU	0.250	2.00	0.50	
Grain sorghum (group II farms)					12
Grain	tons	2.93	43.00	125.99	
Pasture	AU	0.250	2.00	0.50	
Grain sorghum (group III farms)					13
Grain	tons	3.18	43.00	136.74	
Pasture	AU	0.250	2.00	0.50	
Grain sorghum (new farms)					13
Grain	tons	3.2	43.00	137.60	
Pasture	AU	0.250	2.00	0.50	
Alfalfa (group I farms)					11
Grain	tons	4.5	25.00	112.50	
Pasture	AU	1.0	2.00	2.00	
Alfalfa (group II farms)					16
Grain	tons	6.5	25.00	162.50	
Pasture	AU	1.00	2.00	2.00	
Alfalfa (group III farms)					14
Grain	tons	5.6	25.00	140.00	
Pasture	AU	1.0	2.00	2.00	
Sugar beets (groups II & III)	tons	18	11.87	213.66	24
Support payment				35.64	
Wheat (all groups)	cwt	33.6	2.54	85.00	8
Spring lettuce (groups II & III)	cartons	475	2.00	950.00	95
Fall lettuce (groups II & III)	cartons	390	2.30	897.00	89
Barley (group I farms)	cwt	36	2.50	90.00	9
Barley (group II farms)	cwt	39.2	2.50	98.00	9
Barley (group III farms)	cwt	38	2.50	95.00	9
Pima and Pinal Counties					
Long-staple cotton (solid planted)	lb	587	0.445	261.21†	26
Long-staple cotton (skip planted 4 x 4)	lb	743	0.445	331.00†	33
Short-staple cotton (solid planted)	lb	1,033	0.384	396.92†	39

*AUD = Animal unit days; AU = Animal units.

Study Area, rop Enterprise, and overnment Payment	Unit*	Yield	Price per Unit	Gross Return (dollars)	Total Return per Crop (dollars)
and Pinal Counties cont'd					
t-staple cotton					
ip planted 4 x 4)	lb	1,240	0.384	476.35†	476.35‡
y	tons	1.7	50.00	85.00†	85.00‡
sorghum					
rm sizes I and II)	tons	2.07	45.00	93.15	93.15‡
sorghum					
rm sizes III and IV)	tons	2.17	45.00	97.65	97.65‡
'a hay					
thout summer water)	tons	4	25.00	109.50	109.50‡
'a hay					
th summer water)	tons	6	25.00	159.50	159.50‡
t	tons	1.34	55.00	73.70	73.70‡
g lettuce	cartons	475	2.00	950.00	950.00‡
ettuce	cartons	390	2.30	897.00	897.00‡

ment payments, both support and diversion, are included with product revenue.
ents middle pumping depth only.

TABLE A-6

l-Water-Use Relationships for Field Crops, Pinal and Pima Counties, 1966

Crop	Shallow Pumping Lift*		Middle Pumping Lift†		Deep Pumping Lift‡	
	Water Use (acre-feet)	Yield (lb)	Water Use (acre-feet)	Yield (lb)	Water Use (acre-feet)	Yield (lb)
ple cotton,						
planted	6.0	610	5.0	587	4.0	557
ple cotton, skip-row	7.0	766	6.0	743	5.0	713
aple cotton,						
planted	6.0	1,065	5.0	1,033	4.0	996
aple cotton, skip-row	7.0	1,272	6.0	1,240	5.0	1,203
	3.0	3,621	2.5	3,400	2.0	3,107
rghum,						
sizes I and II	3.29	4,350	2.75	4,130	2.17	3,765
rghum,						
sizes III and IV	3.29	4,550	2.75	4,330	2.17	3,965
without summer water)	4.58	4 (tons)	4.58	4 (tons)	4.58	4 (tons)
with summer water)	6.58	6 (tons)	6.58	6 (tons)	6.58	6 (tons)
	3.5	2,888	3.0	2,688	2.5	2,424

eet; 1966 weighted average depth was 315 feet.
) feet; 1966 weighted average depth was 460 feet.
l9 feet; 1966 weighted average depth was 540 feet.

Source: Stults, 1968.

TABLE A-7 — Summary of Per Acre Gross Returns, Operating Costs,

Study Area & Crop Enterprise	Gross Returns ($)			
	All Farms	Per Farm Size		
Yuma County[1]				
Short-staple cotton (solid planted)[2]	572 581			
Short-staple cotton (skip planted 4 x 4)[2]	334 339			
Barley	91			
Sorghum	88			
Wheat	96			
Alfalfa (establish stand)[3]				
Alfalfa (hay only)[4]	175			
Alfalfa (hay and seed)[4]	198			
Alfalfa (hay and grazing)[4]	164			
Alfalfa (green chop)	195			
Bermuda (seed production)[5]	289			
Cantaloupes[6]	812			
Lettuce[6]	967			
Sudan Grass	102			
Graham County[7]		(82 acres)	(284 acres)	(855 acres)
Long-staple cotton		375	358	396
Short-staple cotton		325	317	348
Sorghum		80	72	95
Barley		90	98	95
Alfalfa		151	155	167
Sugar beets		249	249	249
Greenlee County[7]		(67 acres)	(280 acres)	(550 acres)
Short-staple cotton		297	292	303
Sorghum		67	65	65
Barley			82	75
Alfalfa		146	156	152

[1]All estimates are rounded to the nearest dollar. Operating costs **do not** include the cost of water. Source: Jones (1968).

[2]Upper figure includes 50 percent of return from scrap lint. Lower figure includes 100 percent return from scrap lint. Gross return includes government payment of $203.80 per acre of cotton allotment.

[3]No returns are listed for establishing the alfalfa stand. Life of stand is assumed to be three years. Average annual costs can be determined by dividing by three.

[4]Total operating costs include one-third of establishment cost.

[5]No returns are listed for establishing the Bermuda stand. Life of stand is assumed to be eight years. Average annual costs can be determined by dividing by eight. Total operating costs include one-eighth of establishment cost.

Returns Over Operating Costs for Selected Enterprises in 1966 (cont'd)

Total Operating Costs ($)					Net Returns Over Operating Costs ($)				
Per Farm Size					Per Farm Size				
7 es)	(207 acres)	(481 acres)	(980 acres)	(3,912 acres)	(77 acres)	(207 acres)	(482 acres)	(980 acres)	(3,912 acres)
6	269	201			296	303	371		
			209	183				372	398
7	191	150			137	143	184		
			142	130				197	209
9	48	42	40	34	42	43	49	51	57
6	55	50	43	38	32	33	38	45	50
	51	45	43	39		45	51	53	57
3	52	45	44	43					
5	109	71	67	59	60	66	104	108	116
	147	110	103			51	88	95	
		61	59	50			103	105	114
				78					117
	155	131	121			134	158	168	
		662	655	487			150	157	325
		787	779	583			180	188	384
				56					46
s)	(284 acres)	(855 acres)			(82 acres)	(284 acres)	(855 acres)		
	143	143			211	215	253		
	150	151			154	167	197		
	59	58			19	13	37		
	48	48			40	50	47		
	67	53			70	88	114		
	182	182			67	67	67		
s)	(280 acres)	(550 acres)			(67 acres)	(280 acres)	(550 acres)		
	142	144			123	150	159		
	52	59			10	13	6		
	46	46				36	29		
	56	47			74	100	105		

practice is that smaller growers obtain financing and technical aid from packer-shipper, and ns after marketing costs are split fifty-fifty between farmer and packer-shipper. Net returns for and 1,000-acre farms represent the farmer's share, or 50 percent of net return. Large corporate perform all the functions of grower, packer, and shipper and, thus, net returns are not shared.

timates are rounded to the nearest dollar. Operating costs **do not** include the cost of water.

e: Comer (1967).

(cont'd ⟶)

Table A-7 — Summary of Per Acre Gross Returns, Operating Costs,

Study Area & Crop Enterprise	Gross Returns ($)	
	All Farms	Per Farm Size
Salt River Project & Roosevelt Water Conservation Dist.[8]		
Short-staple cotton (solid planted)	464	
Short-staple cotton (skip planted 4 x 4)	552	
Sugar beets	272	
Barley-grain sorghum (double-cropped)	155	
Potatoes	825	
Dry onions	1,230	
Carrots	1,352	
Spring lettuce	950	
Fall lettuce	897	
Wheat	99	
Barley	80	
Grain sorghum (late planted)	75	
Grain sorghum (early planted)	90	
Alfalfa (hay and pasture, 6.5 ton)[9]	175	
Alfalfa (hay and pasture, 4.5 ton)[9]	125	
Alfalfa (hay only, 6.5 ton)[9]	163	
Alfalfa (hay only, 4.5 ton)[9]	113	
Maricopa County Groundwater Area A[10]		
Long-staple cotton (solid planted)	282	
Long-staple cotton (skip planted 4 x 4)	353	
Long-staple cotton (skip planted 2 x 1)	404	
Short-staple cotton (solid planted)	453	
Short-staple cotton (skip planted 4 x 4)	516	
Short-staple cotton (skip planted 2 x 1)	560	
Sugar beets	283	
Safflower	113	
Wheat	99	
Barley	95	
Grain sorghum (early planted)	88	
Grain sorghum (late planted)	77	
Alfalfa (hay and pasture)	134	

[8]All estimates are rounded to the nearest dollar. Operating costs **do not** include the cost of water. Source: Mack (1969).

[9]The two levels of output represent different summer management practices. If water is available dur summer months of heavy water use, additional cuttings of alfalfa can be obtained.

[10]All estimates are rounded to the nearest dollar. Operating costs **do not** include the cost of water. Source: Hock (n.d.)

Returns Over Operating Costs for Selected Enterprises in 1966 (cont'd)

Total Operating Costs ($)			Net Returns Over Operating Costs ($)			
Per Farm Size			Per Farm Size			
(400 acres)	(900 acres)	(1,800 acres)	(100 acres)	(400 acres)	(900 acres)	(1,800 acres)
186	187	182	238	279	277	282
228	227	219	268	324	325	333
158	162	157	90	114	110	115
100	105	100	47	55	50	55
557	574			269	251	
663	673			567	556	
469	484			843	868	
747	769			203	191	
644	662			253	235	
42	46	43	54	57	55	56
43	46	43	33	33	34	37
56	58	56	15	19	16	19
57	59	57	29	33	31	33
111	86	78	62	64	89	97
90	73	65	35	35	53	60
108	84	75	53	54	79	88
87	71	63	26	26	42	50
(540 acres)	(1,200 acres)	(9,500 acres)	(160 acres)	(540 acres)	(1,200 acres)	(9,500 acres)
203	190	186	82	79	92	96
263	247	244	93	90	106	109
269	254	250	143	135	150	154
237	217	213	220	216	236	240
293	272	268	225	223	244	248
297	277	273	271	263	283	287
189	185	184		94	98	99
73	73	66	44	40	40	47
57	54	53	44	42	45	46
55	53	50	41	40	42	45
67	64	60		21	24	28
56	55	50	25	21	24	27
67	78	53	52	67	56	81

(cont'd ⟶)

Table A-7 — Summary of Per Acre Gross Returns, Operating Costs,

Study Area & Crop Enterprise	Gross Returns ($)				
	All Farms	Per Farm Size			
Maricopa County Groundwater Area B[10]					
Long-staple cotton (solid planted)	282				
Long-staple cotton (skip planted 4 x 4)	353				
Long-staple cotton (skip planted 2 x 1)	404				
Short-staple cotton (solid planted)	453				
Short-staple cotton (skip planted 4 x 4)	516				
Short-staple cotton (skip planted 2 x 1)	560				
Sugar beets	283				
Safflower	113				
Wheat	99				
Barley	83				
Grain sorghum (early planted)	88				
Grain sorghum (late planted)	77				
Alfalfa (hay and pasture)	175				
Spring lettuce	950				
Fall lettuce	897				
Potatoes	825				
Cochise County[11]		(86 acres)	(288 acres)	(891 acres)	(N fa
Short-staple cotton (solid planted)		264	325	329	
Sorghum		102	126	137	1
Barley		90	98	95	
Alfalfa		115	163	142	
Sugar beets		249	249	249	
Wheat		85	85	85	
Spring lettuce			950	950	
Fall lettuce			897	897	
Pinal & Pima Counties[12]					
Long-staple cotton (solid planted)	261				
Long-staple cotton (skip planted 4 x 4)	331				
Short-staple cotton (solid planted)	397				
Short-staple cotton (skip planted 4 x 4)	476				
Barley	85				
Grain sorghum	93				
Alfalfa (without summer water)[13]	110				
Alfalfa (with summer water)[13]	160				
Wheat	74				
Spring lettuce	950				
Fall lettuce	897				

[11]All estimates are rounded to the nearest dollar. Operating costs **do not** include the cost of water. Source: Lee (1967).

[12]Three levels of production were used in the models for this study area. Data contained herein are fo the "middle" level only. Complete costs and return for each production level can be found in Burdal

Returns Over Operating Costs for Selected Enterprises in 1966 (cont'd)

	Total Operating Costs ($)				Net Returns Over Operating Costs ($)				
	Per Farm Size				Per Farm Size				
0 es)	(430 acres)	(1,000 acres)	(2,200 acres)	(6,000 acres)	(130 acres)	(430 acres)	(1,000 acres)	(2,200 acres)	(6,000 acres)
1	185	176	174	174	91	97	106	108	108
1	243	232	231	230	102	110	121	122	123
3	242	235	233	233	155	162	169	171	171
3	217	208	202	201	230	236	245	251	252
	273	262	256	254	235	243	254	260	262
7	271	264	257	256	283	289	296	303	304
		175	184	175			108	99	108
	74	72	70	72		39	40	43	41
		53	53	52			46	46	47
)	49	48	48	47	33	34	35	35	36
	63	62		62		25	26		26
	52	51	49	51		25	26	28	26
	84	101	101	101	73	91	74	74	74
		747		759			203		191
		661		663			236		234
		574		574			251		251
s)	(288 acres)	(891 acres)	(New farms)		(86 acres)	(288 acres)	(891 acres)	(New farms)	
	157	153			116	168	176		
	63	55	66		29	63	82	72	
	48	48			40	50	47		
	49	67			46	114	75		
	184	184			65	65	65		
	56	54	54		29	29	31	31	
	747	747				203	203		
	644	644				253	253		
s)	(341 acres)	(675 acres)	(1,705 acres)		(106 acres)	(341 acres)	(675 acres)	(1,705 acres)	
	137	129	125		107	124	132	136	
	154	148	143		158	177	183	188	
	137	129	126		243	260	268	271	
	153	147	143		304	323	329	333	
	38	37	37		46	47	48	48	
	47	42	43		45	46	51	50	
	60	58	57		48	50	52	53	
	81	78	76		78	79	82	84	
	38	38	37		35	36	36	37	
			759					191	
			661					236	

). All estimates are rounded to the nearest dollar. Operating costs **do not** include the cost of water.
e: Stults (1968), Burdak (1970).
a may be grown or allowed to go dormant during summer months, depending upon the
bility of water.

APPENDIX B

Projections of Agricultural Adjustment, 1966–2015

Projections of Future Groundwater Depths

Detailed descriptions of current water conditions are presented in Appendix A. Summarizing briefly, some areas have access to and use recurring surface-water supplies almost exclusively; other areas use recurring surface-water supplies plus water obtained from subsurface sources; a third category of users obtain all water from underground aquifers. These aquifers may differ in several ways. Their shape, depth, material contained, and water yield per given depth may be different in different study areas or even within any given area.

Where surface water is available, it has been assumed that no increase in its cost will take place over the projection period. Groundwater is projected to increase in cost as pumping levels increase.

Three different methods were employed to determine future groundwater decline rates and pumping levels. One method was to determine water declines in aquifers in the recent past, relate this decline to quantities of water withdrawn from the aquifer, and then determine a decline rate per quantity of water withdrawn. For example, if a decline of five feet per year has been experienced during the past ten years and the average quantity withdrawn has been 100,000 acre-feet, then it was determined that the decline rate is one foot per 20,000 acre-feet of water withdrawn. If the quantity of water withdrawn and used decreases because of its increasing cost, the yearly decline rate of the groundwater table also decreases. This ratio method of projecting groundwater declines was employed in all study areas using pump water except in Pinal County, the Salt River Project, and the Roosevelt Water Conservation District.

The second method employed to calculate groundwater decline rates and pumping levels employs an analog model of the groundwater basin (Anderson, 1968; Burdak, 1970). This most detailed method was used only in Pinal County.

An analog model is a physical representation of some system by means of another system. The analog model employed in this study uses

TABLE B-1 — Projected Crop Acreages by Crop, Study Area, and State To

Study Area and Year	Long-staple Cotton	Short-staple Cotton	Sugar Beets	Alfalfa	Ba
1966					
Yuma	0	19,402	0	46,608	48,
Graham	8,680	6,500	300	6,050	7,
Greenlee	0	1,250	0	1,799	
Salt River Project	0	26,171	4,000	47,149	33,
Roosevelt Water Conservation District	0	7,362	850	7,500	2,
Maricopa A	1,692	18,865	6,067	31,650	23,
Maricopa B	5,939	30,262	2,199	15,120	16,
Cochise	200	8,500	4,000	8,272	5,
Pima	2,513	14,982	0	1,916	9
Pinal	7,101	83,810	0	18,511	64,
Totals	26,125	217,104	17,416	184,575	210
1975					
Yuma	0	19,402	0	46,608	48
Graham	8,680	6,500	300	6,050	7
Greenlee	0	1,250	0	1,799	
Salt River Project	0	26,171	4,000	43,871	14
Roosevelt Water Conservation District	0	7,362	850	7,690	3
Maricopa A	1,692	18,930	6,596	31,650	23
Maricopa B	5,939	30,197	1,670	13,250	14
Cochise	200	8,500	4,000	7,432	5
Pima	2,513	14,982	0	1,888	9
Pinal	7,098	83,810	0	13,540	62
Totals	26,122	217,104	17,416	173,778	189
1985					
Yuma	0	19,402	0	46,608	48
Graham	8,680	6,500	300	6,050	7
Greenlee	0	1,250	0	1,799	
Salt River Project	0	26,047	4,000	30,081	4
Roosevelt Water Conservation District	0	7,362	850	7,690	3
Maricopa A	1,692	19,968	6,774	31,650	23
Maricopa B	5,939	29,283	1,492	10,056	13
Cochise	200	8,500	2,000	7,712	4
Pima	2,513	14,982	0	1,916	9
Pinal	7,102	83,810	0	13,335	56
Totals	26,126	217,104	15,416	156,897	17

ervals From 1966 — 2015, Aggregated from Representative-Farm Models

Vheat	Sorghum	Bermuda Grass	Safflower	Cantaloupes	Vegetables	Total Crop Acreages
0	50,488	9,500	0	16,000	17,000	207,946
0	8,857	0	0	0	0	37,562
0	1,338	0	0	0	0	4,957
3,500	11,660	0	0	0	5,600	131,244
200	286	0	0	0	1,540	20,228
5,400	14,600	0	16,200	0	0	117,734
4,400	11,900	0	10,100	0	28,140	124,500
,000	87,300	0	0	0	2,500	127,872
686	17,039	0	0	0	2,200	48,503
0	65,497	0	0	0	7,500	246,916
,186	268,965	9,500	26,300	16,000	64,480	1,067,462
0	50,488	9,500	0	16,000	17,000	207,946
0	8,857	0	0	0	0	37,562
0	1,338	0	0	0	0	4,957
,267	28	0	0	0	5,600	97,722
200	0	0	0	0	1,540	20,942
,400	13,123	0	16,200	0	0	116,851
,853	1,300	0	2,263	0	28,140	101,381
,000	81,828	0	0	0	2,500	117,560
686	17,039	0	0	0	2,200	48,475
0	63,401	0	0	0	7,500	237,707
,406	237,402	9,500	18,463	16,000	64,480	991,103
0	50,488	9,500	0	16,000	17,000	207,946
0	8,857	0	0	0	0	37,562
0	1,338	0	0	0	0	4,957
500	0	0	0	0	5,600	71,707
200	0	0	0	0	1,540	20,942
400	6,215	0	12,568	0	0	107,527
244	382	0	693	0	28,140	92,734
000	83,196	0	0	0	2,500	114,708
686	17,067	0	0	0	2,200	48,531
0	56,586	0	0	0	7,500	224,767
030	224,129	9,500	13,261	16,000	64,480	931,381

Table B-1 — Projected Crop Acreages by Crop, Study Area, and State T

Study Area and Year	Long-staple Cotton	Short-staple Cotton	Sugar Beets	Alfalfa	Ba
1995					
Yuma	0	19,402	0	46,608	48,
Graham	8,680	6,500	300	6,050	7,
Greenlee	0	1,250	0	1,799	
Salt River Project	0	22,876	4,000	19,371	2,
Roosevelt Water Conservation District	0	7,362	850	0	3,
Maricopa A	4,872	23,392	6,958	31,074	18,
Maricopa B	2,759	29,031	1,308	2,648	7
Cochise	200	8,500	2,000	7,992	4
Pima	2,513	14,982	0	1,888	9
Pinal	7,102	83,791	0	9,896	43
Totals	26,126	217,086	15,416	127,326	146
2005					
Yuma	0	19,402	0	46,608	48
Graham	8,680	6,500	300	6,050	7
Greenlee	0	1,250	0	1,799	
Salt River Project	0	19,268	4,000	10,161	1
Roosevelt Water Conservation District	0	7,362	850	0	1
Maricopa A	5,407	26,124	7,056	29,689	17
Maricopa B	2,225	29,907	1,210	1,430	6
Cochise	200	8,500	2,000	8,275	2
Pima	2,513	14,982	0	1,888	9
Pinal	7,102	83,808	0	8,917	37
Totals	26,127	217,103	15,416	114,817	132
2015					
Yuma	0	19,402	0	46,608	48
Graham	8,680	6,500	300	6,050	7
Greenlee	0	1,250	0	1,799	
Salt River Project	0	15,713	4,000	5,215	1
Roosevelt Water Conservation District	0	7,362	850	0	1
Maricopa A	5,797	27,950	7,056	29,251	1
Maricopa B	1,835	31,635	1,210	1,187	[illegible]
Cochise	200	8,500	0	4,032	[illegible]
Pima	2,513	14,982	0	1,446	[illegible]
Pinal*	7,102	83,808	0	8,917	3
Totals	26,127	217,102	13,416	104,505	13

*Same as 2005 period, since Burdak (1970) carried analysis only to that period.

ervals From 1966—2015, Aggregated from Representative-Farm Models (cont'd)

heat	Sorghum	Bermuda Grass	Safflower	Cantaloupes	Vegetables	Total Crop Acreages
0	50,488	9,500	0	16,000	17,000	207,946
0	8,857	0	0	0	0	37,562
0	1,338	0	0	0	0	4,957
,500	0	0	0	0	5,600	56,232
200	0	0	0	0	1,540	13,252
,400	3,247	0	1,183	0	0	94,826
,158	0	0	726	0	28,140	75,147
,000	84,564	0	0	0	2,500	116,606
686	17,067	0	0	0	2,200	48,503
0	45,709	0	0	0	7,500	197,202
,944	211,270	9,500	1,909	16,000	64,480	852,233
0	50,488	9,500	0	16,000	17,000	207,946
0	8,857	0	0	0	0	37,562
0	1,338	0	0	0	0	4,957
,500	0	0	0	0	5,600	42,127
200	0	0	0	0	1,540	11,052
400	2,613	0	192	0	0	94,160
,116	0	0	787	0	28,140	73,391
0	60,032	0	0	0	2,500	84,007
686	17,067	0	0	0	2,200	48,503
0	40,319	0	0	0	7,500	185,145
902	180,714	9,500	979	16,000	64,480	788,850
0	50,488	9,500	0	16,000	17,000	207,946
0	8,857	0	0	0	0	37,562
0	1,338	0	0	0	0	4,957
500	0	0	0	0	5,600	33,146
200	0	0	0	0	1,540	11,052
400	1,994	0	192	0	0	94,849
483	0	0	0	0	28,140	73,057
0	60,032	0	0	0	2,500	77,764
439	17,067	0	0	0	2,200	47,814
0	40,319	0	0	0	7,500	185,145
022	180,095	9,500	192	16,000	64,480	773,292

TABLE B-2 — Agricultural Land and Irrigation W

Year	Totals		I	
	Water* (acre-feet)	Land† (acres)	Water* (acre-feet)	La (ac
Observed				
1966	795,256	144,000	122,760	22,[illegible]
Projected				
1975	671,632	121,630	103,686	18,[illegible]
1985	529,479	95,888	81,741	14,[illegible]
1995	414,116	75,593	64,006	11,[illegible]
2005	329,048	59,590	50,798	9,[illegible]
2015	259,379	46,974	40,040	7,[illegible]

*Total available water per acre is composed of two acre-feet of assessment water, one-half acre-foot normal flow water, one acre-foot stored and developed water, and two acre-feet of project pump water observed total of which was 5.52 acre-feet per acre in 1966. Water availability in projected years is estimated by assuming use of 5.52 acre-feet per acre in all future years as in 1966.

ability, 1966 Through 2015, Salt River Project

Aggregate Size Groups					
II		III		IV	
ter* -feet)	Land† (acres)	Water* (acre-feet)	Land† (acres)	Water* (acre-feet)	Land† (acres)
,224	42,786	207,504	37,728	229,768	41,776
,682	36,124	175,268	31,867	193,996	35,272
,629	28,478	138,171	25,122	152,938	27,807
480	22,451	108,927	19,805	125,571	21,922
,339	17,698	85,866	15,612	95,045	17,281
,730	13,951	67,688	12,307	79,921	13,622

ge projection derived from observed historical relationship $Y_t + 1 = (0.9765)(Y_t)$ where Y equals ed acreage. The acreage projections are derived by applying this relationship to the observed of agricultural land in the Project in 1966. Total acreage is then distributed among size groups basis of observed 1966 distribution.

TABLE B-3 — Aggregate Derived Marginal Den

Yuma		Cochise		Graham		Greenlee	
Price	Acre-feet	Price	Acre-feet	Price	Acre-feet	Price	Acre-f
$116.36	36,399	$67.66	1,500	$50.60	17,975	$42.20	1,4
92.86	64,399	63.66	3,750	43.00	36,300	31.80	2,5
72.36	86,349	63.25	5,750	42.50	43,399	30.00	6,2
67.63	121,725	58.99	8,750	39.39	57,054	13.12	10,5
67.45	148,603	56.22	9,650	33.40	71,684	12.50	18,1
60.60	163,906	39.11	23,343	30.80	76,464	12.00	20,5
59.20	170,061	37.33	39,331	16.66	87,429	9.66	21,2
56.96	180,261	23.42	87,267	15.66	96,294	9.25	27,8
54.54	196,460	22.28	240,791	14.25	113,894	4.33	30,0
44.85	207,659	21.72	249,358	13.33	117,494	3.33	30,8
42.85	224,459	19.00	283,798	12.76	119,069		
31.05	245,017	18.00	377,948	12.33	128,054		
29.20	265,575	16.66	390,248	11.00	154,854		
24.76	275,854	15.66	402,247	8.75	164,454		
22.80	333,966	13.33	408,847	6.33	165,989		
20.40	380,823	13.00	428,847	4.33	172,411		
19.60	433,260	12.50	464,319				
17.20	471,020	12.38	474,819				
17.01	483,046	9.00	485,319				
16.80	499,868	8.85	511,232				
15.67	518,760	8.28	513,781				
15.37	532,450	8.25	532,666				
14.29	631,308						
12.85	814,923						
10.85	826,123						
9.99	842,394						
9.52	881,033						
9.42	933,897						
9.26	943,458						
9.14	967,009						
8.42	970,860						
8.28	982,059						
7.14	991,115						
6.66	991,440						
4.76	1,001,957						
2.63	1,001,472						
2.38	1,021,139						

*Derived marginal demand curves for the Salt River Project and the Roosevelt Water Conservation are given in tables 4-12 and 4-13, respectively. Interpretation of this table is as explained for tables 4-12 and 4-13.

rigation Water by Study Areas, 1966*

Maricopa A		Maricopa B		Pinal		Pima	
ice	Acre-feet	Price	Acre-feet	Price	Acre-feet	Price	Acre-feet
4.78	12,700	$63.07	38,485	$75.00	25,400	$63.33	3,000
4.20	85,053	55.76	70,771	55.49	322,994	58.99	7,800
1.88	103,179	54.88	100,183	54.90	450,894	55.49	71,214
1.30	130,089	54.41	105,171	53.83	509,976	53.83	85,380
3.87	131,538	52.47	110,995	50.66	528,186	53.60	96,620
3.38	135,762	42.00	177,595	31.33	553,586	49.99	121,620
7.52	139,685	41.83	210,937	30.50	564,506	31.33	144,720
6.42	143,896	40.83	256,705	29.50	569,300	30.50	148,956
5.04	147,863	39.33	278,887	26.33	570,758	29.50	149,816
5.88	169,544	38.33	293,167	19.20	669,358	19.20	154,594
5.23	181,328	23.91	299,145	18.80	681,858	18.80	159,094
4.56	264,728	23.77	317,812	18.54	706,993	18.54	171,631
3.50	279,330	23.63	330,522	18.39	712,328	18.18	208,310
2.93	283,053	22.65	333,706	18.18	770,903	16.72	216,560
2.75	326,553	20.26	341,535	16.72	781,628	12.46	227,904
2.64	328,115	18.57	345,425	16.36	784,746	12.00	233,493
.06	402,870	16.54	364,620	12.76	1,464,492	8.09	233,783
.05	450,130	15.66	376,046	12.46	1,747,591		
.72	464,630	15.33	377,819	12.33	1,821,491		
.03	490,730	14.40	416,569	12.00	1,992,157		
.07	559,974	14.00	452,819	11.85	2,029,610		
.35	580,569	13.60	463,068	11.66	2,033,102		
.15	583,010	13.20	469,527	5.73	2,056,671		
.89	629,682	13.05	510,227	5.55	2,066,826		
.92	688,182	10.61	692,839	4.83	2,068,181		
.77	701,729	10.47	702,588	4.65	2,072,639		
.76	705,175	9.00	729,932	3.94	2,394,403		
.41	707,671	8.94	735,229	3.76	2,402,805		
.15	737,158	8.60	743,114	3.04	2,404,179		
.38	746,945	8.40	756,434	2.86	2,431,014		
.49	770,364	8.33	769,734	0.39	2,477,578		
.41	785,788	8.20	778,123				
.74	790,775	7.80	872,584				
		7.50	941,629				
		5.90	944,158				
		5.83	948,594				
		4.00	595,534				

a resistor-capacitor network to represent the groundwater system. The model is a scaled-down electrical version of the actual groundwater system. Resistors represent the energy-dissipation characteristics of the rock matrix through which groundwater flows, and their value is inversely proportional to the transmissibility. Capacitors store electrical energy in a way that is analogous to the storage of groundwater in the pore spaces of an aquifer. The capacitor values are directly proportional to the storage coefficient of the aquifer.

Withdrawal of water from the groundwater system is simulated electrically by the withdrawal of electric current. The change in voltage that occurs in the model as a result of the current withdrawal is analogous to the change in water levels that occurs when groundwater is pumped. In similar fashion, voltage and current in the electrical system are equivalent to the head and volume rate of flow in the groundwater system.

A third method used to project future pumping levels and groundwater cost for irrigation water was to project recent past declines as occurring over the time span of the projection period. This method was used in the Salt River Project (SRP) and Roosevelt Water Conservation District (RWCD).

Since land in the SRP is projected to move from agricultural to urban and industrial uses, it is assumed that groundwater withdrawals will not change significantly, that is, an urbanized or industrialized acre will use a quantity of water equivalent to that of agriculture. The RWCD, lying adjacent to the SRP and withdrawing water from the same aquifer as the SRP, will be affected by SRP groundwater withdrawals. Due to the proximity of these two irrigation districts, their groundwater decline rates in future projections were treated in the same manner. This procedure may cause an exaggeration in groundwater decline rates and future pumping levels in the RWCD, since water and land use are projected to both decline over the projection period with no corresponding reduction in the rate at which groundwater decline rates take place. Were reductions in decline rates to be correlated with reduced groundwater pumping, the cost of groundwater would rise less rapidly, thus causing fewer adjustments to occur, and these adjustments would take place at more distant points in time.

There is some evidence that urban and industrial take-over of project land has somewhat decreased Project water use (Smith, 1968:163). However, Thiele (1965:21) states that,

> Records show a steady increase (in per capita water use) as new household conveniences are developed . . . . The past trends show that commercial and industrial water use increases on a per capita basis (over time). There is nothing to indicate a reversal of these trends in the future.

In light of these conflicting statements, we chose to assume that past water level declines in the SRP would continue at their recent past rate. The direction of the bias that selection of this assumption might cause is consistent with the selection of analytical procedures and assumptions through this study. In any case where there was a choice between two analytical procedures or two assumptions, neither of which was clearly more correct than the other, the procedure or assumption that would most enhance the estimated value of an acre-foot of additional water was selected.

Yuma, Graham, and Greenlee County Groundwater Levels

Graham and Greenlee counties have sufficient recharge to maintain relatively constant groundwater and pumping levels. Thus, no change is projected to occur in the groundwater levels in these two areas.

Groundwater levels in the Yuma County study area are of no significance from the viewpoint of obtaining irrigation water since this area is almost totally served by surface water from the Colorado River. Groundwater levels are of concern due to water-logging of soils and the need for drainage wells. However, these problems have been taken care of and will not significantly affect future water costs.

Salt River Project and Roosevelt Water Conservation District Groundwater Levels

Salt River Project and Roosevelt Water Conservation District groundwater levels are projected to decline at constant rates of 6.5 and 7.0 feet per year, respectively, for the reasons explained above. The total decline for the period 1966-2015 will be 319 feet in the SRP and 333 feet in the RWCD (see table B-4).

Pinal County Groundwater Levels

Average declines in the water level of six subareas of Pinal County (as defined in figure A-2) are shown in table B-5. The average decline in the water level in the Casa Grande area is relatively constant during the first 30 years (1965-1995) of the analysis. Over this period, the water level in this subarea declines at the rate of 50 feet per decade (or five feet each year). It is not until the ten-year period, 1995-2005, that a significant decrease in the projected rate of decline occurs. During this period, the water table declines at the reduced rate of 3.4 feet per year. The reduction in the rate of decline is caused by a substantial decrease in water use in these later years.

The Eloy and Coolidge subareas exhibit the same pattern in this water table decline as does the Casa Grande subarea. However, the rates of decline in these subareas are much less, falling at about 2.8 feet per year during the early years of the analysis and then dropping to a rate of 2.1 feet per year at about 1995.

The Maricopa region undergoes a continuous reduction in the rate of decline of its water table. Early in the analysis (1966-1975), the water of this subarea declines at a faster rate than in any of the other subareas (5.6 feet per year). By the second period, 1975-1985, the water table is falling only 4.0 feet per year. The rate of decline drops to 2.5 feet per year by 1995, less than half of what it was in 1966.

The water level in the Queen Creek area is assumed to decline at the same rate as the water table in the Stanfield subarea. In these two subareas a noticeable increase in the rate of decline of the water levels is seen, beginning in the 1985-1995 period. This effect is because pumpage, as determined by the linear-programming model, is much less than originally simulated in Anderson's analog model of the Stanfield groundwater area. Hence, for many regions in this subarea, the large cones of depression actually rise during the early periods. By the 1985-1995 period, however, effective recovery is no longer occurring, and hence, the average water level in this subarea begins to decline more rapidly (1.7 feet per year) than it had previously (0.8 feet per year).

Maricopa Area A and Area B Groundwater Levels

Projected water level declines in subareas of Maricopa study areas A and B are shown in table B-6. Study area A experiences much lower decline rates in the groundwater levels than does area B, and thus, total groundwater decline in study area A is much less than in area B.

Subareas within each major study area also exhibit variations in both rates of decline between projection periods and in total groundwater decline over all periods. Area A declines are divisible into three decline rates for the six subareas used for the linear-programming models. Two of these subareas show slightly increasing rates of decline. This is because of the in-transfer of cotton from the Salt River Project as cotton is forced out owing to urban and industrial expansion onto Project land. Land which was formerly idle in these subareas is used to grow transferred cotton, thus using water and increasing total water use, with the result of lowering the groundwater level at faster rates.

Study area B subarea groundwater declines can be grouped into rates. Most subareas have a slight slowdown in the rate at which the water level declines through the first four projection periods. In the final period, however, there is a slight increase in the rate of decline caused by transferring cotton allotments into these subareas. The Harquahala Valley area shows by far the greatest slowdown in its decline rate as well as the greatest total decline in the groundwater level over the projection period.

Pima County Groundwater Levels

Pima County projected water level declines by projection period are shown in table B-4. The three areas are defined in figure A-3. The irrigated area of Pima County overlies two separate groundwater basins, with pumpage by the City of Tucson for municipal and industrial use, also having effect on water levels and decline rates. Pima County areas A and B, although having different initial period declines, both show increasing declines in each of the following four projection periods. These increases occur due to projected municipal and industrial pumping from the same aquifer that serves agriculture. Agricultural water use in these two areas of Pima County is projected to change very little. Area C of the Pima County study area is projected to experience very little change in groundwater decline rates. Only one change in the groundwater decline rate is indicated in the 1995-2005 period, where the ten-year decline falls from 50 feet to 41 feet.

Cochise County Groundwater Levels

Groundwater levels in the Cochise study area are projected to change as shown in table B-4. These declines are quite stable during the first four projection periods. Very little change in water withdrawals occurs during this time. The final 2005-2015 period shows a marked decrease in the decline rate, indicating reduced withdrawals from the aquifer during this projection period.

Projections of Future Pumping Costs

Irrigation water is projected to increase in price over the projection period because of the ever-increasing depths from which it must be pumped. Tables B-7 through B-10 show the expected per-acre-foot variable costs of irrigation water to the farms in each projection period for each study area or subareas within study areas. Except for the Salt River Project, the costs shown are the weighted average costs to the farm, where costs were weighted by projected pumping depths, sizes of wells and types of pumping equipment used in the area (electric or natural gas), the costs of power in the area, the efficiency of water delivery (related to farm size), and the expected quantity of surface water available. Estimates for the Salt River Project are pumping costs only – not the water cost to the farmer. The SRP area has substantial quantities of surface water as well as large power revenues with which to subsidize its water producing and delivery activities. Therefore, projected water costs to the farmers in the SRP are relatively constant over the projection period and much lower than projected pumping costs.

TABLE B-4

Projected Average Declines (in feet) in the Groundwater Level in the Salt River Project and the Roosevelt Water Conservation District and in Cochise and Pima Counties, 1966 to 2015

Period	Study Areas*					
	SRP	RWCD	Pima			Cochise
			Area A	Area B	Area C	
1966 to 1975	59	63	26	45	45	68
1975 to 1985	65	70	36	52	50	70
1985 to 1995	65	70	39	50	50	69
1995 to 2005	65	70	46	62	41	70
2005 to 2015	65	70	57	71	41	51
Total decline (1966 to 2015)	319	333	204	280	227	328

*Subareas refer to areas within the major study areas for which separate linear-programming models were constructed. Even though groundwater declines were the same in two or more subareas, the original pumping levels, cropping patterns, or farm sizes may have been different. See figures A-1 and A-3 for subarea boundaries.

TABLE B-5

Projected Average Declines (in feet) in the Groundwater Level in Pinal County, 1966 to 2015

Period	Subareas*					
	Casa Grande	Coolidge	Eloy	Maricopa	Stanfield	Queen Creek
1966 to 1975	45	27	28	50	7	7
1975 to 1985	49	27	29	40	9	9
1985 to 1995	51	28	29	36	17	17
1995 to 2005	34	21	21	25	21	21
2005 to 2015†	34	21	21	25	21	21
Total decline (1966 to 2015)	213	103	128	176	75	75

*Subareas refer to areas within the major study areas for which separate linear-programming models were constructed. Even though groundwater declines were the same in two or more subareas, the original pumping levels, cropping patterns, or farm sizes may have been different. See figure A-2 for subarea boundaries.

†Burdak (1970) carried analysis only to the 1995-2005 period. The 2005-2015 projection, assumed from the previous period, is probably too high because as water reaches greater depth, less would be used.

TABLE B-6

Projected Average Declines (in feet) in the Groundwater Level in Study Areas A and B of Maricopa County, 1966 to 2015

Period	Area A*			Area B*					
	RID	BID; ARL; SRV, ARV	GB	MAR; AD; LMP	TON	HAR	AG	RB	QC
6 to 1975	35	26	21	69	32	153	39	49	58
6 to 1985	39	29	20	72	33	112	44	56	61
6 to 1995	36	27	18	68	33	84	44	44	60
6 to 2005	33	30	14	58	47	60	29	39	59
6 to 2015	31	30	14	59	47	57	29	40	58
ecline 6 to 2015)	174	142	87	326	192	466	185	228	296

eas refer to areas within the major study area for which separate linear-programming models constructed. Even though groundwater declines were the same in two or more subareas, the al pumping levels, cropping patterns, or farm sizes may have been different. Identification is as vs. Also see figure A-1.

ID Roosevelt Irrigation District
ID Buckeye Irrigation District
RL Arlington Canal Company
RV Farms not in an irrigation district located south and west of the Salt River Project extending west to Buckeye.
RV Area along Centennial Wash west of Arlington Canal Company service area.
B Area between Gillespie and Painted Rock Dams.

AR Maricopa County Municipal Water Conservation District No. 1.
D Adaman Mutual Water Company.
MP Pump water area located around Litchfield Park, Marinette and Peoria.
ON Tonopah area located west of the Hassayampa River.
AR Harquahala Valley
G Aguila
B Rainbow Valley
C Queen Creek area in eastern Maricopa County outside of the Salt River Project and Roosevelt Water Conservation District.

TABLE B-7

Projected Per-acre-foot Weighted Variable Water Cost (in dollars per acre-foot) to the Farmer in the Salt River Project, Roosevelt Water Conservation District, and Pima and Cochise Counties, 1966 Through 2015

Year	Study Areas*					
	SRP†	RWCD	Pima			Cochise
			Area A	Area B	Area C	
1966	6.44	8.50	3.55	6.53	7.10	6.11
1975	8.13	9.69	4.17	7.56	7.94	8.10
1985	9.37	10.91	4.99	8.75	8.87	10.16
1995	11.32	12.11	5.89	9.91	9.81	12.21
2005	12.91	13.33	6.94	11.34	10.57	12.70
2015	14.50	14.54	8.24	12.96	11.34	13.58

*See figures A-1 and A-3 in Appendix A for area definitions.

†Projected Salt River Project pumping cost but not water cost to the farmer. This area has substantial quantities of surface water as well as large power revenues with which to subsidize its water-producing operation.

TABLE B-8

Projected Per-acre-foot Weighted Variable Water Costs (in dollars per acre-foot) to the Farmer in Study Area A of Maricopa County, 1966 Through 2015

Year	Subareas*					
	RID	BID	ARL	SRV	ARV	GB
1966	4.89	2.71	3.70	2.55	3.97	5.11
1975	5.52	3.19	4.17	3.02	4.32	5.48
1985	6.32	3.78	4.76	3.62	4.77	5.92
1995	7.06	4.33	5.31	4.17	5.19	6.33
2005	7.72	4.94	5.92	4.78	5.65	6.66
2015	8.36	5.56	6.54	5.39	6.12	6.97

*See figure A-1 for subarea definitions.

TABLE B-9

Projected Per-acre-foot Weighted Variable Water Costs (in dollars per acre-foot) to the Farmer in Study Area B of Maricopa County, 1966 Through 2015

Year	Subareas*							
	MAR	AD	LMP	TON	HAR	AG	RB	QC
1966	10.62	10.00	9.28	6.48	6.54	12.03	5.22	10.89
1975	11.89	11.25	10.54	7.05	8.64	12.75	5.89	11.93
1985	13.36	12.75	12.01	7.72	10.08	13.65	6.75	13.18
1995	14.75	14.15	13.40	8.40	11.39	14.55	7.44	14.40
2005	15.94	15.30	14.59	9.36	12.31	15.14	8.04	15.61
2015	17.14	16.50	15.79	10.32	13.20	15.73	8.66	16.79

*See figure A-1 for subarea definitions.

TABLE B-10

Projected Per-acre-foot Weighted Variable Water Costs (in dollars per acre-foot) to the Farmer, Pinal County 1966 Through 2015

Year	Subareas*					
	Casa Grande	Coolidge	Eloy	Maricopa	Stanfield	Queen Creek
1966	10.06	9.49	8.18	9.99	10.95	10.56
1975	11.11	10.12	8.71	11.16	11.12	10.71
1985	12.28	10.76	9.27	12.10	11.33	10.92
1995	13.52	11.42	9.84	12.94	11.72	11.33
2005	14.13	11.92	10.24	13.53	12.21	11.83
2015	15.11	12.42	10.65	14.11	12.50	12.33

*See figure A-2 for subarea definitions. Costs presented herein are for farm size III, with a "middle" pumping lift. The representative-farm linear-programming models for Pinal County were modeled with a shallow, medium, and deep pumping lift for each area, along with four farm sizes. Thus, a total of 72 (3 pumping lifts $\times$ 6 areas $\times$ 4 sizes $=$ 72) pumping-cost estimates were used for each projection period.

APPENDIX C

Import and Export Estimates for Arizona, 1958–2020

Projected outputs by producing sectors, as shown in table 6-18, were derived by injecting import and export estimates into the Input-Output model so as to achieve consistent estimates for all sectors of the Arizona economy. These import and export estimates, developed as documented by Finster (1970), are presented in tables C-1 to C-4.

Table C-1 shows the import-export picture for the adjusted base year (1958) economy which one can compare with the alternative posited trade patterns, as shown in tables C-2 to C-4, where aggregate and sectoral exports and imports under each alternative trade pattern for each projection year are displayed. The sectors are arranged according to the water-trade price of water embodied in the products of each. This arrangement was made to highlight the extent to which exports embodying high-priced water are substituted for those embodying low-priced water, and imports embodying low-priced water substituted for those embodying high-priced water in each posited external trade pattern. In moving from the Trade Pattern I through increasingly more water-conservation-oriented trade patterns, these substitutions become more extensive.

TABLE C-1

Distribution of Adjusted Base Year (1958) Exports and Imports Among Arizona Sectors

Producing Sector	Water Trade Price (dollars)	Exports (thousand dollars)	Distribution of Exports Among Sectors (%)	Competitive Imports (thousand dollars)	Distribution of Imports Among Sectors (%)
Trade & transportation	19,181.71	32,067	3.0	0	0
Petroleum	15,618.41	0	0	89,282	9.9
elected services	12,169.89	77,735	7.1	28,305	3.1
ircraft & parts	11,690.44	100,496	9.3	0	0
onstruction	8,324.80	0	0	0	0
nallocated services	8,173.27	7,590	0.7	5,089	0.6
abricated metals & machinery	7,610.29	13,867	1.3	241,508	26.8
tilities	3,603.64	43,044	4.0	3,656	0.4
ining	3,551.77	310,846	28.6	9,707	1.1
ther manufacturing	3,531.66	627	0.1	235,877	26.2
rimary metals	2,586.73	117,444	10.8	50,610	5.6
hemicals and fertilizers	1,774.56	10,969	1.0	106,461	11.8
anning, preserving, freezing	984.45	0	0	24,432	2.7
isc. agric. processing	467.31	0	0	42,537	4.7
eat & poultry processing	173.67	0	0	24,156	2.7
egetables	151.92	85,316	7.9	0	0
airy products	110.48	0	0	7,506	0.8
eat animals & products	107.10	150,866	13.9	5,287	0.6
ruits & tree nuts	97.78	631	0.1	4,606	0.5
isc. agriculture	97.02	6,455	0.6	0	0
itrus fruits	84.45	10,543	1.0	0	0
rain mill products	74.82	0	0	3,186	0.4
otton	67.13	94,448	8.7	0	0
oultry & eggs	63.28	0	0	19,311	2.1
arm dairy products	56.64	0	0	0	0
ood & feed grains	22.92	14,301	1.3	225	0
orage crops	21.23	6,757	0.6	0	0
Total		1,084,002	100.0	901,741	100.0

TABLE C-2 — Exports and Imports by Sector in 1980 U

	Producing Sector	Water Trade-Price (dollars)	Trade Pattern I	
			Exports	Imp
25	Trade and transportation	19,181.71	90,140	
17	Petroleum	15,618.41	0	25[illegible]
24	Selected services	12,169.41	218,512	7[illegible]
19	Aircraft and parts	11,690.44	282,492	
27	Construction	8,324.80	0	
26	Unallocated services	8,173.27	21,335	[illegible]
18	Fabricated metals and machinery	7,610.29	38,980	67[illegible]
23	Utilities	3,603.64	120,996	[illegible]
22	Mining	3,551.77	873,782	2[illegible]
21	Other manufacturing	3,531.66	1,762	66[illegible]
20	Primary metals	2,586.73	330,133	14[illegible]
16	Chemicals and fertilizers	1,774.56	30,834	2[illegible]
14	Canning, preserving, freezing	984.45	0	[illegible]
15	Miscellaneous agricultural processing	467.31	0	1[illegible]
12	Meat and poultry processing	173.67	0	[illegible]
6	Vegetables	151.92	239,822	
13	Dairy products	110.48	0	[illegible]
1	Meat animals and products	107.10	424,081	[illegible]
7	Fruits and tree nuts	97.78	1,774	[illegible]
10	Miscellaneous agriculture	97.02	18,145	
8	Citrus fruits	84.45	29,636	
11	Grain mill products	74.82	0	
5	Cotton	67.13	265,491	
2	Poultry and eggs	63.28	0	[illegible]
3	Farm dairy products	56.64	0	
4	Food and feed grains	22.92	40,200	
9	Forage crops	21.23	18,994	
	Total		3,047,109	2,5[illegible]
	Noncompetitive imports		...	5[illegible]
	Total exports and imports		3,047,109	3,0[illegible]

rnative Trade Patterns (thousands of 1958 dollars)

Trade Pattern II		Trade Pattern III		Trade Pattern IV	
ports	Imports	Exports	Imports	Exports	Imports
0,940	0	131,753	0	131,753	0
8,940	299,205	18,051	297,867	18,051	297,867
7,441	67,638	393,870	62,472	393,870	62,472
4,603	0	519,702	0	519,702	0
0	0	0	0	0	0
5,943	7,008	40,206	7,474	40,206	7,474
9,399	546,107	202,650	564,843	202,650	564,843
3,016	10,861	139,110	11,334	139,110	11,334
5,065	30,515	549,632	30,599	549,632	30,599
2,241	514,900	2,355	503,265	2,355	503,265
2,112	175,270	274,407	177,081	274,407	177,081
5,749	224,311	25,046	215,245	25,046	215,245
0	53,775	0	57,530	0	57,530
0	96,590	0	114,857	0	114,857
0	44,226	0	60,543	0	60,543
0,150	0	117,237	0	117,237	0
0	13,809	0	19,046	0	19,046
1,043	3,967	121,948	6,809	121,948	6,809
1,099	9,931	962	10,678	962	10,678
6,335	0	14,056	0	14,056	0
2,561	0	20,900	0	20,900	0
0	21,737	0	25,054	0	25,054
9,054	0	112,531	0	41,997	0
0	28,225	0	39,267	0	39,267
0	0	0	0	0	0
1,486	4,761	14,076	0	0	9,354
0	7,252	0	18,236	0	18,236
5,795	2,160,088	2,698,492	2,222,200	2,613,882	2,231,554
...	396,707	...	382,328	...	382,328
5,795	2,556,795	2,698,492	2,604,528	2,613,882	2,613,882

TABLE C-3 — Exports and Imports by Sector in 2000 U

	Producing Sector	Water Trade-Price (dollars)	Trade Pattern I	
			Exports	Imp
25	Trade and transportation	19,181.71	198,204	
17	Petroleum	15,618.41	0	55
24	Selected services	12,169.89	480,474	17
19	Aircraft and parts	11,690.44	621,158	
27	Construction	8,324.80	0	
26	Unallocated services	8,173.27	46,913	3
18	Fabricated metals and machinery	7,610.29	85,711	1,49
23	Utilities	3,603.64	266,052	2
22	Mining	3,551.77	1,921,314	5
21	Other manufacturing	3,531.66	3,875	1,45
20	Primary metals	2,586.73	725,912	31
16	Chemicals and fertilizers	1,774.56	67,798	65
14	Canning, preserving, and freezing	984.45	0	15
15	Miscellaneous agricultural processing	467.31	0	26
12	Meat and poultry processing	173.67	0	14
6	Vegetables	151.92	527,331	
13	Dairy products	110.48	0	4
1	Meat animals and products	107.10	932,490	3
7	Fruits and tree nuts	97.78	3,900	2
10	Miscellaneous agriculture	97.02	39,898	
8	Citrus fruits	84.45	65,165	
11	Grain mill products	74.82	0	1
5	Cotton	67.13	583,775	
2	Poultry and eggs	63.28	0	11
3	Farm dairy products	56.64	0	
4	Food and feed grains	22.92	88,393	
9	Forage crops	21.23	41,464	
	Total		6,700,127	5,5
	Noncompetitive imports		. . .	1,1
	Total exports and imports		6,700,127	6,7

native Trade Patterns (thousands of 1958 dollars)

Trade Pattern II		Trade Pattern III		Trade Pattern IV	
orts	Imports	Exports	Imports	Exports	Imports
9,842	0	364,483	0	364,483	0
0,559	748,142	18,899	746,368	18,899	746,368
7,628	98,435	1,100,344	88,171	1,100,344	88,171
0,195	0	1,322,621	0	1,322,621	0
0	0	0	0	0	0
7,730	0	142,744	0	142,744	0
5,819	986,756	641,863	1,092,980	641,863	1,092,980
0,735	26,437	349,989	29,974	349,989	29,974
4,097	56,295	601,276	57,014	601,276	57,014
3,398	848,511	3,499	841,706	3,499	841,706
5,920	488,182	520,220	497,706	520,220	497,706
3,027	388,194	48,745	358,947	48,745	358,947
0	97,648	0	112,940	0	112,940
0	183,501	0	312,849	0	312,849
0	63,557	0	178,277	0	178,277
,671	0	151,478	0	151,478	0
0	22,586	0	46,152	0	46,152
,333	4,031	92,104	37,261	92,104	37,261
,756	18,262	0	19,286	0	19,286
,684	0	17,519	8,814	17,519	8,814
,717	0	25,630	0	25,630	0
0	76,159	0	56,065	0	72,991
,937	0	114,568	0	0	0
0	31,567	0	103,789	0	103,789
0	0	0	1,099	0	1,099
0	12,661	16,250	0	0	18,375
0	19,055	0	25,130	0	42,924
,048	4,169,979	5,532,232	4,632,903	5,401,414	4,667,623
...	806,069	...	733,791	...	733,791
,048	4,976,048	5,532,232	5,366,694	5,401,414	5,401,414

TABLE C-4 — Exports and Imports by Sector in 2020 Ur

	Producing Sector	Water Trade-Price (dollars)	Trade Pattern I	
			Exports	Imp
25	Trade and transportation	19,181.71	390,057	
17	Petroleum	15,618.41	0	1,086
24	Selected services	12,169.89	945,554	344
19	Aircraft and parts	11,690.44	1,222,415	
27	Construction	8,324.80	0	
26	Unallocated services	8,173.27	92,323	61
18	Fabricated metals and machinery	7,610.29	168,676	2,937
23	Utilities	3,603.64	523,579	44
22	Mining	3,551.77	3,781,074	118
21	Other manufacturing	3,531.66	7,627	2,869
20	Primary metals	2,586.73	1,428,567	615
16	Chemicals and fertilizers	1,774.56	133,425	1,294
14	Canning, preserving, freezing	984.45	0	297
15	Miscellaneous agricultural processing	467.31	0	517
12	Meat and poultry processing	173.67	0	293
6	Vegetables	151.92	1,037,768	
13	Dairy products	110.48	0	9
1	Meat animals and products	107.10	1,835,106	6
7	Fruits and tree nuts	97.78	7,675	5
10	Miscellaneous agriculture	97.02	78,518	
8	Citrus fruits	84.45	128,243	
11	Grain mill products	74.82	0	3
5	Cotton	67.13	1,148,848	
2	Poultry and eggs	63.28	0	23
3	Farm dairy products	56.64	0	
4	Food and feed grains	22.92	173,955	
9	Forage crops	21.23	82,191	
	Total		13,185,601	10,96
	Noncompetitive imports		...	2,21
	Total exports and imports		13,185,601	13,18

...rnative Trade Patterns (thousands of 1958 dollars)

Trade Pattern II		Trade Pattern III		Trade Pattern IV	
...orts	Imports	Exports	Imports	Exports	Imports
2,275	0	763,293	0	763,293	0
3,027	1,629,812	20,818	1,636,224	20,818	1,636,224
0,960	155,538	2,230,589	51,652	2,230,589	51,652
4,395	0	2,761,890	0	2,761,890	0
0	0	0	0	0	0
0,623	0	301,102	0	301,102	0
4,736	1,441,223	1,195,809	1,662,872	1,195,809	1,662,872
2,906	61,864	743,952	70,798	743,952	70,798
5,949	102,049	674,379	152,806	674,379	152,806
9,060	1,234,420	9,338	1,178,401	9,338	1,178,401
6,759	958,206	684,152	996,770	684,152	996,770
3,613	582,745	84,631	530,870	84,631	530,870
0	168,566	0	198,850	0	198,850
0	338,114	0	618,847	0	618,847
0	101,326	0	489,950	0	489,950
2,835	0	128,430	0	10,396	0
0	39,590	0	88,301	0	88,301
4,646	2,868	94,125	32,752	20,338	32,752
2,555	32,177	0	32,223	0	33,222
,898	0	7,749	56,221	7,749	56,221
,444	0	15,300	0	15,300	0
0	177,810	0	98,327	0	115,520
0	0	112,346	0	0	0
0	39,239	0	186,527	0	186,527
0	0	0	3,026	0	3,026
0	30,962	12,100	0	0	19,701
0	38,394	0	17,300	0	32,472
,681	7,134,933	9,840,003	8,102,717	9,523,736	8,155,782
...	1,539,748	...	1,367,954	...	1,367,954
,681	8,674,681	9,840,003	9,470,671	9,523,736	9,523,736

Bibliography

Anderson, T. W. *Electric-Analog Analysis of Groundwater Depletion in Central Arizona.* Geological Survey, Water-Supply Paper no. 1860. Washington, D.C., 1968.

Arizona Academy. *Fourth Arizona Town Hall on Arizona's Water Supply.* Research Report prepared by the University of Arizona for meetings held April 6-8, Phoenix, 1964.

Arizona Agricultural Experiment Station and Extension Service. *Arizona Agriculture,* Annual. Tucson, 1946-1970.

Arizona Crop and Livestock Reporting Service. *Arizona Agricultural Statistics,* Annual. Phoenix, 1967-1971.

Arizona Revised Statutes. Quoted by Fred C. Struckmeyer, Jr., and Jeremy E. Butler, in *Water: A Review of Rights in Arizona.* Phoenix: Arizona Weekly Gazette, April, 1960.

Arizona State Land Department, *Annual Report on Groundwater in Arizona,* Water Resources Reports nos. 2, 5, 6, 7, 10, 11, 15, 19, 24, 32, 36, and 38, Phoenix.

Bain, Joe S., Richard E. Caves, and Julius Margolis. *Northern California Water Industry,* Resources for the Future, Inc. Baltimore: The Johns Hopkins Press, 1966.

Burdak, Thomas G. "Projections of Farmer Response to a Falling Groundwater Table: A Marriage of Economy and Hydrologic Models." Unpublished master's thesis, University of Arizona, Tucson, 1970.

Clark, Robert Emmet. *New Mexico Water Resources Law,* Division of Government Research, University of New Mexico, Albuquerque, 1964.

Comer, Billy M. "Aspects of Resource Combination and Enterprise Selection on Eastern Arizona Farms." Unpublished master's thesis, University of Arizona, Tucson, 1967.

Corollo, John A. *Waterworks Report for the Valley Metropolitan Area of Phoenix, Arizona.* Phoenix: John Corollo Engineers, 1968.

Cross, Jack L., Elizabeth H. Shaw, and Kathleen Scheifle, eds. *Arizona: Its People and Resources.* Tucson: University of Arizona Press, 1960.

Daly, Rex F. "Demand for Farm Products at Retail and the Farm Level. Some Empirical Measurement and Related Problems." American Statistical Association Proceedings, Annual meeting of the Business and Economics Statistics Section, 1957.

Easterlin, Richard A. "State Income Estimates," in *Population Redistribution and Economic Growth in the United States,* 1870-1950. Edited by Simon Kuznets. Philadelphia: American Philosophical Society, 1957.

Farris, Martin T., and Joseph F. Scott, eds. *Project Rescue – A Seminar on the Central Arizona Project.* Arizona State University Bureau of Business Research and Service, Tempe, Arizona, 1964.

Finster, Ronald D. "Water Policy Implications of a Changing Economic Structure for Arizona." Unpublished Ph.D. dissertation, University of Arizona, Tucson, 1970.

First National Bank of Arizona. *Profile of Arizona.* Phoenix, November, 1968.

Harshbarger, John W., D. D. Lewis, H. E. Skibitzke, W. L. Heckler, and L. R. Kister. *Arizona Water.* United States Geological Survey, Water-Supply Paper no. 1648, Washington, D.C., 1966.

Hock, Kenneth J. "Agricultural Adjustments to a Falling Groundwater Table in Central Arizona, 1967-2020." Ph.D. dissertation in preparation, University of Arizona, Tucson.

Hochwald, W. "Conceptual Issues of Regional Income Estimation," in Regional Income, Studies in Income and Wealth, vol. 21. National Bureau of Economic Research, Princeton University Press, 1957.

Jones, Douglas M. "Economic Aspects of Agricultural Use of Colorado River Water in Yuma County, Arizona." Unpublished Ph.D. dissertation, University of Arizona, Tucson, 1968.

Lee, Ivan M. *Conditional Projections of California Economic Growth.* Giannini Foundation Monograph Number 19, California Agricultural Experiment Station, Berkeley, 1967.

Lee, V. Wilson. "Economic Factors Affecting the Long Term Outlook for Irrigated Farming in Sulphur Springs Valley, Arizona." Unpublished master's thesis, University of Arizona, Tucson, 1967.

Lessing, Lawrence. "Where the Industries of the Seventies Will Come From." *Fortune,* vol. 75, no. 1, 1967.

Mack, Lawrence. "Economic Implications of a Dynamic Land and Water Base for Agriculture in Central Arizona." Unpublished Ph.D. dissertation, University of Arizona, Tucson, 1969.

Modern Arizona Industry, Inc. "Electronics Gain Shown in Arizona." *Modern Arizona Industry,* vol. 2, no. 12, 1969.

Nelson, A. G., and C. D. Busch. *Cost of Pumping Irrigation Water in Central Arizona.* Technical Bulletin 182, Arizona Agricultural Experiment Station, Tucson, 1967.

Office of Business Economics, United States Department of Commerce. "Table 50, Personal Income by Major Sources, Arizona." *Survey of Current Business,* relevant monthly issues.

Office of Business Economics, United States Department of Commerce. "Table 70, Industrial Sources of Civilian Income Received by Persons for Participation in Current Production, by States and Regions." *Survey of Current Business,* relevant monthly issues.

Perloff, Harvey S. "Problems of Assessing Regional Economic Progress." *Regional Income, Studies in Income and Wealth,* vol. 21, National Bureau of Economic Research, Princeton University Press, 1957.

Salt River Project, *Annual Reports.* Phoenix, Arizona, 1962-1970.

Salt River Valley Water Users' Association. "Statistical Report." Irrigation Department, Phoenix, 1962.

Smith, Courtland L. "The Salt River Project of Arizona: Its Organization and Integration with the Community." Unpublished Ph.D. dissertation, University of Arizona, Tucson, 1968.

Smith, H. V. *The Climate of Arizona.* Arizona Agricultural Experiment Station, Bulletin 279, University of Arizona, Tucson, 1956.

Smith, H. V., G. E. Draper, and W. H. Fuller. *The Quality of Irrigation Water.* Arizona Agricultural Experiment Station Report No. 223. Tucson, 1964.

Stults, Harold M. "Predicting Farmer Response to a Falling Water Table: An Arizona Case Study." Unpublished Ph.D. dissertation, University of Arizona, Tucson, 1967.

Struckmeyer, Fred C., and Jeremy E. Butler. *Water: A Review of Rights in Arizona.* Phoenix: Arizona Weekly Gazette, 1960.

Thiele, Heinrich J. *Present and Future Water Use and Its Effects on Planning in Maricopa County, Arizona.* Maricopa County Department of Planning and Zoning, Phoenix, 1965.

Tijoriwala, Anilkumar G., William E. Martin, and Leonard G. Bower. *The Structure of the Arizona Economy: Output Interrelationships and Their Effects on Water and Labor Requirements: Part I, The Input-Output Model and Its Interpretation,* Arizona Agricultural Experiment Station Technical Bulletin 180; and "Part II, Statistical Supplement," Department of Agricultural Economics File Report 68-1. University of Arizona, Tucson, 1968.

United States Bureau of the Census. *United States Census of Agriculture 1940.* Washington, D.C.: Government Printing Office, 1941.

United States Bureau of the Census. *United States Census of Agriculture 1954.* Washington, D.C.: Government Printing Office, 1956.

United States Bureau of the Census. *County Business Patterns, First Quarter 1962,* Part 9, Mountain States. Washington, D.C.: Government Printing Office, 1963.

United States Department of Agriculture. *Farm Income-States Estimates, 1949-1967.* Economic Research Service, Washington, D.C., 1968.

United States Department of Agriculture. "Population Estimates for 1965 with Projections to 1980, 2000, and 2020 on an Economic and a 'Hydrologic' Basis, Lower Colorado Region." Economic Research Service, Economics Work Group, Tucson, Arizona, 1969.

United States Department of Commerce. *Census of Population.* Washington, D.C.: Government Printing Office, 1940, 1950, 1960.

United States Department of Commerce. *Growth Patterns in Employment by County, 1940-1950 and 1950-1960, Volume 5 Southwest.* Washington, D.C.: Government Printing Office, 1965.

United States Department of Commerce. *Exports from Arizona – 1966.* Bureau of International Commerce, Washington, D.C., 1966a.

United States Department of Commerce. *The National Income and Product Accounts of the United States, 1929-1965; Statistical Tables.* Office of Business Economics, Washington, D.C., 1966b.

United States Department of Commerce. *Industrial Location as a Factor in Regional Economic Development*. Economic Development Administration. Washington, D.C.: Government Printing Office, 1967a.

United States Department of Commerce. *Survey of Current Business,* vol. 47, no. 4, 1967b.

United States Department of Commerce. *Growth Pace Setters in American Industry 1958-1968*. Business and Defense Services Administration. Washington, D.C.: Government Printing Office, 1968a.

United States Department of Commerce. *Population Estimates: Summary of Demographic Projections,* series P-25, no. 388. Bureau of the Census, Washington, D.C., 1968b.

United States Department of Commerce. *Statisticals Abstract of the United States*. Bureau of the Census, Washington, D.C., 1968c.

United States Department of Commerce. *Survey of Current Business,* vol. 48, no. 7, 1968d.

United States Department of Commerce. *Survey of Current Business,* vol. 48, no. 8, 1968e.

United States Geological Survey. *Annual Report on Groundwater in Arizona,* Water Resources Report no. 36. United States Department of the Interior and Arizona State Land Department cooperating, Phoenix, 1968.

United States Geological Survey. *Annual Report on Groundwater in Arizona,* Water Resources Report no. 38. United States Department of the Interior and Arizona State Land Department cooperating, Phoenix, February, 1969.

United States Geological Survey. *Annual Report on Groundwater in Arizona,* Water Resources Report no. 42. United States Department of the Interior and Arizona State Land Department cooperating, Phoenix, December, 1969.

United States Geological Survey. *Annual Report on Groundwater in Arizona,* Water Resources Report, relevant years, 1963-1969.

United States Geological Survey. *Compilation of Records of Surface Waters of the United States through September 1950: Part 9, Colorado River Basin,* United States Geological Survey Water-Supply Paper 1313, United States Department of the Interior, Washington, D.C., 1954.

United States Geological Survey. *Quality of Surface Water for Irrigation; Western States, 1965*. United States Geological Survey Paper 1967, United States Department of the Interior, Washington, D.C., 1969.

United States Department of the Interior. "Data Book on Power Districts, Irrigation Districts, and Cooperatives." Bureau of Reclamation, Boulder City, Nevada, 1965.

Valley National Bank. *Arizona Statistical Review,* Phoenix, Arizona, 1948, 1958, 1968.

Wildermuth, John R., William E. Martin, and Victor H. Riech. *Costs and Returns Data for Representative General Crop Farms in Arizona,* report 253. Arizona Agricultural Experiment Station, 1969.

Young, Robert A., William E. Martin, and Dale L. Shaw. *Data for Arizona Crop Farm Planning*. Department of Agricultural Economics, University of Arizona, Tucson, 1968.

Index